87877

AIR
CONSERVATION

The Report

of the

AIR CONSERVATION COMMISSION

of the

American Association for the Advancement of Science

Publication No. 80 of the

AMERICAN ASSOCIATION FOR THE ADVANCEMENT OF SCIENCE

WASHINGTON, D. C.   1965

Printed and bound by The Horn-Shafer Company

Baltimore, Maryland, U.S.A.

The Air Conservation Commission

JAMES P. DIXON, President, Antioch College, Yellow Springs, Ohio (*Chairman*)

JOHN W. BODINE, President, Academy of Natural Sciences of Philadelphia, and President, Pennsylvania-New Jersey-Delaware Metropolitan Project, Inc., Philadelphia, Pennsylvania

HERBERT R. DOMKE, Director, Allegheny County Health Department, Pittsburgh, Pennsylvania

FRANCOIS N. FRENKIEL, Applied Mathematics Laboratory, David Taylor Model Basin, Washington, D.C.

M. MASON GAFFNEY, Chairman, Department of Economics, University of Wisconsin-Milwaukee, Milwaukee

JOHN R. GOLDSMITH, Head, Air Pollution Medical Studies Unit, California State Department of Public Health, Berkeley

ARIE J. HAAGEN-SMIT, Division of Biology, California Institute of Technology, Pasadena

HOWARD HIGMAN, Department of Sociology, University of Colorado, Boulder

JAMES P. LODGE, Staff Chemist, National Center for Atmospheric Research, Boulder, Colorado

MARTIN MEYERSON, Dean, College of Environmental Design, University of California, Berkeley

NORTON NELSON, Chairman, Department of Environmental Medicine, New York University Medical Center, New York

FRITS W. WENT, Desert Research Institute, University of Nevada, Reno

iii

Acknowledgments

The Air Conservation Commission wishes to acknowledge its debt to the following authorities, who contributed to this report by writing or reviewing chapters, by providing needed information, or by expressing their views in writing or at a hearing conducted by the Commission in December 1963 in Washington, D.C. The positions and affiliations indicated are those that were current at the time.

E. M. ADAMS, Assistant Director, Biochemical Research Department, Dow Chemical Company, Midland, Michigan

A. P. ALTSHULLER, Robert A. Taft Sanitary Engineering Center, Cincinnati, Ohio

HARRY C. BALLMAN, Manager, Air Pollution Control Division, National Coal Association, Washington, D.C.

DANIEL BIENSTOCK, Central Experiment Station, Bureau of Mines, U.S. Department of the Interior, Bruceton, Pennsylvania

ALLEN BRANDT, Manager, Industrial Health Engineering, Bethlehem Steel Company, Bethlehem, Pennsylvania

C. S. BRANDT, Chief, Agricultural Section, Laboratory of Medical and Biological Sciences, Division of Air Pollution, Robert A. Taft Sanitary Engineering Center, Cincinnati, Ohio

LESTER BRESLOW, Chief, Division of Preventive Medical Services, California State Department of Public Health, Berkeley

F. STEWART BROWN, Chief, Bureau of Power, Federal Power Commission, Washington, D.C.

FORREST H. BUMFORD, Director, Occupational Health Service, Department of Health and Welfare, Concord, New Hampshire

R. D. CADLE, National Center for Atmospheric Research, Boulder, Colorado

JOHN D. CAPLAN, Chairman, Automobile Combustion Products Committee, General Motors Corporation, Warren, Michigan

ELLIS DARLEY, Air Pollution Research Center, University of California, Riverside

JOHN HENRY DENTON, State-Wide Coordinator of Continuing Education in Real Estate, University Extension, University of California, Berkeley

CHARLES L. DUNHAM, Director, Division of Biology and Medicine, Atomic Energy Commission, Washington, D.C.

MERRILL EISENBUD, New York University–Bellevue Medical Center, New York

ERIK ERIKSSON, International Atomic Energy Agency, Vienna, Austria

W. L. FAITH, Consulting Chemical Engineer, San Marino, California

IRVING FOX, Vice-President, Resources for the Future, Inc., Washington, D.C.

LEO GOODMAN, Secretary, Atomic Energy Technical Committee, Industrial Union Department, AFL–CIO, Washington, D.C.

LEE HANSON, Department of Economics, University of California, Los Angeles

LYNN HARRISS, Executive Director, American Society of Landscape Architects, Washington, D.C.

JOHN M. HESLEP, Chief, Bureau of Radiological Health, California State Department of Public Health, Berkeley

J. Z. HOLLAND, Chief, Fallout Studies Branch, Division of Biology and Medicine, Atomic Energy Commission, Washington, D.C.

CHRISTIAN JUNGE, Meteorologisch-Geophysikalisches Institut, Mainz-Universitat, Germany

HAROLD W. KENNEDY, County Counsel, Office of the County Counsel, Los Angeles, California

HAROLD KNAPP, Weapons Systems Evaluation Group, Pentagon, Washington, D.C.

ALLEN V. KNEESE, Economist, Resources for the Future, Inc., Washington, D.C.

HELMUT E. LANDSBERG, U.S. Weather Bureau, Washington, D.C.

WRIGHT H. LANGHAM, Assistant Division Leader, Biomedical Research, Los Alamos Scientific Laboratory, Los Alamos, New Mexico

RALPH E. LAPP, Quadri-Science, Inc., Washington, D.C.

BENJAMIN LINSKY, Professor of Sanitary Engineering (Air Pollution), Department of Civil Engineering, West Virginia University, Morgantown

LESTER MACHTA, Director, Air Resources Laboratory, U.S. Weather Bureau, Washington, D. C.

VERNON MACKENZIE, Chief, Division of Air Pollution, U.S. Department of Health, Education, and Welfare, Washington, D.C.

JULIUS MARGOLIS, School of Business, University of California, Berkeley

EDWARD MARTELL, Nuclear Chemist, Research Staff, National Center for Atmospheric Research, Boulder, Colorado

JERRY MCAFEE, Vice-President and Executive Technical Adviser, Gulf Oil Corporation, Pittsburgh, Pennsylvania

JAMES E. MEEKER, Robert A. Taft Sanitary Engineering Center, Cincinnati, Ohio

MALCOLM H. MERRILL, Director of Public Health, California State Department of Public Health, Berkeley

IRVING MICHELSON, Director, Public Service Projects, Consumers Union of the United States, Inc., Mount Vernon, New York

JOHN T. MIDDLETON, Director, Air Pollution Research Center, University of California, Riverside

GEORGE MILLY, Director, Operations Research Group, Edgewood Arsenal, Maryland

HOWARD P. MORGAN, Member, Federal Power Commission, Washington, D.C.

MORRIS NEIBURGER, Chairman, Department of Meteorology, University of California at Los Angeles, Los Angeles

NORMAN C. NELSON, Bureau of Power, Federal Power Commission, Washington, D.C.

R. R. NEWELL, U.S. Naval Radiological Defense Laboratory, Hunter's Point, San Francisco, California

WILLIAM NISKANEN, Economist, Office of the Controller, Department of Defense, Washington, D.C.

WILLIAM W. PAYNE, Deputy Associate Director for Field Studies, National Cancer Institute, National Institutes of Health, Bethesda, Maryland

HARALD H. ROSSI, College of Physicians and Surgeons, Columbia University, New York

EUGENE SAWICKI, Robert A. Taft Sanitary Engineering Center, Cincinnati, Ohio

JEAN J. SCHUENEMAN, Chief, Technical Assistance Branch, Division of Air Pollution, Robert A. Taft Sanitary Engineering Center, Cincinnati, Ohio

TIBOR SCITOVSKY, Department of Economics, University of California, Berkeley

RAYMOND SMITH, Chief, Air Pollution Control Section, Philadelphia Department of Public Health, Philadelphia, Pennsylvania

JEROME F. THOMAS, Associate Professor of Sanitary Chemistry, Sanitary Engineering Research Laboratory, Richmond Field Station, Richmond, California

BENJAMIN VAN DUUREN, Associate Professor of Environmental Medicine, Department of Environmental Medicine, New York University Medical Center, New York

WILLIAM VICKREY, Department of Economics, Columbia University, New York

Introduction

The AAAS Committee on Science in the Promotion of Human Welfare asserted in its report of July 1960 that the scientific community "should accept the obligation to determine how new advances in our understanding and control of natural forces are likely to affect human welfare, to call these matters to public attention, to provide for the public and its social and political agencies the objective statements of the facts and of the consequences of alternative policies that are required as the basis for informed decisions on the relative merits of proposed courses of action." In December 1960, the Committee identified air conservation as "an excellent illustration of the main thesis of the Committee report [to the AAAS Council], that the accelerating progress of science is creating social issues of unprecedented magnitude." The Committee expressed its intention of appointing expert groups to examine some of the social problems that have resulted from scientific progress, an intention that led within a short time to the appointment of the Air Conservation Commission.

The Committee, in its charge to the Commission, referred to the need for the scientific community to assemble facts and to identify alternatives. The Committee charged the Commission "with responsibility to define the issues and the consequences that may be anticipated from these alternatives, so far as available facts permit."

The Commission met for the first time in the spring of 1962, and its deliberations spanned the next 2 years. It reviewed available data, solicited and received papers from its members and from other authorities in the fields of air conservation, pollution control, pollutants and their effects, law, economics, meteorology, public health, public opinion, and government. At a hearing in December 1963, it invited representatives of industry, labor, government, and private agencies concerned with the problem of air pollution to present their points of view.

The Commission decided to design its final report so that it would be useful to scientists in a wide variety of disciplines and to laymen interested in the subject of air conservation. To that end, this report is in three parts. Part 1, Air Conservation and Public

Policy, is directly responsive to the Committee charge, and was written to be of interest to the broadest possible readership. Part 2, Summary of the Facts, is a concise report on the state of scientific knowledge. It, too, was designed for broad readership. Part 3, Background Reports, consists of seven chapters, some of them fairly technical in nature and of interest principally to scientists and specialists in other disciplines. However, every effort has been expended to make the material readable without sacrificing scientific accuracy, and it should present no insurmountable problem to the interested nonscientist or nontechnical reader.

Clearly, the Commission could not hope to include in one report all that man knows about air conservation, air pollution, and the formulation of public policy. To make the report manageable, a considerable amount of material had to be condensed or omitted. Thus, for example, the section on radioactive pollution of the atmosphere, although the largest single paper in the report, does not begin to cover so complicated a subject; and thus, too, the Commission decided to omit reference to airborne biota.

Despite these obvious limitations, the Commission believes that the information contained in the report will be of value to scientists, public bodies, and the public during the next several years. The Commission's specific task is completed; but a far greater task now remains for all of us.

This report is the result of the efforts not only of the members of the Commission, but of the large number of authorities in many fields of endeavor whose names appear in the list of acknowledgments. However, special mention should be made of the work of Miss Molly Day, who served ably as Executive Secretary of the Commission, and of Mr. Richard Landau, Associate College Editor, Antioch College, who edited the report.

JAMES P. DIXON, *Chairman*
Air Conservation Commission

Contents

PART 1

Air Conservation
and
Public Policy

Air Conservation and Public Policy

Every living thing contaminates its environment. To live, it must react with its environment, and in the process of reacting—by the very fact of living and reacting—it produces and casts off wastes.

Any environment must be self-cleansing in order to sustain life. Unless the environment can dispose of life's by-products, life will cease.

Man evolved in a sea of air of definite composition. Like other air-breathing creatures, he contributes his burden of wastes to the air he breathes. However, man's contribution is not limited to his exhaled air; he has developed processes that produce huge quantities of airborne debris. These processes have profound economic, political, medical, social, and military significance. They affect man's comfort, his health, his wealth, his power, and his security. Indeed, to tamper with these processes is to tamper with human civilization. But to ignore their by-products is to ignore a threat to human survival.

Man's environment has the necessary characteristic of any life-sustaining environment: It is self-cleansing. A substantial part of the wastes that man produces by living and by the processes of his civilization is dispersed by the winds, is converted to less harmful substances, is washed away by rain, and is dissolved in the sea. But sometimes there is no wind, and the air may fill with fetid wastes. And when there is a wind, it may carry the wastes to neighboring communities. Sometimes the effluvia are changed very slowly, and during the process new, even more toxic, substances may be formed. And, in recent years, some of the pollutants that man has produced, capable of affecting fundamental life processes, threaten not only this generation but also generations as yet unborn.

When wastes are produced so rapidly, or when they accumulate in such concentrations that the normal, self-cleansing or dispersive propensities of the atmosphere cannot cope with them, we call the air "polluted." Some kinds of pollution affect visibility; and some pollutants, in sufficient concentrations, may cause discomfort to man or animals, may damage property, or may actually injure man, animals, and plants. Even when levels are so low that they cannot be detected except with special instruments, some pollutants may harm living creatures exposed for long periods of time.

Information about air pollution and its possible effects is still far from complete, but however obscure the missing facts may be, some of them can be found with increased effort. Far more difficult than the scientific problem is a philosophical one: Given the state of man's knowledge, what are its implications for man's conduct?

Stated perhaps too simply, some authorities believe that the information now available warrants grave concern and prompt, broad, preventive action. Others believe that this information should be seriously considered, but that, until additional evidence is available to suggest stronger action, efforts should be directed primarily toward eliminating pollutants that are known to be toxic and toward eliminating or reducing others when it is economically or militarily possible.

The Air Conservation Commission has not attempted to resolve the differences that exist. But it has attempted to present a variety of policies so that, with informed discussion and consideration, the differences may be ultimately resolved.

*   *   *   *   *   *

Although the air has a great capacity for coping with pollutants, it is not limitless. The Air Conservation Commission has considered air as a natural resource, similar in some ways to water. Throughout its deliberations, the Commission has been concerned not only with problems of *air pollution*, but also with the need for *air conservation*. The Commission has been impressed with the need not only to control pollution, but also to develop programs to conserve the air.

Assumptions

The Air Conservation Commission has reviewed the available facts on sources of pollutants, the effects of pollutants at different concentrations, atmospheric reactions and relevant meteorological phenomena, and levels of pollutants in the world today. It has examined the economic implications of air pollution, the variety of public policies at the several levels of government, and how public attitudes are formed and how they affect the formation of public policy.

In the course of its deliberations, the Commission identified four basic assumptions that are essential for any rational consideration of the problem.

1) *Air is in the public domain.* Such an assumption is necessary if air pollution is to be considered a public problem, of concern not only to those who discharge the pollution but also to those who may suffer as a result. This assumption does not challenge the concept of ownership of air space above a parcel of land, but it does exclude from such property rights the flowing air, which cannot be controlled by the owner of the land, and which carries its pollution in whatever directions meteorology and topography permit.

2) *Air pollution is an inevitable concomitant of modern life.* There is a conflict between man's economic and biologic concerns, and, in the past, this conflict was recognized only after air pollution disasters, such as those that claimed lives in Donora, London, and the Meuse Valley. Evidence of the effects of air pollution in major metropolitan areas in the United States and in other countries has, until now, been viewed as an isolated phenomenon, obscuring the need for systematic development of policies and programs to conserve the atmosphere for its most essential biological function.

3) *Scientific knowledge can be applied to the shaping of public policy.* Information about the sources and effects of air pollution is far from complete, and a great deal of work is needed to develop and improve control devices. Nevertheless, sufficient information is now available to make possible substantial reductions in air pollution levels both locally and throughout the world. Man does not have to abandon either his technology or his life, but he must use his knowledge.

4) *Methods to reduce air pollution must not increase pollution in other sectors of man's environment.* Some industries reduce hazards from industrial exposure by venting wastes to the outside air where they can pose a threat to the entire community. Other industries control wastes in the air by dissolving them in water and by pouring the polluted water into streams. Such methods may be expedient, but they do not solve the important problem of helping the environment to sustain life.

*   *   *   *   *   *

Recommendations

Employing these assumptions, and taking into account the factual information at its disposal, the Air Conservation Commission developed four basic recommendations.

1) The Commission recommends that scientists in all disciplines become familiar with the available information about air pollution, and that they play active roles in informing both the public and public policy bodies of the facts and their significance.

The Commission recognized that this was no small task, but it saw no acceptable alternative. If scientists failed to assume this responsibility, ineffective and uninformed efforts would be made to control the amounts and kinds of pollution that emptied into the air. We may expect pollution to steadily increase, with an ever-increasing danger to man, animals, property, and plant life. And we may expect injustices to result from the enforcement of defective policies. Not only must scientists participate in formulating public policy, but they must also be prepared to reevaluate existing policies regularly in order to insure that they reflect scientific advances.

2) The Commission recommends that the decisions on what to do about the facts—the actual weighing of risks versus benefits—should be a responsibility of the entire community, including scientists.

The scientist's special knowledge imposes upon him the burden of informing; but the final decisions on public policy must rest with those who are affected by the decisions. Scientists alone should not be expected to make decisions that affect the lives and well-being of a community, a nation, or the world.

For example, the Commission suggests that when standards are developed for ambient air quality, conscientious use should be made of the available information, and that the standards should include documentation on the substances, their concentration and duration, and their effects. Standards may be set at the several levels that reflect the range of effects that the pollutants are expected to have. But the adoption of such standards is the responsibility of public policy bodies, and should not be the responsibility of scientists alone. Each area should make its own decision with regard to the air quality it wants and needs. Such air quality standards usually have immediate value when a community faces costly problems of air pollution; but ultimately their greatest value may be in their use in air conservation efforts.

3) The Commission recommends that air pollution be viewed as a problem that transcends political boundaries and as one that has global significance.

The most effective air conservation program is one that applies to an area that includes both the sources of pollution and those affected by it. Defining such an area is a complex task but the Commission believes that with suitable application of meteorologic and topographic criteria, specific areas will be able to define the proper boundaries for air conservation purposes.

Pollution is not only a problem in a given locality or metropolitan area, but it is also a global problem. Thus, nuclear weapons tests may inject debris high into the stratosphere, and from there it descends on vast areas of the globe and for long periods of time. Other pollutants also have global significance. The gradually increasing concentration of carbon dioxide in the earth's atmosphere may cause a slow increase in world temperature, and it may cause glacial melting and higher sea levels. Such a change, if it is occurring, or if it should occur, would be difficult or impossible to stop.

4) The Commission recommends that communities, metropolitan areas, states, and appropriate federal agencies should give special consideration not only to the elimination or reduction of air pollution, but also to air conservation planning.

Public policies may be devised not only to correct the mistakes of the past, but also to prevent new mistakes. The adoption of ambient air quality standards, for example, is an important step in the development of an air conservation program since the standards can be designed to reflect a community's goal for air quality. If such standards are not developed, the increasing levels of pollution will eventually require remedial action, which is often more costly than preventive action. Thoughtful planning can be an effective way of conserving air by applying the information now available.

Public Policy Alternatives

Because the number of alternative policies that are available to public bodies is enormous, the Commission has attempted, in this part of the report, to define them only in the broadest terms. More detailed policy alternatives and their probable consequences are suggested, explicitly and implicitly, in other parts of the report; but even these are not, and cannot be, exhaustive.

Community and Metropolitan Air Pollution

Some communities have no obvious air pollution problem other than the one they share with the rest of the world. Such communities are usually small, are not near a large metropolitan center, and have few or no industries that produce toxic airborne wastes in large quantities. However, as our population grows, the number of people living in such communities is dwindling rapidly; also, more and more Americans are moving into burgeoning metropolitan areas. Furthermore, even if a community has no problem today, it may be able to avoid future problems by adopting a sound air conservation program now.

The local government agencies in the areas where most Americans live face a fundamental policy alternative: to recognize air conservation as an important need, or to ignore it.

To ignore it is to invite a host of consequences. Industries, homes, and the ubiquitous automobile pour toxic wastes in ever-increasing quantities into the air. Under certain meteorological conditions—conditions not at all unique—these wastes can accumulate in relatively high concentrations. Certain pollutants, particularly those emitted by motor vehicles, can be converted by sunlight into especially unpleasant substances. In a typical city, the air may be burdened with sulfur compounds, carbon monoxide, carbon dioxide (at levels higher than are normally found in "clean" air), oxides of nitrogen, compounds of lead and other metals, particles of various sizes and character, and many other wastes. Areas near certain industrial plants may have relatively high concentrations of fluorides in the air. Even communities in sparsely settled rural regions may have concentrations of economic poisons in the air after crop dusting.

Work still needs to be done in order to determine the exact effects of acute and chronic exposure to these pollutants. (Efforts have been made to determine whether or not pollutants play a role in the formation of cancers.)

The lack of definitive information about the health effects of air pollution does not mean that health is not adversely affected. And, quite apart from such effects, is the damage that these pollutants can do to plants and property. Although the cost of such damage is usually spread thinly over the population, the total cost to the community might be impressive.

If a community chooses not to ignore the question—if it chooses action as its alternative—it faces consequences of a different kind. For then it must formulate an effective and equitable program that will reflect accurately the community's standards of air purity.

Metropolitan air pollution can be ascribed to four major sources: (i) motor vehicles, (ii) thermoelectric power stations, (iii) assorted industries, and (iv) householders, through heating their homes and burning rubbish. Individual citizens, by their use of cars, by the demands they make for more electric power, and by the running of their homes, are the principal contributors to community-wide air pollution in most modern cities. The detailed policies that are needed for an air conservation program depend substantially on the particular situation in the community. But whatever kind of program is needed, public bodies should consider certain basic needs: a monitoring program, methods for identifying sources and effects, the advice of experts, formulating regulations based on available data, and enforcement of any regulations developed.

Air pollution control programs and air conservation efforts should take into account (i) the volume and mobility of the air mass overlying the area where emissions occur; (ii) the interaction of pollutants and the self-cleansing attributes of the atmosphere; (iii) the topography of the region and any effects it may have on dispersing pollutants; (iv) the variables of meteorology; (v) the existing pattern of industrial practices, transportation, use of land, production of energy, and all matters that pertain to their further development; and (vi) the range of sensitivity of the human beings, plants, and animals in the region.

Underlying the complex variety of technical procedures that are suitable for air pollution control and prevention are several social and administrative principles. These include, first, voluntary restraints, based on the views of acceptability, on good neighborliness, and on what might be called "common decency." Such voluntary restraints are often backstopped by the courts in applying and interpreting the legal doctrine of nuisance.

The second basic principle is the development and application of regulations based, as they generally are, on the police powers of government. These regulations may be used to ban certain kinds of activity, to prohibit specified types of emissions at certain times, and to require the use of protective devices when there is a likelihood of emission, and finally, they may be used as a basis for permitting certain types of activities under specified conditions in certain areas, for example, by zoning regulations. All of these, however, are based upon the use or potential use of police powers.

The third general type of restraint, one that has not been used very much in air pollution control and air conservation, is what might be called "flexible social controls." Here the major example would be the use of market economics. Air zoning, that is, allowing specified types and amounts of pollution to be emitted into a given body of air under specified conditions, as opposed to land zoning, might also be considered one of the more flexible social restraints.

The choice of mechanism depends in part upon the effect to be prevented; for example, more rigid mechanisms would seem justified for preventing effects on human health. In general, the more disruptive and costly the constraint, the greater is the need for valid evidence relating the likelihood of effects to the acts of emitting pollutants.

Many communities may wish to use multiple methods. However,

areas with acute air pollution problems probably will need to make more extensive use of police powers, while those with threatened problems may want to rely on flexible social restraints.

Preventing Avoidable Emissions

The most suitable general policies for controlling local and metropolitan air pollution are those that are designed to prevent avoidable emissions. In some communities, such policies are in effect, are firmly established, and seem to be well accepted by industry and government. In others, a variety of obstacles seems to hinder their adoption. Just as communities and their problems differ, so do the needs for and the approaches to air conservation. Local air pollution problems are often so complex or are so costly to abate that the simple principle of prevention cannot be easily applied. Two major obstacles are often cited for lack of progress: lack of adequate devices for effective control and excessive cost. The cost, however, is frequently considered relevant only to the emitter, and no estimate is made of the cost to the community.

The experience of many air pollution control agencies suggests that constructive solutions to local emission problems can be developed through a reasonable approach to industrial management, especially when the approach is by individuals and agencies with an adequate fund of information. In some cases, control of air pollutants leads to net savings for the industry; and in other cases, when all the costs of pollution to the community are considered, the control or prevention may provide a net saving for the community.

(Industry, of course, is not the only source of community air pollution. Automobiles, for example, add a great deal to the total burden, although the contribution of a single vehicle may be small.)

Using Price Mechanisms

Because of its possible contribution to air conservation, communities might consider the use of price mechanisms—permit fees or flexible emission charges—for the privilege of using air to dispose of wastes. This approach would be particularly suitable when questions of impairment to health are not involved.

The adoption of such a proposal would imply recognition of the inevitability of some pollution. It would also imply that the air is a limited natural resource, and that the community might legitimately impose a charge for using it. Pollution would become a cost of operation, and the charge would be less for a more efficient operation. And it would compensate the community, at least to some extent, for the economic effects of polluted air.

The proposal assumes that air has a natural self-cleansing capacity, and that, given certain patterns and rates of emission, and specified pollutants and mechanisms for removing them, it can be estimated within limits prescribed by meteorology and topography. The use of air for waste disposal might be considered similar to the use of water for the same purpose; in some areas, such a use of water has been subject to regulation by market economics.

There is no *a priori* reason why charges cannot be levied for using air as a waste disposal system, whether these charges are based on the amount of emissions or on a permit system with or without graded fees. However, applying such economic restraints is complicated by the difficulty of determining fair and equitable charges.

The Air Conservation Commission is aware that the use of these restraints is untested, and it reserves judgment as to whether they are practical. It has no reservations, however, on the need for additional work on the economic aspects of pollution, its abatement, and the conservation of the atmosphere. The alternatives to more research could be an economically unnecessary increase in pollution on the one hand, or a technically unnecessary control on the other.

Zoning

In metropolitan areas with acute or threatened problems, particularly where rapid change in industry, transportation, use of land, or energy production is contemplated, the allocation of air resources through the zoning of land is worth further study. Communities that have detailed information on pollutant emissions, on the probable distributions of their atmospheric trajectories, and on other details concerning the magnitude and behavior of the airshed, may also consider zoning the air. In general, such policies should be designed so that the unavoidable sources of emission are located in areas that are likely to have rapid dispersion, or the most effective processes of atmospheric self-cleansing, or where the effluent will do the least damage because of the absence of sensitive receptors.

Zoning in air conservation, whether it is based on the use of land or air, implies a permit to add pollutants to the atmosphere. This can be justified only when there is some reason to believe that the added pollutants will not produce effects undesirable for the community. Such a decision requires technical information about the dilution capacity and self-cleansing potential of the airshed.

Prohibition

Metropolitan areas with acute problems, or those that are threatened with an acute problem, might consider a policy of not allowing any new industry that would produce significant emissions. Such a policy might, for example, require that power plants be located only in areas where their emissions could not produce undesirable effects during the period of their expected useful life. (Such a plan would require a prediction of the likelihood of sensitive receptors being located in the immediate vicinity during the same period of time.) A variation of such a policy would be one that barred an industry with preventable pollution from establishing itself without effective control equipment.

Such policies might curtail the rate of industrial growth in a community, or they might increase the costs of industrial products or electrical energy. The evaluation of such policies, including an evaluation of the costs of existing air pollution or the cost of future air pollution, is quite difficult. Nevertheless, methods for obtaining these cost estimates can be developed, and the fact that the effort is rarely made only emphasizes the need for more attention to the problem.

Better Use of Land

Some methods of utilizing the land are believed to increase natural atmospheric self-cleansing. For example, some believe that forests or greenbelt areas naturally facilitate the cleansing of pollutants from the atmosphere. However, careful quantitative studies are needed, including study of the various patterns for using land and their relative effectiveness for a given pattern of total emissions.

Among the alternatives for areas with acute air pollution problems might be the adoption of a policy of not permitting any additional allocation of land for residential or industrial use. While the consequence of such a policy would appear to be economic stagnation, this may not be the case, particularly when associated with other policies for optimal land use of already developed areas within a region. Policies already in effect in limited areas exclude commercial or industrial operations through conventional zoning regulations. The application of such regulations, however, to an area as large as a single airshed would have radically different effects on local government, on revenues from property taxes, and on the relative value of real property.

Even if such policies were adopted, an increase in per capita use of energy and changing patterns of transportation could still lead to deterioration of air quality. An alternative policy would be to permit residential, industrial, or commercial development when the effects of the policy on air quality can be clearly determined in advance and found to be tolerable. Ambient air quality standards may be used to define tolerable levels. (Such effects should be extrapolated to a reasonable period in the future with reasonable trends in quantitative and qualitative aspects of emissions.)

Power Plants

The consequences of emissions from thermoelectric power installations deserve special consideration because of (i) the steady increase in the per capita and gross consumption of prime energy, and (ii) the desire to develop power-generating facilities that will produce the maximum amount of power at a minimum cost. These factors encourage the location of these facilities along the shoreline of urban areas on the West Coast and in the center of metropolitan areas on the East Coast because of the availability of large amounts of ocean or river water for cooling and condensing steam. The location of such plants, however, produces a source of emissions almost inevitably upwind of major concentrations of population and human enterprises. Many observers believe that, in the

West, such power installations should be in the interior desert areas, and in the East, they should be at the pithead of the major coal-producing areas. Existing technology now permits the economical long-distance transmission of electrical power at high voltages. (While the pollutant potential of coal- or oil-fired power plants is substantially different from that of nuclear power installations, the pollution distribution patterns, and hence the policies concerning location, may be very similar for such plants.) One alternative policy is to use such fuels as natural gas, rather than coal, for power installations that must be located where their emissions could have a substantial effect on metropolitan air quality.

Motor Vehicles

Because the contribution of motor vehicle emissions to metropolitan air pollution has been well documented, the planning and development of urban transportation must take this factor into account.

In the presence of a stringent urban industrial control program, the major air pollution problem remaining in Los Angeles is the photochemical reaction of motor vehicle pollutants. The urban transportation complex in Los Angeles is based on the unstated assumption that the freeway system is the equivalent of a mass rapid transit scheme. This assumption is one factor in the complexity of the Los Angeles air pollution problem.

A number of alternatives are theoretically available for attacking the motor vehicle exhaust problem: (i) Taxation or other devices might be used to restrict the size of motor vehicles and to penalize fuel consumption or fuel inefficiency. (ii) Efforts could be made to develop principles of fuel combustion that would be inherently more efficient. (iii) Efforts might be directed toward developing a competitive system of mass rapid transit. (iv) Policies might require the development and installation of systems to control motor vehicle exhaust.

Alternative (i) might result in a drastic rearrangement of the economic factors with respect to residence and transportation patterns. Alternative (ii) suggests the engineering developments that are needed, but perhaps incentives for these developments could be strengthened. For alternative (iii), there are many justifications in the long run, and air conservation is only one of them. The tendency to defer the development of transit planning in many communities will only tend to aggravate the matter. Alternative (iv) is the one that has been adopted in California. But even its effect will be costly and, as long as the population and the use of motor vehicles continue to increase, it will yield only temporary benefit—temporary viewed in terms of 5 to 15 years.

Radioactive Air Pollution

Certain radioactive pollutants are highly persistent and, when forced into the stratosphere during a nuclear weapons test, may fall out slowly. They cannot be made harmless by any means now known to man. Some of the pollutants can cause damage to various parts of the body and can produce changes in genetic material—changes that are irreversible.

It is extremely difficult to assess the possible effects of radioactive pollution on man. The effects may be masked, since they are the kind that might be produced by pollution or they might also be produced by other factors. Under such circumstances, any assessment of effects must depend heavily on statistical data. But man is both the observer and the observed; the life span of the scientist and his subject are the same. It might be several generations before the scientist will have the evidence necessary to say that pollution probably does or does not produce certain effects. And here is the heart of the matter. If the evidence did show that there had indeed been an effect, and that the effect was undesirable, the knowledge would be of limited use by that time. The damage would have been done, it would be irreversible, and the persistent, steady fallout of radioactive contaminants might continue to inflict damage.

At the same time, nuclear devices are the major weapons in the arsenals of the major world powers. Any nation with pretensions to such status feels compelled to develop its own arsenal, and in the development, to test nuclear weapons. In addition, the test ban agreement that exists not only does not cover new members of the "nuclear club," but its effectiveness also depends on the willingness of its participants to honor it. Resumption of tests by one nation tempts others to do the same, presumably because additional tests advance the knowledge and the sophistication of a nation's weaponry.

Even if, by some flash of wisdom that has not yet illuminated man's political horizons, the threat of war and the desire for testing should vanish, the problem of radioactive pollution would not. For nuclear energy offers too many possibilities in its peacetime applications to be ignored.

The problem of radioactive pollution of the atmosphere represents a great challenge to the scientific community. The scientist who decides to take part in formulating public policy on this problem engages himself in an activity where the stakes are high and the disagreements are intense. But if he fails to engage himself, he leaves the problem to others—others who perhaps are less well informed on a matter of critical importance. The scientist is not being asked to abandon the objectivity that he cherished in the laboratory; rather he is being asked to bring it out of the laboratory so that it can play an important role in decisions that affect man's fate.

The Tasks Ahead

The quality of the air that our children and their children will breathe depends to a large extent on what we do or fail to do during the next several years. The tasks ahead are many and complex. If they seem too overwhelming, we may derive some small comfort from the fact that the sooner we start the more easily they will be accomplished.

Tasks of the Scientific Community

The Air Conservation Commission believes that the scientific community must undertake three broad tasks:

1) To engage in more extensive research on the nature of air pollutants, how they interact, what their effects are, how they can be controlled more effectively and economically, and how they are

carried from one place to another, including how such transmission can be predicted.

2) To become familiar, if they are not already, with information about air conservation and air pollution, even if the information is outside immediate professional concerns.

3) To participate in the process of informing public bodies and the public about the nature of air pollution and the possibilities for air conservation.

The Commission is, in effect, calling upon scientists to recognize that the products of the efforts of the scientific community have imposed new obligations and offer new opportunities.

The Tasks of Government

The Commission believes that the appropriate levels of government should undertake five tasks:

1) To recognize and state the need for air conservation efforts, and to gather the information needed to develop the necessary programs.

2) To support appropriate research.

3) To establish monitoring systems.

4) To develop air conservation and air pollution control programs, making use of necessary enforcement procedures.

5) To support and participate in educational programs that are aimed at the broadest possible public understanding of air pollution problems and air conservation needs.

Different levels of government can perform some of these functions more effectively than others. Thus, gathering basic data and sponsoring basic research can be performed most effectively by the federal government; but some states and several metropolitan areas may also be able to make significant contributions. Federal and state governments and international agencies could probably handle monitoring most effectively. The development of air conservation and control programs have, until now, been viewed as tasks for local governments; and this is proper. But both federal and state governments might also have an interest in cooperating with local areas.

The Task of the Citizen

The best program in the world can founder on the rock of public antipathy, or it can sink in the sea of public apathy. The Air Conservation Commission believes that the public should undertake three tasks:

1) To become familiar with information about air conservation and air pollution, calling upon the scientific community and the government for assistance.

2) To consider the problems of all segments of the community: industries, utilities, and private citizens.

3) To urge, permit, and require that the appropriate governments take the action needed to insure that the quality of the air is at the level desired by the people within its jurisdiction, and to take the necessary steps to insure that this air quality is maintained.

A Challenge and an Opportunity

Man has been extravagant and wasteful with the world in which he lives. He has ravaged its forests and soils and has plundered its mineral wealth. He has squandered and soiled its waters. And he has contaminated its air.

No reasonable person would suggest that man should not use his environment. And no reasonable person would suggest that man revert to his primitive past. But no reasonable person would condone the wasteful excesses that have characterized man.

The problem of air pollution will probably never be "solved." But, if man is willing to recognize that the problem exists, if he is prepared to bring to it his political wisdom, scientific knowledge, and technological skills, and if he is willing to work with nature instead of against it, then he can leave to his children and his children's children something more valuable and more necessary to human life than any of the manufactured products of his civilization. He can bequeath to them the blessing of clean air.

PART 2

Summary

of the Facts

Summary of the Facts

The initial evolution of man took place in an environment that, whatever its other hazards, was characterized by the virtually unlimited availability of what we now refer to as "pure air." That is, man's respiratory apparatus was evolved to breathe a mixture of nitrogen, oxygen, water vapor, and small traces of carbon dioxide, the rare gases, and a few other simple substances. Although there were natural outbreaks of pollution from volcanoes and the like, the usual response was migration; there was not enough preference for one area over another to hold a tribe in an uncomfortable location. Then mankind began to build or seek shelter for itself, and discovered the use of fire—the deliberate release of stored energy to modify the local environment.

The discovery of how to control fire also marked the start of air pollution. As tribes settled in villages, and villages grew into cities, the levels of concentration of the combustion products, and of the other by-products of human living, increased. This early urbanization was accompanied by the first evidences of industrialization, which further added to the general pool of atmospheric substances to which man was not genetically accustomed. However, since the average human life span was only a few decades, the slow chronic workings of airborne toxicants probably did not have time to seriously affect the human system before death claimed it.

The past century has seen a radical change in man's existence. Improvements in nutrition, agriculture, communication, hygiene, and medicine have extended the human life span tremendously. During this same period, improvements in heating methods and

23

standards of sanitation were so great that the level of insult to the organism probably decreased substantially. As industry continued to introduce new substances into the air, it also put into effect improved industrial hygiene practices, which further decreased the exposure of the individual to high concentrations of many toxic materials.

This environmental improvement, however, much as it may have ameliorated conditions inside homes and factories, was accomplished in most cases by removing the objectionable substances to the outside air. This process, accompanied by rapid industrial development and concentration, began producing, in the outdoor air of the cities, the phenomena that had previously occurred indoors. There were even a few catastrophic, acute pollution episodes, such as the one at Donora, Pennsylvania.

Meanwhile, increasing population and increasing longevity, together with a high standard of living, generated pressure from all population groups for cleaner air. The youngest, the oldest, and those whom medicine had spared without fully curing make up groups who are especially sensitive to pollutants. The younger adults, with long lives ahead, object to any threat to longevity. All ages and conditions have become intolerant of discomfort and annoyance.

Finally, the enormous increase in world population now taking place, an increase apparently destined to continue, raises an entirely new kind of problem. The oxygen in our atmosphere is not a permanent feature, but is rather the result of a delicate balance between its formation in the photosynthetic process and its removal by animals, by combustion, and principally by the slow oxidation of minerals on the earth's surface. This balance completely renews the oxygen supply in the atmosphere in the course of a very small number of millenia. A change of a few percent in the rate of either production or removal could well result in an enormous change in the steady oxygen level.

Although it is unlikely that man or his machines could "breathe" enough oxygen to seriously contribute to upsetting this balance, he could, either through nuclear war or through sheer numbers, destroy enough green plants to seriously decrease the renewal rate of atmospheric oxygen. At present there are no data on which to base a quantitative statement; however, the possibility seems very real. It has also been postulated that the amount of carbon dioxide that human activities are injecting into the atmosphere may be sufficient to upset the global balance.

These considerations suggest that the time has come for man to stop regarding the atmosphere as unlimited and to undertake its conservation.

It may be worthwhile at the outset to restate the fundamental nature of atmospheric pollution. All creatures live by a process of converting one form of energy into another. Man has raised himself above the animal level to the extent that he deliberately converts this energy by processes outside the limitations of his body. All extensions of the human senses, of the human frame, and of the human muscle, which is to say, our tools and the trappings of civilization, use this energy. Energy conversion has certain material by-products. When they become airborne, in sufficient concentrations to be troublesome to man, we call the resulting airborne material "air pollution." At a very high stage of technology, pollution may also occur from by-products of processes other than the liberation of energy, but they are seldom as widespread as the energy by-products.

Some material by-products from this process of energy conversion are inevitable. The only choices are the relative proportions of the various by-products and the way in which they will be removed. Nothing is gained by removing them from the air if we thereby pollute the waters of nearby streams and make them unusable, or contaminate the soil to the extent that it will not support vegetation. In some respects, the problem resembles the old one of attempting to bury a pile of dirt.

In order to obtain an optimum balance of benefit and risk for ourselves and for our posterity, the problem of air conservation is to select the appropriate means for either disposing of or using these by-products and to employ appropriate forms of energy. The definition of such an optimum—the risks we are prepared to take for the benefits we enjoy—is not a matter of scientific judgment, but rather one of moral and ethical judgment; hence, it will not be discussed here. Mankind will probably face enough moral decisions during the next decade to keep occupied; probably the precise setting of an optimum balance will not receive a great deal of attention. However, mankind must ultimately make such a decision; it must decide what the balance of risk and benefit will be. We cannot abandon our technology without relapsing into savagery. But we cannot continue our present course of technological development without the risk of making the earth unfit for human habitation.

The Pollutants

The sources, then, of air pollutants are anywhere that energy is converted under human direction. From the smallest hearth fire to the latest factory, all contribute their share. The pollutants are even greater in number than the sources. However, a small number of groups of substances comprise the vast bulk of human emissions to the atmosphere and they have been singled out for special attention in this report.

The greatest single product of the energy conversion processes is of least concern here—water. Only in very rare instances can it qualify as a pollutant. Occasionally, the vapor from the stack of a large factory may reduce visibility on a nearby highway. But normally, water vapor does not represent an air pollution problem.

Carbon dioxide is next in quantity of the waste products produced by our use of organic fuels. It is naturally abundant in the atmosphere, and mankind is well adapted to living with widely varying levels of it. However, while water vapor precipitates out of the atmosphere to join the oceans, carbon dioxide normally remains in a gaseous state for a long time. The liberation of this gas has been so great that we have already increased the global concentration by a substantial figure—around 5 percent; the exact figure is still in dispute. This increase has had no effect on any known living organism. However, carbon dioxide is intimately involved in the mechanism that maintains the overall temperature of the earth. Although so many factors are involved in this overall atmospheric heat balance that it is impossible to evaluate the effect of any given increase in atmospheric carbon dioxide, a continued increase over a long period could possibly change the global climate. And, if such a change were to involve an increase of the earth's temperature, thereby causing a large portion of the global ice caps to melt and the oceans to rise, available land area would be reduced at precisely the time when more land is needed for an increasing population. In the light of this possibility, the use of fossil fuels as the principal source of our energy should be continually evaluated.

The complete combustion of carbonaceous fuels produces carbon dioxide; the incomplete combustion, characteristic of many processes involving the conversion of energy, yields carbon monoxide. In American cities, the primary source of this gas is the automobile. Carbon monoxide begins to be hazardous to most human beings at concentrations of about 100 parts per million (ppm) if experienced over a period of several hours. Particularly susceptible individuals may be affected at lower levels. Although the toxic level seems very high when compared with other pollutant gases, this level has actually been reached occasionally in areas where traffic is heavy; more frequent occurrences may be expected unless automotive emissions can be effectively controlled.

In addition to substances emitted in massive amounts, there are a variety of materials that normally occur in much lower concentrations. However, these materials are much more toxic. Sulfur dioxide and the sulfuric acid that forms when the gas comes in contact with air and water seldom reach levels above a few parts per million. However, the present consensus is that these two substances have been principal factors in all the air pollution disasters of recent history, including the London smog of 1952 in which some 4000 persons died. (There are many scientists who believe that factors as yet undiscovered contributed materially to these deaths, but most of them would identify sulfur dioxide and sulfuric acid as the major causative agents, perhaps combined with soot or other particles.) Sulfur dioxide results primarily from the combustion of coal or oil, both of which contain substantial percentages of sulfur in various chemical forms. To some extent in the combustion itself, and to a greater extent in the external atmosphere, sulfur dioxide is converted by the action of atmospheric oxygen and water to sulfuric acid. Sulfur dioxide by itself is extremely irritating to the upper respiratory tract in concentrations of a few parts per million. Sulfuric acid appears as a fine mist that can be carried deep into the lungs to attack sensitive tissues. In addition, droplets of sulfuric acid carry absorbed sulfur dioxide far deeper into the system than the free gas alone could penetrate, thus spreading the effect of this irritant over the entire respiratory tract. On the other hand, because of the ease with which sulfur dioxide is converted into sulfuric acid and sulfates, its lifetime in the atmosphere is seldom more than a few days. Consequently, it would not be expected to accumulate in the atmosphere.

Hydrogen sulfide can result from a variety of industrial and other processes, but it usually enters the atmosphere as a result of the accumulation of industrial wastes in stagnant waters. Here bacterial action reduces the sulfur-containing compounds to hydrogen sulfide, which is relatively insoluble in water. It has the well-known odor of rotten eggs and it is highly objectionable. In high concentrations, it is also rapidly lethal. However, there are only a few cases in which concentrations of hydrogen sulfide in the open atmosphere exceeded the level of mere nuisance. (In one such case, a score of deaths resulted from an accidental release from a refinery in Poza Rica, Mexico.) The bacterial processes described constantly occur in nature, and by far the bulk of the total sulfur found in the atmosphere comes from natural causes. However, concentrations at any one place are usually not sufficient to be' detected by the senses, or, in fact, by any but the most delicate measuring devices.

There are six known oxides of nitrogen, and there is presumptive evidence for a seventh. However, only two are normally considered as pollutants: nitric oxide and nitrogen dioxide. These are what might be called "status symbol" pollutants. Only a highly mechanized and motorized community is likely to suffer serious pollution from them. Nitric oxide, the primary product, is formed when combustion takes place at a sufficiently high temperature to cause reaction between the nitrogen and oxygen of the air. Such temperatures are reached only in highly efficient combustion processes or when combustion takes place at high pressure. A great deal of nitrogen is fixed in the latter way in automobile cylinders. Electrical power plants and other very large energy-conversion processes will also fix nitrogen in this fashion. However, in most cities, automobiles are the largest single source.

Nitric oxide is generally emitted as such into the atmosphere. However, a complex of processes, some of them photochemical in nature, may convert a substantial portion of the nitric oxide to

nitrogen dioxide, a considerably more toxic gas and the only important and widespread pollutant gas that is colored. As a result, nitrogen dioxide can significantly affect visibility. Nitrogen oxides are
also liberated from a variety of chemical processes, such as in the
manufacture of guncotton and nitric acid. In large-scale pollution,
these sources are usually less significant than the broad area source
represented by vehicular traffic.

There is little or no ozone emitted as such into the atmosphere.
However, this gas, which is extremely toxic, is formed in the atmosphere on sunny days as a result of the interaction of nitrogen oxides
with certain organic compounds.

In addition to the inorganic gases just mentioned, nearly any other
objectionable inorganic gaseous material that is used in industry
can become a pollutant if it escapes into the atmosphere. However,
these are not the general emissions of what might be called the
metabolic processes of civilization and they are likely to be restricted to a few locations. Consequently, only one of them, hydrogen fluoride, deserves separate attention. Because of its extreme
toxicity for some living organisms, it is likely to be an acute problem wherever materials containing fluorides are processed. Hydrogen fluoride is apparently taken up from the air by nearly all plants,
and certain species are damaged by concentrations as low as 1 part
per billion. Furthermore, since vegetation tends to concenetrate the
fluoride that it receives, continuing low atmospheric levels of fluoride can produce toxic levels in forage and probably in some leafy
vegetables as well. The manufacture of phosphate fertilizer, the
smelting of certain iron ores, and the manufacture of aluminum
are all sources of hydrogen fluoride gas as well as of some particulate
fluoride.

The organic gases are very numerous. The chemical process industries inevitably release into the atmosphere some of almost
everything they manufacture. However, only a few general classes
need separate consideration since a number of the organic materials
that can be identified in the atmosphere appear to have no adverse
effects.

Probably the simplest organic substance significant to air pollution is ethylene. Aside from its participation in the "smog" reaction,
it is a potent phytotoxicant (plant damaging agent) in its own right.

Concentrations of a few parts per billion, for example, are extremely damaging to orchids, and only slightly higher concentrations adversely affect the growth of tomatoes. Ethylene, like the bulk of other simple hydrocarbons, emanates in part from industrial sources, but it is primarily a product of automotive exhaust.

The higher members of the series to which ethylene belongs, the olefins, appear to have no direct effect upon vegetation or animal life. However, when they (together with several other classes of organics) are exposed to sunlight in the presence of nitrogen dioxide or nitric oxide, an extremely complex reaction sequence ensues. The end products appear to be ozone, aldehydes, and a variety of organic compounds that contain nitrogen. In adequate concentrations, this mixture injures plants and irritates the eyes and mucous membranes in human beings. There is some indication that animals are also affected. This reaction was first noticed in Los Angeles, and is therefore popularly referred to as the "Los Angeles smog reaction." The substances needed for this reaction can be produced by the right combination of industries, but they are present in almost ideal concentrations in automotive exhaust. Consequently, the presence of this type of pollution is characteristic of areas having a high density of automobile traffic.

Some of the aldehydes characteristic of the Los Angeles smog can also arise from other sources. Formaldehyde and acrolein, which are particularly irritating to the eyes and nose, are found in the smoke of poorly operating incinerators and also in stockyards and a number of other sources.

Mercaptans, which are organic substances related to hydrogen sulfide, are among the most odorous materials known. Aside from chemical processes that directly employ or produce these compounds, they are undesired by-products of Kraft paper mills and of some petroleum refineries.

Finally, there is a large class of organic vapors generally referred to as "solvents." They escape from such processes as dry cleaning and painting. They are very diverse chemically, and some of them can probably participate in the smog reaction. Others have objectionable odors. Most of them are toxic to some degree, although it would be difficult to produce toxic concentrations over any period of time in the open air.

Aside from these gases and vapors, large quantities of more or less finely divided particulate matter are put into the air or are formed there as a result of human activities. The largest single particle in nearly all urban atmospheres is dust. This word is used here to denote soil from areas denuded of vegetation, whipped up by natural wind, by the passage of vehicular traffic, or by agricultural activities. For the most part it is without physiological effect, but it is a very substantial nuisance. The particle sizes are usually large, so that, under most circumstances, such dust will not travel great distances. Obvious exceptions occur during times of high winds, as was demonstrated during the dust storms of the middle 1930's.

In many cities, the next most prevalent substance among the airborne particles is soot. Soot is very finely divided carbon clumped together into long chains and networks. Because the individual particles are so fine, they present an enormous surface per unit weight. This surface is extremely active, and it can absorb a large variety of substances from its environment. Soot generally carries with it a substantial load of heavy hydrocarbons that are formed simultaneously with it in smoky flames. These hydrocarbons include organics that are either known or are suspected causes of environmental cancer on sufficiently prolonged contact. Soot can also act under some circumstances in the same manner as sulfuric acid mist; that is, it can absorb vapors that would normally be removed in the upper respiratory tract and carry them deep into the lungs. In addition to all the known or suspected physiological effects, soot is a nuisance because it obscures visibility and soils buildings and clothing. The fall of combined soot, dust, and other particulate materials on a single square foot of horizontal surface in a city may easily exceed a pound per year.

Another variety of fine particles is one of the end results of the photochemical smog reaction. The nature of the particulate matter formed is not understood, but it is oily, not easily wetted, and of a size that is highly effective in obscuring visibility.

The typical urban atmosphere also contains particles caused by practically every process carried on within the city. There are lead salts from the combustion of leaded gasoline and particles of airborne ash from all the solid and liquid fuels burned in the area. The metallurgical industries, the manufacture of fertilizer, the storing of

grain, and the milling of flour all add particles that are characteristic of their own processes.

Finally, there is a quantity of material generally referred to as
"resuspended matter," refuse dropped into the streets or onto the
ground, there to be slowly pulverized and blown into the air. Bits
of newspaper, residue of plant matter, particles of glass and tire
rubber, all go to make up the complex found suspended in the
atmosphere of a typical city.

There are two additional classes of particulate matter which,
while not of peculiarly urban origin, have had a substantial impact
on human well-being and have received a great deal of attention
recently. The first of these are the economic poisons. They include
insecticides, herbicides, and other chemicals used by man. A number of them are normally disseminated through the air, and some
portion may well find its way substantial distances from the intended
site of application. While many of them are toxic to man, they can
also harm other forms of life not intended as their targets.

The second category is radioactive material. There are three major
sources of radioactive gases and particles. The first is research, which
is generally not an important source of contamination except in the
case of a major accident. The second is nuclear power plants, which
almost continuously give off some gaseous materials. There is no
evidence to date that their accumulation in the atmosphere is a
major hazard. The nuclear power industry is said to be one of the
most carefully controlled of all industries on the face of the earth.
However, an accidental discharge can distribute highly toxic concentrations over a rather large area. The final source is, of course,
nuclear weapons. They belong in a special category, not because
of any chemical or physiological difference in the compounds involved or in their effects, but because the political and economic
considerations that govern their use are so special.

Transport of Pollutants

Once a pollutant, or a group of pollutants from a given source, has
been ejected into the air, its movement with the air will depend
upon a number of factors.

Particles larger than approximately 1 micron are significantly affected by gravity. They tend to settle out from the air and are eventually deposited, the distance from the source usually depending on the size of the particle. In addition to gravity, the movement of pollutants is affected by turbulent diffusion. The wind contains many eddies, ranging in size from millimeters to miles, and these eddies tend to disperse the cloud of pollutants.

Less important over short distances, but of crucial importance on a large scale, are the effects of aggregation and growth. Particles in a pollution cloud tend to increase in size, sometimes by collisions that form larger aggregates, and sometimes by the condensation of vapors on them, with or without chemical reaction. This process may occur in and under water clouds, where the water droplets may form on the particles, thereby increasing their size, or falling raindrops may collide with the particles, thereby carrying them to the ground.

At substantial wind speeds, pollutants are rapidly removed from the point of origin and turbulent diffusion usually dilutes them below the level of significant effect within a short distance. However, under some conditions, turbulence can bring the plume from a stack to the ground in great loops at a point quite close to the source and before extensive dilution has occurred, resulting in brief exposure to extremely high concentrations. Thus, a period of strong winds is likely to be characterized by low mean values of pollutants, with occasional high peaks of short duration near the point of origin. When the air is still, both horizontally and vertically, all pollutants tend to stay near their source and to blend in slowly with other sources in the same area. Generally the result is a very high average level of pollution with a few abrupt short-term variations.

While the horizontal travel of pollutants is largely controlled by wind velocity, the primary factor that regulates the vertical dispersal of pollution is the vertical profile of temperature. The rate of temperature change with height is referred to as the "lapse rate." In the lower atmosphere the temperature usually decreases with increasing height.

A substantial amount of misinformation has been disseminated concerning the effect of lapse rate on pollution. The facts are rather simple. According to well-established physical law, if a parcel of air is carried from a low altitude to a high one, it will expand with the decreasing pressure and its temperature will decrease, provided there is no exchange of heat with its surroundings. By the same token, if the parcel of air is taken to a lower altitude without gaining or losing heat, its temperature will increase. For a given change of altitude, the corresponding temperature change is constant and determinable. This rate of change is referred to as the "adiabatic lapse rate."

If the actual lapse rate is greater than this theoretical rate, a parcel of surface air that begins to rise will continue to do so. This situation is called "unstable." If, on the other hand, the change in temperature with height is less than the adiabatic rate, surface air that begins to rise will tend to sink back to the surface; this is called a "stable" lapse rate. If there is no change in temperature with altitude, or an increase, the atmosphere will be particularly stable. The difference between this and the unstable situation is one of degree, not of kind. An increase in temperature with altitude, a so-called inversion, is not a unique phenomenon.

During unstable conditions, there is a great deal of vertical mixing, in addition to whatever horizontal dispersion the wind may induce, and so the dilution of pollutants takes place in three dimensions. On the other hand, under conditions of high stability, vertical dispersion will be greatly inhibited; if this is accompanied by low winds, a layer of highly polluted air may build up over a large area, such as an entire city or an entire basin.

Shifts from stable to unstable conditions and back are set in motion by three major forces. Since winds tend to have vertical eddies, and since rapid vertical air motions tend to be adiabatic, the wind helps to establish a precisely adiabatic lapse rate. The sun, by heating the surface more than the air, tends to steepen the lapse rate and thus acts as a force for instability. Conversely, at night the ground loses more heat by radiation than the air does, which tends to make the surface colder than the layer overlaying it. This cooling of the ground is a force working for stability. Under most circumstances, there is a continuous diurnal cycle from stability to instability and back. When, for a variety of reasons, this cycle is broken, a serious accumulation of pollutants is possible.

The Fate of Pollutants

For virtually every known pollutant, there are natural processes that tend to remove it from the atmosphere, thus preventing man from smothering in his own by-products.

Reference was made earlier to the tendency of particulate pollutants to coagulate, to increase in size, and to fall. Rain and snow carry large amounts of both particulate and gaseous pollutants out of the atmosphere and into the soil and the water of the earth. Trees and grasses act like the fibers of an enormous filter mat to collect particles and some gases.

The oxygen of the air combines with many pollutants, either directly or indirectly, gradually changing them into forms that are more readily removed. In many cases, sunlight plays a role in this reaction, and frequently particulate matter is formed from gases. These particles can then enter the cycle of filtration, aggregation, and washout, and can thus be removed from the atmosphere. It is worth noting that the droplets of sulfuric acid that have been implicated by many as contributing to the death toll in London, and the photochemical smog that is characteristic of the West Coast, are actually steps in the atmosphere's own process of self-purification. The misfortune is that these intermediate products are physiologically active and that they frequently form in heavily inhabited areas.

A few miscellaneous substances do not participate rapidly enough in the reactions of photochemical oxidation to be removed by that process. The outstanding examples are methane and a few of its relatives and carbon monoxide. They are ultimately destroyed by oxidation, entirely in the gas phase, and become carbon dioxide, although the rate of destruction is not known. Carbon dioxide appears to be removed effectively by direct solution in the ocean, the disposal point for most of the soluble inorganic substances. The capacity of the ocean to ultimately consume such materials by dilution is enormous. However, our rapid production of carbon dioxide seems to be outstripping the ocean's ability to remove it from the atmosphere. It appears that roughly one-third of the carbon dioxide put into the air by combustion remains there and, as noted earlier, it may have an effect on the world's weather.

Thus, the atmosphere has tremendous powers to dilute, disperse, and destroy a large variety of substances that man, for one reason or another, elects to discharge into it. Pollution occurs when these processes cannot keep up with the rate of discharge, and when this happens, only one more factor is needed to constitute pollution—a susceptible receptor, such as man.

Man removes some of the pollutants from the air, for if he did not, the pollutants would not affect him. (The only exception is when pollution is manifested by loss of visibility. This can have economic repercussions in delaying aircraft schedules, in increasing automobile accidents, and by making a location less favorable to paying tourists, or its effect may be purely aesthetic.)

Pollutants collect on, and may affect, buildings, plants, and animals, including man. They enter the lungs of creatures that breathe the air. With the pollution density of the atmosphere increasing rapidly, the possibility of any pollutant leaving the atmosphere without contacting man, his property, plants, or animals is becoming increasingly small. Although it is certainly necessary to use the atmosphere as one of the places to dispose of our wastes, it is going to become more and more difficult to find a parcel of air that can be used for waste disposal and that can adequately detoxify its load of pollutants before it is needed again.

Control

The first and most obvious solution, historically, to the problem of a "dirty" industry is to move it out of town. This has also been, historically, a quite unsatisfactory solution; the town has often promptly grown out until it encompassed the industry. Attempts have been made to segregate industry in areas generally downwind of the residential portion of the city. This has at least two weaknesses. The first arises from the problem of transporting workers to these segregated sites, and sometimes the pollution from the workers' automobiles has added as much pollution as the industry would have had it been close to the population center. The other weakness arises from the facts of meteorology. The wind simply does not blow from the prevailing direction at all times. Consequently, this particular approach can succeed only where it is possible for industry to suspend emissions during periods of adverse wind.

Another widely used technique, particularly in the power industry, is the erection of extremely tall stacks, which usually also have very high air velocities in them. As a result, pollutants are discharged into the atmosphere at high levels, and their vertical velocity tends to carry them still higher. It is thus hoped that the dispersive processes in the atmosphere will have diluted the effluents below the level of physiological significance before they reach the ground. This technique has considerable merit, but it is not a complete guarantee against an occasional very high concentration reaching the ground. As noted before, during periods of high wind, the turbulent processes of the atmosphere can bring clouds of undiluted effluent into inhabited areas.

In most industries it is at least theoretically possible, and in many cases it is economically feasible, to remove the bulk of the pollutants from the effluent stream before it is discharged into the atmosphere. There are devices for removing nearly all particulate pollutants and the bulk of the gases if they are in sufficiently high concentrations. However, some industries are characterized by an enormous total volume of effluent that contains impurities at rather low concentrations. The actual discharge in terms of tons per hour may be quite large, but the concentration in the effluent air stream can be so low that efficient removal of the pollutants is extremely expensive.

Another very general problem with techniques for cleaning the air is the disposal of the collected material. It is generally unacceptable to solve an air pollution problem by generating a water pollution problem. In some industries the recovered material may have substantial economic value. In other cases, extensive research may be necessary to find uses for these materials. Economics may become extremely important in the problem; for example, the potentially recoverable by-product sulfur from all present emissions into the atmosphere considerably exceeds the entire primary production of sulfur in the United States. The sudden entrance of this recovered sulfur into the market could be disruptive.

In some cases, it is possible to avoid emissions into the atmosphere by simply modifying the processes being used. The main obstacle frequently is tradition. Certainly those cities that have changed from heating homes by coal to gas have greatly cut down on their concentrations of soot and sulfur compounds in the atmosphere. Tradition is partly to blame for the air pollution problems of English cities, since central heating, even by coal, is considerably cleaner than the traditional coal fire in every room. But it is also true that the first cost of conversion to central heating is also a deterring factor. Sometimes a troublesome emission of solvents into the atmosphere can be averted by changing to a less volatile solvent. The advent of latex-based paints has decreased the amount of turpentine given off in painting homes. These last examples are perhaps trivial, but they illustrate in familiar terms the potential of modifying a process.

A final and little-explored approach is simply better collaboration with nature. It was noted earlier that air pollution is the result of man's conversion of energy, which he applies in order to oppose or to overcome nature—to create heat when it is cold, to create light when it is dark, and to substitute the strength of machines for the weakness of the human frame. This opposition to nature has become so much a part of him that he now sometimes chooses the more difficult way simply because it is more in opposition to nature. Thus, he builds houses in hot climates without the large roof overhang that would decrease the necessary air conditioning load and he builds houses in cold areas with enormous windows, and thereby increases the amount of fuel burned.

There is, of course, no panacea for air pollution. The intelligent location of sources of pollution is an important first step. Discharge of pollutants high in the air will compensate to some degree for the inevitable eventual crowding together of activities in the horizontal plane. Proper choice of fuels and raw materials will decrease process effluents. The removal of some of these effluents before they are emitted into the atmosphere will further decrease the burden that the atmosphere is called upon to destroy. Finally, an intelligent program of general conservation—the use of energies available in nature, the avoidance of certain frills that produce pollution out of balance with the benefits they create, and the selection of alternatives to highly polluting activities—will decrease the incidence of high levels of pollution. None of these taken alone can solve any substantial portion of the problems that face mankind in its attempt to conserve its atmosphere.

Sociological Aspects

The foregoing has summarized the state of knowledge in the physical and medical sciences and in engineering with regard to pollutants, their effects, and their control. Although the aim of this summary is didactic, not polemic, it leads inescapably to the conclusion that limits must be placed on pollution. The question that remains to be answered is how the scientist-as-citizen can be effective in applying his knowledge as a scientist in order to bring about this necessary curtailment of pollution.

It will be noted later that society generally solves its problems, if they are solved, by first going through a period of trial and error, then finally settling down to a rational study, which leads to the forming of workable policies. A portion of the United States has gone through the first stages of this process and is now in the midst of the final study. One obvious role of the scientist is to assist in disseminating information that can prevent or minimize the trial-and-error stage in his community, thus shortening the time between the initial recognition of an air pollution problem and the formulation of policies, programs, and (usually) laws to meet it.

Law is public policy particularized and systematized. In general, it is not necessary to its enactment that a majority of the public demand a statute, although it is useless to enact a statute that is opposed by the majority. The public excuses itself of concern for detail in law by electing legislators who are supposed to sense the general needs and desires of their constituencies and to translate them into legislation. The legislator usually succeeds in meeting a sufficient portion of the needs and desires of the community to satisfy the majority, or he is not reelected.

However, air conservation is an issue on which the public is unlikely to take a clear stand; the arguments on the opposing side are sufficiently technical so that only the educated minority can grasp them, and after the fact a legislator can claim success regardless of the outcome. If statutes for controlling air pollution are strengthened, he has brought the public cleaner air. If they are relaxed, he has protected their paychecks, and if they are unchanged, he has championed conservatism.

Hence, except in the unlikely event of a public referendum, total public opinion is unlikely to become a motivating force for air conservation. Rather, it is necessary to identify the influential groups on whom the legislators depend for guidance in matters of this sort; they are usually called *opinion leaders*. The opinion leaders, in this case, may or may not be the same individuals who exert primary influence on public opinion in referendums and similar cases in which the opinion of the general public is of consequence. The findings of a number of studies suggest that there are several hierarchies of leaders, depending on the area under consideration.

Such leaders will, in general, hold several value systems involving health, money, aesthetics, tradition, and public image. If there has been no previous air pollution statute, they may well be unaware of the way in which air conservation issues impinge on these value systems. They will also generally have little knowledge of the physical sciences. On the other hand, they will almost certainly be knowledgeable in matters of applied politics.

A number of devices can be utilized to reinforce the impact of the individual on leadership. It is frequently possible to induce local service clubs to schedule programs on air conservation; these are especially effective if the legislator or opinion leader is asked to make the talk. School children who are assigned to write themes on local air pollution problems can be counted on to badger local authorities and local factories for information. Citizens' "anti-smog" committees, while seldom directly effective, serve to inject comment into the news media and to create a climate favorable to the acceptance of pollution control.

Different geographical areas will vary to some degree in the importance attached to the values affected by air pollution. An approach through pure aesthetics is seldom fruitful, unless it is coupled with other values. An argument that pollution obscures the view has little weight of itself. However, an area highly dependent on tourists will immediately see an economic value in the loss of the view. The presence of unpleasant odors is generally evaluated, not for its own sake, but as an assurance (justified or otherwise) that some effects on health are being produced.

An attempt to motivate action for air conservation through an appeal to health values is extremely tempting. It is, as has been noted previously, an area in which the public is sensitive. In any geographical area, there is usually a department of public health that has most of the machinery for carrying out a program of air conservation. Two cautions are in order. The first is that scare tactics seldom produce the desired result. Experience has shown that messages conveying mild anxiety are far more likely to produce reactions than frightening ones. Most individuals seem to tune out highly emotional material.

The other problem is the extreme difficulty of clearly demonstrating that air pollution can be a hazard to health. There is, obviously, an effect in the most acute cases. However, unequivocal proof of chronic effects is still lacking and it may not be available for many years. While it is true that police power does not demand total knowledge, action based entirely upon a health hazard is extremely vulnerable if a legal protest is organized. Although concern for effects on health can certainly be a strong motivating force for air conservation, it is difficult to uphold them as the sole basis for action.

Particularly among cost-conscious individuals, the economic approach is most likely to carry weight. The New York City Department of Air Pollution Control has taken as its slogan, "Clean air costs money; dirty air costs more." Although much work remains to be done on precisely evaluating the cost of dirty air, the existence of a cost is now clearly proved. The best available estimate is of the order of $65 per capita per year for the entire United States. It can also be demonstrated that it is less expensive for industry if a well-designed air pollution statute is in effect before the industry is admitted to the area. Controls can always be built in more cheaply than they can be added at a later date, assuming that there are controls available for the industry. This is a strong argument for action before a serious pollution situation exists.

An economic approach also suggests some interesting alternatives to a flat prohibition of emissions—ways to recover the cost of pollution from individual industries in which the cost of control may exceed either the profit margin on the product or the damage caused.

Air conservation legislation may take many forms, depending on the level of government involved and the purpose to be accomplished. Legislation designed directly to control pollution falls into a small number of categories. The emission of certain substances in objectionable amounts may constitute a nuisance at common law and may be the basis for a damage suit or an injunction. Or, such emissions may be prohibited by exercising the police power of the jurisdiction, by analogy to speed limits, and other necessary limitations of activity. The economic approach suggested has not yet been tried, possibly because legislatures have shied away from a law that explicitly permits air pollution. Finally, the application of the body of laws for the conservation of other resources has not yet been investigated, but it might afford still another approach.

A control statute must be worded so that its interpretation is unequivocal and enforcement is possible. (Laws not having these characteristics are likely to be stricken down by the courts.)

State or federal statutes are less likely to control pollution directly and are more apt to simply facilitate such control. Examples of such statutes are those that state that cities, counties, or larger geographic areas can organize to control pollution and those that establish offices for research, development, training, consultation, and aid to local areas in defining their problems and in drafting their own legislation. Since statutes are confined to the jurisdiction of the legislative bodies enacting them, while air pollution knows no such boundaries, there is an increasing need for legislation that covers entire airsheds with uniform control ordinances.

Legislation to control air pollution directly often specifies legal limits on the emission of pollutants. In this respect, at least two cautionary notes are in order. Legislative inertia can make it extremely difficult to amend these levels in either direction at a later date in the light of new findings. If this sort of problem can be expected, it is frequently preferable to delegate the establishment of such levels to the agency that will be responsible for their enforcement, either the public health agency or an especially created body. The inclusion of requirements for publicity, reasonableness, and the possibility of appeal is generally a sufficient guarantee against

arbitrary action. The second caution is that analyses of air pollutants are seldom absolute. For example, the quantity of settled dust
per unit area is highly dependent upon the shape of the container
used for measuring and its location. It is relatively easy to produce
differences of a factor of 5 by changing the measuring technique.
Thus, airborne concentrations are very likely to be a function of
the measuring technique, and this needs to be specified. On the
other hand, progress in analytical methods is rapid. Many cities are
now faced with the statutory use of outmoded instruments and
methods that have become embalmed in the legal structure. Once
again, the best approach is probably delegating this decision to the
authority that is concerned with the rest of the pollution problem.

Reference has been made to permitted levels of emissions without
suggesting how they might be determined, or what they mean.
There are several techniques for arriving at such figures, some of
which are based more firmly on scientific grounds than others.

If a community has any air pollution legislation whatsoever, it
probably has a statutory limitation on permitted smoke emission.
While this is a highly desirable rule, in most communities it appears
to be based on the legal theory that if you look guilty, you are
guilty.

In other areas, emission standards are based on the state of technology at the time the law is passed, that is, on the thesis that if this
is the best control available to the industry, nothing is gained by
demanding more. This is in accord with the theory of not passing
an unenforceable law. On the other hand, this approach does not
consider the effects on the population and on property that the technologically attainable limit may produce. Furthermore, unless there
is a provision for ready amendment, such a law can become extremely permissive in a short time as technology improves. This
approach also fails to take advantage of the economic approaches
mentioned earlier that would permit some recovery of damages
from industries unable to control their emissions below the damage
point.

Obviously, the above techniques have legislative advantages or
they would not have been enacted. From the scientific standpoint,
it seems more desirable to set standards of cleanliness for the community air, to compare these standards with present performance,

and to infer from them the degree of reduction that is needed to bring the ambient air within safe limits. This approach has been taken in Russia and Czechoslovakia, is in progress in West Germany, and is very well along in California and Colorado as well as in some other states. These standards must be based on the criteria of demonstrable effects on persons, property, plants, and animals, and also on aesthetic values.

The existence of standards based on scientific criteria has a number of salubrious effects. It is still possible to adjust the demands made on various industries to their ability to control their emissions. However, one does so with an idea of the degree to which the area will fail to meet the standards, and with a strong motivation to seek better control methods as soon as possible. Standards can also underline the need for interjurisdictional control measures. If the air that enters the community is already substandard, no amount of cleaning is likely to bring it within standards. Finally, while rules or laws to govern emissions can (theoretically, at least) change with the whim of the controlling authority, standards of air quality change only with the scientific refinement of criteria. They thus serve as a sort of conscience for the community.

It seems likely that if society is to achieve true air conservation, it will need a conscience.

Unsolved Problems

It is unquestionably true that a community can achieve air of almost any desired purity, up to the level of the air entering the area, provided the community is willing to pay the price. In many cases, the present price of pure air far exceeds what the community is willing to pay. The end purpose of continued study must therefore be to decrease the cost of achieving pure air in order to put it within reach of all communities.

Within the pat statements of the nature of pollution are concealed a large number of unresolved problems. Our knowledge of the chemical nature of pollution is at best fragmentary. For example, it has not been possible to synthesize a mixture that has the toxic properties of the London "killer smog" of 1952 by combining all the known contaminants that were measured in it. There are numerous aspects of photochemical pollution that are not yet understood. Our attempts at control can stop being completely empirical only when we understand the chemistry of the pollutant systems.

Too little is known about the processes by which the atmosphere purifies itself. In the field of particulate materials there is a considerable body of knowledge, but even here there are many gaps. The processes by which gaseous pollutants are removed are only now beginning to be explored. Very little is known about the chemical changes in both particulate and gaseous pollutants during their airborne state.

In many cases, such studies, even if undertaken, would yield equivocal results because of shortcomings in the means of determining the individual pollutants. It is, therefore, a matter of high priority to further improve and extend the methods for analyzing polluted atmospheres. There must also be better dissemination of information about the strengths and shortcomings of existing methods. It is now almost impossible for someone new to the field to determine which of the many published methods will actually work under the conditions of the experiments that he plans.

Our knowledge of the physical dispersion processes of the atmosphere is also far less than might be wished. There are excellent equations, both theoretical and empirical, to approximate the long-term average results of dispersive mechanisms. On the other hand, there is almost no information about very short-term averages and the effects of many sources in the same geographic area.

Means of controlling a substantial number of pollutants are now available. On the other hand, as noted above, there are economical means to purify large volumes of extremely dilute mixtures. Further research and development are also needed on ways of disposing of or economically using the collected pollutants once they have been removed from the atmosphere. No serious study has been made so far on developing techniques to remove pollutants or to transform them into less toxic species once they have entered the atmosphere.

This discussion began with a statement to the effect that the motivation for air pollution research today is economic. However, there seems to be no satisfactory technique for totally assessing the cost of air pollution (although estimates have been made) or the cost of avoiding pollution.

Conservation implies an optimum apportionment of use between the present and the future. Without valid yardsticks, it is impossible to accurately determine an optimum.

Not only is our knowledge of the material costs of air conservation inadequate, but we are also unable to clearly define the cost in terms of human health. Knowledge of acute toxicities of most of the species identified in polluted atmospheres is fairly complete. However, the chronic effects of lower concentrations, particularly in a mixed system that contains aerosols, is clearly insufficient. Although standards of air quality have been promulgated in many cases, and must certainly be written in the immediate future, they cannot be considered final until there has been a tremendous amount of additional research to gird them with demonstrated scientific fact.

The scientist has three primary duties with regard to air conservation. As a scientist, he must examine his area of competence to see whether there are specific contributions he can make to further the knowledge of air conservation. As an educated person, he must inform himself of developments in fields other than his own in order to maintain a factual knowledge of the problems and the progress toward solving them. As a citizen he must, on the basis of this knowledge, both speak out and vote in behalf of the conclusions to which this knowledge impels him.

PART 3

Background

Reports

CHAPTER 1

Meteorology

The most critical cases of atmospheric pollution and those that have been most commonly discussed in recent years have occurred in large urban areas with many kinds of pollution sources: industry, automobiles, house heating, and refuse disposal. To a great extent, the production of large quantities of atmospheric pollution has become an unavoidable part of modern life.

Meteorologic or topographic conditions in some areas favor the accumulation of pollutants, and the contamination of the atmosphere in such areas may hasten deterioration of buildings, may affect public health, and may detract from the appearance of a city. It may also become a public nuisance to the surrounding areas and to more distant communities. Pollutants emitted by such sources include solid particles, liquid droplets, vapors, and gases. The heavier particles often fall to the ground near the pollution sources and are therefore eliminated before leaving the area. However, lighter particles, vapors, and gases will move through the community and spread out into the surrounding areas, other communities, other states, or even other countries. During this dispersion, the nature of the pollutants may be changed by natural physical or chemical processes, such as solar radiation, rain, fog, or interaction with the normal constituents of the atmosphere. Pollutants originating from the same or from different sources may also interact among themselves and be transformed into still other pollutants. The result of these transformations will not always be harmful and in some cases, could be beneficial. Some pollutants formed in this way will remain in the atmosphere or be continuously re-formed

49

for such extensive periods of time that they will be considered a normal part of the atmosphere. Most pollutants eventually reach land or sea, are washed out by the rain, or escape into outer space.

The Pollution Cycle

Atmospheric pollution starts with the *production* of pollutants, often as undesirable or incidental consequences of various industrial processes. An airborne cycle begins with the *emission* of pollutants, which is followed by *transfer* through the atmosphere. The cycle is completed by the *contact* of pollutants with people, livestock, vegetation, and other objects. This contact may result in eliminating pollutants from the atmosphere, or it may be followed by the repetition of a similar cycle. In its final stage, atmospheric pollution may cause *damage* to health and property. At each stage of an atmospheric pollution cycle attempts can be made to reduce the dangers and inconveniences of atmospheric pollution. It may, however, be quite impractical to completely get rid of atmospheric pollution. A community, like a human being, breathes in clear air and breathes out pollutants. The very life of the community is accompanied by air pollution. The main problem is to prevent it from reaching such a magnitude that it becomes a great inconvenience and danger to the population. Technical methods for cleaning the air of our polluted communities do exist. However, many of these methods may be difficult to apply and may be expensive in terms of both capital and operating costs. Atmospheric pollution control is not so much a technical problem as it is an economic one. An important part of air pollution studies, therefore, should be a comparison of the costs and inconveniences of various control measures with the effects that they may have on reducing contamination levels.

Large urban areas, with their concentration of human activities and major industrial centers, are the most frequent sources of air pollution. There are, however, numerous small communities, hamlets, isolated sources, and other contributors to the overall pollution of the atmosphere. Although the contamination in these locations may seldom be noticeable, either because the local concentrations do not reach dangerous levels or because there is only a small population, a large number of such sources adds to the overall pollution of the atmosphere and forms a background for the other pollution sources.

Dispersion

The dispersion of pollutants in the atmosphere is caused by two principal factors: (i) the general "mean" air motion that carries them downstream and (ii) the "turbulent" velocity fluctuations that disperse them in all directions. Added to these factors is the effect of the size and the weight of the pollutants, which is related to the speed at which they fall to the ground or are buoyed upward.

The most important factor affecting the vertical dispersal of pollutants is the vertical profile of temperature. The rate of temperature change in this vertical profile is known as the "lapse rate." Under normal conditions in the lower atmosphere, temperature falls as altitude increases.

Although facts about the lapse rate are relatively simple, its role in air pollution has been the subject of a great deal of misunderstanding. Stated in its simplest terms, if a parcel of air is carried from a low altitude to a high one, it will expand because of the decrease in pressure, and its temperature will drop, assuming that there is no exchange of heat with its surroundings. If a parcel of air is taken to a lower altitude, again without an exchange of heat with its surroundings, its volume will decrease and its temperature will rise. For a given change in altitude, the corresponding temperature change is constant and determinable. This rate of change is known as the "adiabatic lapse rate." In a dry atmosphere, the adiabatic lapse rate is 1° Centigrade per 100 meters, or 5.4° Fahrenheit per 1000 feet.

When the actual lapse rate is greater than this theoretical rate, a parcel of air that begins to rise will continue to do so, and the atmospheric condition is called "unstable." If, however, the actual lapse rate is less than the adiabatic rate, the surface air that begins to rise will tend to sink to the surface, and the atmospheric condition is called "stable."

The difference between the two conditions is one of degree rather

meteorological consultant (*1*). Forecasts of stagnation situations emanate from the various Weather Bureau forecast centers. Special research on air pollution in relation to weather is conducted by the Weather Bureau research group attached to the U.S. Public Health Service's Taft Sanitary Engineering Center, Cincinnati, Ohio.

Mathematical Models

Los Angeles provides an interesting example of a community with dispersion problems. The Los Angeles Basin is bounded on the north and east by mountains and during many days of the year it is covered by an inversion layer. During the day the pollutants that are produced in the basin are blown toward the mountains and accumulate under the inversion layer. Large quantities of ozone and other pollutants are produced and build up over several days. If the general meteorological conditions break up the inversion layer, the pollution clouds may be driven away over the mountains and move into the Mojave Desert at some distance from the Los Angeles Basin. (Pockets of ozone could well move long distances in a stable atmosphere, disperse at a relatively slow rate, and result in appreciable concentrations even far away from their origin.)

The extensive data that have been gathered in the Los Angeles area make it a particularly appropriate proving ground for studying a method by which the pollution pattern can be related to the meteorological conditions and to the distribution of pollution sources. As a basis for determining the meteorological conditions in the Los Angeles Basin, Frenkiel (*2*) used the data on stream lines for surface winds as determined for successive hours during September 1947. These stream lines represented mean wind-velocity fields that were obtained by averaging the air flow for each hour of the day for all days of September. In addition to the "mean" motion of the wind, there was, of course, a "turbulent" dispersion whose intensity can be estimated.

Using such data, a mathematical model of the atmosphere over an urban area can be developed to study the probable pollution patterns (*2*). A simple model can be constructed by including the distribution of pollution sources, their emission conditions, and the micrometeorological characteristics that directly affect the dispersion of pollutants. The mean concentration distribution of pollutants caused by each source of pollution can be determined, and the effects of the several sources can be added. The mean concentration pattern of pollution as a function of time can then be found, and the relative contributions of each source of pollution to the contamination at various points of the area can be analyzed. In the mathematical model a thermal inversion will be represented by proper boundary conditions. This method of analysis can be extended to include the patterns of pollution that originate from many sources of pollution. Some might be individual point sources, such as a large power station or a steel mill; others might be area-wide sources, such as automobile traffic, taking into account the appropriate hourly variations and variable geographic distribution.

Such a mathematical model could be used to determine (i) temporary emergency measures to be taken when atmospheric pollution threatens to reach the allowable concentration levels, (ii) efficacy of various plans to reduce the pollution in an urban area, (iii) effects of a new pollution source on the mean concentration patterns, (iv) pollution patterns for an expanding city, and (v) effectiveness of the various solutions in urban planning for handling predicted pollution levels.

Similar mathematical models with appropriate characteristics could be developed to estimate the probable pollution patterns that would follow industrial expansion and population increases in an urban area. The possible effects of increased combustion efficiency and other factors in industrial and vehicle operations, as well as the effects of changes in traffic patterns, on present and future pollution could be examined and the results could be used in urban planning.

The receptor of air contaminants usually comes in contact with combined pollution that emanates from a number of sources. In some cases two sources may produce nonharmful pollutants that will interact at a distance from their origin to become an objectionable contamination. On the other hand, a pollution source close to the receptor may be chiefly responsible for contamination in a given area. The relative responsibility of all sources could be evaluated by taking into account the quantity of pollutants that is emitted by each source and the meteorological conditions that may contribute to dangerous contamination levels. While such estimates can be based on a scientific analysis, their application to a legal procedure may lead to some difficulties.

Air Zoning

Evaluation of the detriments and benefits that are associated with air pollution should be related to the basic needs of the community, including its need for clean air. Each community should be aware that certain benefits might become liabilities because of their potential as a danger and nuisance that could contribute to atmospheric contamination, and that to have clean air might mean risking economic penalties. However, in most cases there is room for improvement without taking such a risk, and even the most critical pollution areas need not cripple their growth or impose too severe and often ineffective restraints in order to avoid harmful air contamination.

The air pollution problem for large cities becomes more serious each year. Much can be done to modify conditions and many industries have largely eliminated the danger of contamination but only by quite expensive methods. The ultimate answer may be "air zoning." Land zoning is now an established practice to prevent deterioration of residential neighborhoods, the growth of slums, and so forth. Zoning the air above communities, however, would be a much more difficult problem, involving knowledge of the possible sources of pollution, local geographic and weather conditions, chemical changes of pollutants in the atmosphere, necessity for applying purification methods, and several other factors.

Zoning could prove to be a good method for controlling pollution. It should be noted, however, that insofar as air pollution is concerned, it is not the land that should be zoned but the atmosphere. Such zoning would differ from the usual land zoning in that it does not necessarily lead to unconditional restrictions for the location of a pollution source in any desired area. (However, considerations other than air conservation might result in the imposition of such a restriction on a source.) Air zoning could be based on an analysis of meteorological conditions and take into account the willingness of the population in some communities (or parts of a community) to tolerate the contamination to a greater degree than a standard established for a state, a nation, or the world. In order to accomplish such zoning, a pollution source could be given the choice between several appropriate restrictions, or a combination thereof, that would vary according to the location of the source in the community. The pollution source might, for example, be given a choice among (i) a fixed limitation on the manner and the rate at which each pollutant can be emitted, (ii) the collection of pollutants or the reduction of the emission rate when weather conditions are not favorable and full emission when the conditions are again favorable, and (iii) complete interruption of the emission of pollutants under emergency circumstances.

The possibility of selecting among several alternate restrictions, depending on location, might enable a polluting source to estimate and compare the costs in investment and operation that would be required by the various choices. Standards for air pollution tolerance, based on both their temporary and their lasting effects, would have to be established. These standards would not have to be rigid, but could include some margin within which a departure from the basic standards could be authorized. This would lead to the creation of giant "smoking lounges" where higher contamination tolerances would be accepted. Authorization for a departure from the basic standards could be given if the community involved should decide that the benefits derived from the pollution sources justified a certain amount of nuisance and the damages that were produced by the pollutants.

Use of the atmosphere is one of the most economic ways to dispose of pollutants. While the atmosphere has often been misused as a waste dump, its ability to disperse most contaminants without harmful effects can be increased. The main problem in air conservation stems from the distribution of pollutants in the lower atmosphere as a function of time and space rather than the overall quantity of each pollutant in the world atmosphere. At the same time we must be concerned with the possibility of saturating the world atmosphere with some pollutants to the degree that they become harmful.

References

1. For private groups, names of qualified consultants are available from the American Meteorological Society, 45 Beacon Street, Boston, Mass.
2. Frenkiel, F., "Atmospheric pollution in growing communities," from the *Smithsonian Report for 1956,* pp. 269–299 (Smithsonian Institution, Washington, D.C., 1957). This material was also published in a report prepared by the University of California, Los Angeles.

CHAPTER 2

Pollutants and Their Effects

1. SULFUR AND ITS COMPOUNDS

Sulfur occurs in trace quantities as an element in the atmosphere, and in its reduced form as unpleasant-smelling hydrogen sulfide and mercaptans. Most of the sulfur in the atmosphere is in an oxidized form; sulfur dioxide is probably the most widespread of the man-made air pollutants and is the one most intensively studied.

Oxides of Sulfur

Sources

Oxides of sulfur, primarily sulfur dioxide, are produced by the combustion of sulfur-containing fuels, such as coal and fuel oils, in sulfuric acid plants and in metallurgical processes involving ores that contain sulfur. In New York City, 1.5 million tons of sulfur dioxide are discharged yearly from the burning of coal alone (1), and in Great Britain, 5.8 million tons (2). Based on statistics available from some of the industrialized countries, the annual worldwide emission of sulfur dioxide in recent years totals about 80 million tons: 50 to 60 million tons from coal, about 11 million tons from crude oil refining (most of this in the United States), 11 to 12 million tons from copper smelters, and 3.5 to 4 million tons from lead and zinc smelters (3). The burning of wood and solid wastes, such as paper, cardboard, and rubber tires, also adds sulfur dioxide to the atmosphere.

Reactions

In the combustion of sulfur-containing materials, most of the sulfur is converted to sulfur dioxide and a small percentage is oxidized further to the trioxide stage. The formation of sulfur trioxide may be increased by using excess oxygen and by the catalytic action of ash constituents, especially iron oxides (formed on boiler tubes and walls) (4). Sulfur trioxide reacts rapidly with water vapor to become sulfuric acid, resulting in an irritant mist. This conversion often is the cause of the bluish-white plumes emitted in industrial and power-plant operation.

60

When gases, including oxides of sulfur, leave a stack, turbulent diffusion usually lowers the sulfur dioxide concentration rapidly to only a few parts per million several hundred feet away, and further oxidation to sulfur trioxide proceeds at a slow rate. Nevertheless, in time, substantial conversion to sulfur trioxide will take place, contributing, because of the trioxide's affinity for water vapor, to the haze that is characteristic in many industrial areas. Oxidation is accelerated by the catalytic action of metal oxides in water droplets, a factor that may be of great importance during conditions of high humidity such as those that exist during London fogs. Under different weather conditions—at lower humidities and in bright sunshine—strongly oxidizing substances, such as those found in the Los Angeles-type smog, will speed oxidation (5).

Effects and Concentrations

Sulfur oxides can injure man, plants, and materials, and can interfere with visibility. At sufficiently high concentrations, sulfur dioxide irritates the upper respiratory tract of human beings because of its high solubility in body fluids. At low concentrations, the main potential effect of sulfur dioxide is to make breathing more difficult by causing the finer air tubes of the lung to constrict.

Although the concentration of sulfur dioxide has been measured regularly for many years and in many places, the concentration was determined during only one of the three well-known dramatic air pollution disasters (London, Meuse Valley, and Donora). The average concentration of sulfur dioxide during a 2-day period at the height of the London smog of December 1952 was 1.34 parts per million (ppm) (6). Higher concentrations may have existed for shorter periods of time, but this average figure is well below the maximum that has been measured in other cities not in the midst of a disaster. Concentrations of up to 3.2 ppm have been recorded in the commercial and industrial sections of cities that use a great deal of solid fuel, such as Chicago and Pittsburgh (6).

The more usual concentrations for community air pollution are about a few parts per hundred million. Although these levels are far below those regarded as hazardous to the industrially employed, there is growing evidence that lower concentrations may adversely affect health in special cases (7). [A discernible physiological response, produced by concentrations as low as 1 ppm, has been reported, but there is disagreement with the finding (8).]

A concentration of 0.6 ppm of sulfur dioxide will produce no detectable response in healthy human beings; in the range between 1 and 5 ppm, most persons will begin to show a detectable response (8). There is no sound evidence that chronic exposure to concentrations below 5 ppm of sulfur dioxide, by itself, has any persistently ill effects. Most people can detect 5 ppm, and it produces a distinctive gross physiological response; exposure for 1 hour causes choking (9). Most people find 10 ppm quite unpleasant; an exposure for 1 hour to this concentration produces severe distress.

A study of people who, because of their occupations, were regularly exposed, indicates that a moderate degree of resistance may develop from continuous exposure to sulfur dioxide concentrations of 5 ppm and above (8). They can scarcely smell the gas at these concentrations, and experience little or no irritation of the respiratory tract. Pattle and Cullumbine reported that repeated exposure may also be associated with increased sensitivity (10). They found that a small proportion, perhaps 1 percent, of the population suffers from bronchial constriction when inhaling low concentrations of sulfur dioxide that do not affect others. When exposed experimentally, some of these individuals experienced a sensation of tightness in the chest at concentrations as low as 1 ppm. They reported that one such individual had unusual breathlessness when he exercised during a London fog.

The toxic effects of sulfur dioxide appear to be greater when the gas combines with aerosols than when it is alone. Simultaneous exposure to low levels of sulfur dioxide and sulfuric acid aerosol produces a greater physiological reaction than the sum of the reactions to the substances alone (1). In an experiment, unanesthetized guinea pigs that were exposed to a mixture of sulfur dioxide and sodium chloride at near air pollution levels experienced greater difficulty in breathing than did those exposed to a corresponding concentration of sulfur dioxide alone (11). Many believe that the illnesses and deaths in the Meuse Valley episode must be attributed primarily to a mixture of sulfur dioxide and sulfuric acid mist, and to other aerosols in conjunction with sulfur dioxide. [Others attribute the Meuse Valley disaster to hydrogen fluoride that accidentally escaped from a zinc factory (*12*).]

Lawther recently reported that mortality in London increased significantly when 750 micrograms per cubic meter of suspended smoke were present at the same time that sulfur dioxide was in excess of 0.25 ppm. He also reported that with 300 micrograms of smoke per cubic meter, 0.21 ppm of sulfur dioxide was associated with a deterioration in health of patients with chronic bronchitis (*13*).

Why certain combinations should prove to be so toxic is still not certain. Possibly the molecules of the irritant gas attach themselves to the aerosols and are transported deeper into the lungs than they could travel by themselves (*1*). Such a theory might help to explain how sulfur dioxide has, at times, been able to seriously harm people with no record of cardiorespiratory disease (*11*).

Experimental exposure of both animals and man to sulfur dioxide—or, rather, its hydrate, sulfuric acid—shows that it is a very strong irritant, much stronger than sulfur dioxide, and can cause choking at relatively low levels of concentration (*1*). Unfortunately, there are few data concerning levels and particle sizes of sulfuric acid as a community air pollutant. Sulfuric acid must have been the principal cause of the air pollution disasters in the Meuse Valley, Donora, and London (*8*). It produces, on a molar basis, from 4 to 20 times the physiological response in animals as sulfur dioxide does (*8*). The effect of sulfuric acid mist is greatly influenced by the size of the mist particles; those of intermediate size (about 1 micron in mean diameter) appear to be most injurious.

Sulfur dioxide causes both acute and chronic injury to the leaves of plants. The gas is phytotoxic to some species in concentrations above 0.1 to 0.2 ppm; the effect depends upon the length of exposure (*14*). It is absorbed through the stomata and, below 0.4 ppm, the sulfur dioxide tends to be oxidized to sulfate in the cells as rapidly as it is absorbed. In such cases, there may be a temporary partial inhibition of photosynthesis while the gas is present, but if the leaves are not permanently damaged, the normal level of photosynthesis is rapidly regained after the fumigation has stopped. At higher levels of exposure, the cells die, interveinal tissues collapse and take on a water-soaked appearance, and drying and bleaching occur later. It seems clear that the oxidation-reduction properties of sulfur dioxide, rather than its acidity, are responsible for its toxic effect on plants (14).

Chronic injury to plants is caused either by rapid absorption of an amount of sulfur dioxide somewhat less than the amount needed to cause acute symptoms, or by exposure over a long period of time to sublethal concentrations (usually under 0.4 ppm). The leaves gradually turn yellow, and later become white; areas affected are half as active as normal ones (15). While the injured areas of the leaves never recover, the uninjured parts quickly and fully regain their functions and new leaves develop normally.

High light intensity, high relative humidity, adequate moisture, and moderate temperatures cause the stomata to open and the leaf therefore absorbs more sulfur dioxide. Maximum sensitivity to the gas occurs in late spring or early summer during the growing season. The stomata of most plants close at night and plants are therefore much more resistant to sulfur dioxide during that time.

Different species of plants and even different varieties of a species may vary considerably in their susceptibility to sulfur dioxide. These differences seem to be caused primarily by variations in the rate of absorption of the gas by the leaves. Plants with thin leaves of high physiological activity, such as alfalfa, grains, squash, cotton, and grapes, are generally sensitive. Plants with fleshy leaves or needles, such as citrus and pine, tend to be resistant except when the leaves are newly formed (before cutinization).

Sulfur dioxide is one of the oldest known air pollutants recognized as causing significant damage to vegetation. Indeed, in several instances damage to vegetation has been the first indication that the air in the vicinity was polluted; plants are often used to detect mixtures of gaseous air pollutants. Although it is possible to confuse the effects of sunscald and frost with those caused by sulfur dioxide, sulfur dioxide damage to vegetation can be identified with high specificity if proper precautions are taken.

The presence of nontoxic concentrations of sulfur dioxide has been found to lessen the oxidant damage to plants in the Los Angeles area (16). At higher concentrations, however, this protective effect has not been noticed (17).

Sulfuric acid aerosol appears to be toxic to vegetation only under special circumstances. In the vicinity of industrial plants, vegetation has been damaged by large droplets containing sulfuric acid.

Both sulfur dioxide and sulfuric acid are responsible for accelerating the corrosion and deterioration of certain materials. Especially when moisture is present, they attack iron and steel, copper, nickel, and aluminum, although the latter appears to be fairly resistant to the concentrations of the sulfur oxides that are normally found in polluted atmospheres (18). Also, the familiar greenish coating formed by sulfur oxides on copper and copper alloys in many urban and industrial areas is extremely resistant to further atmospheric attack and acts as a protective film. But these same reaction products are detrimental when they form on electrical contacts made of copper because they increase the electrical resistance of the contacts.

Sulfur dioxide and sulfur trioxide also attack building materials, particularly limestone, marble, roofing slate, and mortar, all of which contain carbonates that are converted to relatively soluble sulfates that can be leached away by rainwater.

The small amounts of metallic impurities in paper accelerate the conversion, in the presence of moisture, of absorbed sulfur dioxide to sulfuric acid, which makes the paper extremely brittle. Sulfur dioxide also causes leather to lose much of its strength and to eventually disintegrate, and brings about the deterioration of a number of natural and synthetic fibers used in textiles, particularly cotton and wool. Women's nylon hose appear to be damaged either by extremely small atmospheric particles that contain absorbed sulfur dioxide, or by tiny droplets of sulfuric acid that have formed around particles (18).

Control

The control of sulfur oxide emissions has been studied for many years. Although much progress has been made, both source and abatement controls are beset with many difficulties and more engineering research and development are needed.

The concentration of sulfur dioxide in waste gases from metallurgical operations is usually relatively high and, at a great number of smelters, processes have been installed that recover many hundreds of tons of valuable sulfur products daily. For example, in 1930, the stacks of a large lead-zinc smelter at Trail, British Columbia, were emitting up to 20,000 tons of sulfur dioxide per month. The crops and forests in Canada and in the adjacent part of the United States suffered such widespread damage that a large new industry was created for converting waste sulfur gases to sulfuric acid, ammonium sulfate and nitrate, and phosphate fertilizer. Today, about 91 percent of the sulfur dioxide formerly wasted is recovered at this smelter by converting it to these valuable by-products (3). In a similar situation at two copper smelters near Ducktown, Tennessee, most of the sulfuric acid regained is used by phosphate plants in the South for producing fertilizer. In some years, the income from this by-product exceeds the value of the copper refined (19).

The concentration of sulfur dioxide in sulfuric acid waste gases and in the stack gases that result from the combustion of fuels is low when compared with the waste gases in metallurgical operations; but the total discharge of sulfur dioxide into the air may be enormous. In these cases, economic removal and recovery of sulfur dioxide is difficult, and therefore the effort has been made at only a few places. The Battersea and Bankside stations in London are probably the only power plants that attempt full-scale removal of sulfur dioxide from stack gases (20). This practice has not spread because (i) no product of direct value is produced, and (ii) while the sulfur dioxide is being removed, the flue gases are cooled so thoroughly that they tend to settle near the power stations and the residual sulfur dioxide plus a great cloud of water droplets distress nearby residents. There seem to be more complaints since the sulfur dioxide removal was initiated than there were before (21). Although reheating the gases would cure this ill, it would also add to the cost of operating the plant. Apparently the community is not willing to pay this price or is unaware of the possibilities of control. (The control system used in the British power plants is extremely expensive and requires a great deal of maintenance. The obvious alternative is the recovery of sulfur in a form in which it may be returned to commerce. Both in the United States and in the world at large, the tonnage of sulfur emitted into the atmosphere is approximately twice the consumption (22, 23). Some economists fear that successful recovery would upset the economy of sulfur production. The fears are groundless at the moment; no recovery technique now known will economically produce practicable quantities of sulfur from all emissions.)

The electric power industry has attempted to control the visible stack emissions, often caused by ash constituents, through the use of electrostatic precipitators or baghouses. Objectionable plume opacity, caused by sulfur trioxide, has been reduced by raising stack gas temperatures and by using alkaline reagents to bind free sulfuric acid. The formation of sulfur trioxide, and consequently sulfuric acid, is reduced further by minimizing the use of air and by properly cleaning the boilers.

These measures will reduce fallout of acid droplets and ashes in the neighborhood of the plants. Methods to improve the appearance of the smoke plumes are important from a public relations point of view; they do not, however, control objectionable sulfur dioxide emissions.

A comparative cost estimate of eight different processes for the recovery of sulfur dioxide in power plants shows that the operating cost ranges from 20 to 100 percent of the fuel cost, while the initial cost for a 175,000-kilowatt unit is estimated to range from $3 to $25 million (24).

There is an increasing tendency of plants to "solve" the problem of controlling the discharge of sulfur dioxide by using tall stacks that emit the sulfurous gases at such a height that ground-level concentrations are negligible. When high stacks are objectionable and when drastic measures, such as relocation and building plants outside the airshed, are not feasible, a solution is to burn fuels of low sulfur content. These fuels may be low in sulfur either naturally or as a result of sulfur reduction during fuel production and preparation.

Because of the problems of emission control, much thought has been given to extracting sulfur from fuel before it is burned. It is possible to do so, but it is costly. Present techniques for removing sulfur from the residual oils that are used for generating steam in power plants are not now commercially feasible. It is estimated that the removal of sulfur and minerals from residual oil would cost about 50 percent of the fuel price (24). However, research is continuing on methods to improve fuels at a reasonable cost before they reach the consumer.

During recent years several large cities have progressively decreased the average atmospheric concentrations of sulfur dioxide by increasing the use of coal with a lower sulfur content and by using natural gas and light fuel oil for space heating. Air pollution control measures in St. Louis have reduced the use of high sulfur coal. Los Angeles has reduced its pollution level of sulfur dioxide by about 75 percent (25) by removing sulfur from refinery fuel gases and by using natural gas in place of high sulfur-containing fuels. This latter measure was made mandatory year-round as of January 1964 as long as natural gas was available. Some students of air conservation believe that there will be a considerable reduction in sulfur dioxide pollution and smoke because of the trend in North America toward consumption of natural gas instead of coal for space heating and for some industrial operations (3). However, the increased use of coal in power plants and in other industrial operations runs counter to this trend, and unless full use is made of presently available control methods there may be no significant improvement. In addition, since petroleum and natural gas constitute only 6 percent of the total world resources of fossil fuels and recoverable coal constitutes 73 percent (26), natural gas cannot be indefinitely substituted for coal and high sulfur-containing fuel oil.

Global Implications

As mentioned earlier, the total world production of sulfur dioxide is estimated to be approximately 80 million tons per year. If sulfur dioxide were to remain in the air and be distributed evenly over the globe, the increase per year would be about 0.006 ppm. This is, of course, an extremely small amount; moreover, sulfur dioxide does not remain in the air. It may last an average of 43 days (27), probably less.

A large percentage of the sulfur dioxide in the air oxidizes to sulfur trioxide, which forms sulfuric acid mist. The sulfuric acid in the aerosols reacts with other materials in the air and forms, among other things, ammonium and calcium sulfate. The available evidence suggests that a substantial portion of the atmospheric sulfur dioxide is directly neutralized by ammonia, calcite dust, or one of the many other airborne alkalies and is then rapidly oxidized to the corresponding sulfates (28). Precipitation finally removes these salts from the air. Sulfur oxides may, therefore, be of little global concern from a long-range point of view. However, without systematic study, it is not certain whether or not there is a global increase in sulfur dioxide or sulfate. If they are increasing, it will be important to raise the question of the consequences.

Other Sulfur Compounds

Mercaptans and hydrogen sulfide are produced in large quantities in the processing of petroleum, in the coking of coals, and in the operating of paper pulp mills using the Kraft process. They are also evolved in the distillation of tar, natural gas refining, manufacture of viscose rayon, and in certain chemical processes. Other sources include inadequately treated sewage, dumps, and other environments in which anaerobic bacteria can function. As a rule, however, these substances are not liberated in appreciable quantities by industrial operations in urban communities. Relatively low concentrations of hydrogen sulfide, less than 0.10 ppm, have been found in a small number of observations in some cities (3).

Effects

Hydrogen sulfide and mercaptans are objectionable because of their distinct and unpleasant odor even at very low concentrations. They cause odor nuisances when they are present in the air at concentrations 10 to 100 times smaller than the lowest concentration of sulfur dioxide detectable by smell. Some mercaptans are perceptible at 0.03 of a part per billion (29), and people can smell hydrogen sulfide in concentrations of approximately 0.035 to 0.10 ppm (3).

Silver and copper tarnish rapidly in the presence of hydrogen sulfide. House paint that contains lead compounds darkens rapidly in the presence of even low concentrations of hydrogen sulfide by forming black lead sulfide.

The air pollution problem that results from the presence of hydrogen sulfide is, therefore, largely associated with nuisances from odors and from harm to the above materials. It is unusual to find levels in the atmosphere that are high enough to cause damage to vegetation, irritation of the eyes and respiratory system, systemic effects, or death (8). These higher concentrations can result from accidental industrial discharges from point sources rather than from community-wide emissions.

Just such an industrial accident occurred at Poza Rica, Mexico, in November 1950. Twenty-two deaths and the illness of 320 persons were caused by the spillage of hydrogen sulfide gas. The gas caused loss of the sense of smell and severe irritation to the respiratory tract. [Exposure for 2 to 15 minutes to 100 ppm or more will impair the sense of smell (8).] These symptoms and other circumstances indicated that the gas concentration must have reached extremely high levels over a period of about 1 hour. Persons of all ages were affected and preexisting disease did not seem to have much bearing on which individuals were afflicted.

Control

Many industries have taken extensive measures to remove mercaptans and hydrogen sulfide before they become a nuisance. It is becoming standard practice in the petroleum industry to recover hydrogen sulfide for the production of sulfur, which is sometimes used later for manufacturing sulfuric acid. Under the pressure of community requirements, more paper mills are improving control measures. The Kraft paper mills, however, have not yet succeeded in reducing the mercaptans and hydrogen sulfide sufficiently to eliminate the annoying odor threshold at the plant gates.

Global Implications

There is no accumulation of mercaptans or hydrogen sulfide in the atmosphere; direct and photochemical oxidation convert them to sulfate. More than 75 percent of the total airborne sulfur enters the atmosphere as hydrogen sulfide from natural sources. This amounts to about 300 million tons of hydrogen sulfide per year. These sources are so diffuse, and the lifetime of hydrogen sulfide in the air so short, that perceptible concentrations are seldom encountered (30).

References

1. Heiman, H., "Effects on human health," in *Air Pollution,* WHO Monograph No. 46, pp. 159–220 (World Health Organization, Geneva, 1961).
2. Meetham, A. R., *Atmospheric Pollution: Its Origins and Prevention* (Pergamon Press, New York, ed. 2, 1956).
3. Katz, M., "Some aspects of the physical and chemical nature of air pollution," in *Air Pollution,* WHO Monograph No. 46, pp. 97–158 (World Health Organization, Geneva, 1961).
4. Engdahl, R. B., "Combustion in furnaces, incinerators, and open fires," in *Air Pollution,* A. C. Stern, Ed., vol. 2, pp. 3–99 (Academic Press, New York, 1962).
5. Haagen-Smit, A. J., "Reactions in the atmosphere," *ibid.,* vol. 1, pp. 41–64.
6. Tebbens, B. D., "Residual pollution products in the atmosphere," *ibid.,* pp. 23–40.
7. *Air Pollution Manual,* part 1 (American Industrial Hygiene Association, Detroit, 1960).
8. Goldsmith, J. R., "Effects of air pollution on humans," in *Air Pollution,* A. C. Stern, Ed., vol. 1, pp. 335–386 (Academic Press, New York, 1962).
9. *Technical Report of California Standards for Ambient Air Quality and Motor Vehicle Exhaust* (California State Department of Public Health, Berkeley, 1960).
10. Pattle, R. E., and H. Cullumbine, "Toxicity of some atmospheric pollutants," *Brit. Med. J.,* **2,** 913 (1956).
11. Stokinger, H. E., "Effects of air pollution on animals," in *Air Pollution,* A. C. Stern, Ed., vol. 1, pp. 282–334 (Academic Press, New York, 1962).
12. Went, F. W., Henry Shaw School of Botany, Washington University, St. Louis, personal communication, 1963.
13. Lawther, P. J., "Compliance with the Clean Air Act: Medical aspects," *J. Inst. Fuel,* **36,** 341 (1963).
14. Thomas, M. D., "Effects on plants," in *Air Pollution,* WHO Monograph No. 46, pp. 233–278 (World Health Organization, Geneva. 1961).
15. Thomas, M. D., and R. H. Hendricks, "Effect of air pollution on plants," in *Air Pollution Handbook,* P. L. Magill, F. R. Holden, and C. Ackley, Eds., section 9, pp. 1–44 (McGraw-Hill, New York, 1956).
16. Haagen-Smit, A. J., E. F. Darley, M. Zaitlin, H. Hull, and W. Noble, "Investigation on injury to plants from air pollution in the Los Angeles area," *Plant Physiol.,* **27,** 18–34 (1952).
17. Haagen-Smit, A. J., Division of Biology, California Institute of Technology, Pasadena, personal communication, 1963.
18. Yocum, J. E., "Effects of air pollution on materials," in *Air Pollution,* A. C. Stern, Ed., vol. 1, pp. 199–219 (Academic Press, New York, 1962).
19. Katz, M., "City planning, industrial-plant location, and air pollution," in *Air Pollution Handbook,* P. L. Magill, F. R. Holden, and C. Ackley, Eds., section 2, pp. 1–53 (McGraw-Hill, New York, 1956).
20. Gartrell, F. E., "Water pollution potential of air pollution control devices," in *Air Pollution,* A. C. Stern, Ed., vol. 2, pp. 387–398 (Academic Press, New York, 1962).
21. Barker, K., and W. A. Macfarlane, "Fuel selection and utilization," in *Air*

Pollution, WHO Monograph No. 46, pp. 345–363 (World Health Organization, Geneva, 1961).

22. U.S. Bureau of Mines, *Minerals Yearbook,* vol. 1 (Government Printing Office, Washington, D.C., 1961).

23. Junge, C. E., *Air Chemistry and Radioactivity* (Academic Press, New York, 1962).

24. Haagen-Smit, A. J., "Studies of air pollution control by Southern California Edison Company," *J. Eng. Power,* **81,** 1–6 (1959).

25. *Summary of Air Pollution Statistics for Los Angeles County* (Los Angeles County Air Pollution Control District, Los Angeles, 1963).

26. Brown, H., J. Bonner, and J. Weir, *The Next Hundred Years* (Viking Press, New York, 1961).

27. Junge, C. E., and R. T. Werby, "The concentration of chloride, sodium, potassium, calcium, and sulfate in rain water over the United States," *J. Meteorol.,* **15,** 417 (1958).

28. Van Den Heuvel, A. P., and B. J. Mason, "The formation of ammonium sulfate in water droplets exposed to gaseous sulfur dioxide and ammonia," *Quart. J. Roy. Meteorol. Soc.,* **89,** 271–275 (1963).

29. Moncrief, R. W., *The Chemical Senses* (University Press, London, 1944).

30. Erikksson, E., "The yearly circulation of sulfur in nature," *J. Geophys. Res.,* **68,** 4001–4008 (1963).

2. CARBON MONOXIDE

Sources

Carbon monoxide is one of the three most common products of fuel combustion; carbon dioxide and water vapor are the other two. Most of the carbon monoxide in the atmosphere results from incomplete combustion of carbonaceous materials.

Automobiles are especially notorious for producing this gas. In Los Angeles County, more than 3 million motor vehicles each day pollute the air with 8000 tons of carbon monoxide (1), which amounts to an average of more than 5 pounds per vehicle per day. The Los Angeles Air Pollution Control District found that the 1963 concentrations of carbon monoxide at four locations in the County Basin were 215 percent of the 1956 readings (Fig. 1). The mass emission of carbon monoxide as a result of fuel combustion in the United States was estimated, as of June 1962, at about 100 million tons per year (2), a quantity that approximately equals the combined total of all other industrial contaminants.

Description

Carbon monoxide is quite stable in the atmosphere. It is probably converted to carbon dioxide, but the rate of conversion (not known exactly) is slow. Because it remains unchanged for several days, carbon monoxide has been used to calculate the dispersal volume of other pollutants.

Carbon monoxide is an odorless and colorless gas and in this lies part of its danger.

Effects and Concentrations

Carbon monoxide is a poisonous inhalant and no other toxic gaseous air pollutant is found at such relatively high concentrations in the urban atmosphere (3). Carbon monoxide is dangerous because it has a strong affinity for hemoglobin, which carries oxygen to body tissues. The effect of carbon monoxide is to deprive the tissues of necessary oxygen.

73

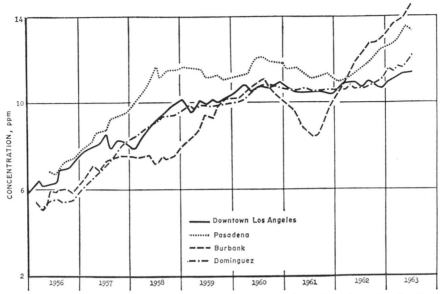

Fig. 1. Trend of carbon monoxide observed at four locations in the Los Angeles Basin and expressed as 12-month moving averages. Averages are plotted at midpoint of observation period, 1956–1963. [Los Angeles County Air Pollution Control District]

At concentrations of slightly more than 1000 ppm, carbon monoxide kills quickly (3). One hundred parts per million is generally considered the upper limit of safety in industry for healthy persons within certain age ranges when exposure may continue for an 8-hour period (4). Los Angeles has set its three alert levels for carbon monoxide at 100, 200, and 300 ppm. Most people experience dizziness, headache, lassitude, and other symptoms at approximately 100 ppm (5).

Present measurements do not show that this level is often exceeded in cities of the United States (6). In the commercial and industrial districts of Cincinnati, the concentrations of carbon monoxide have ranged from 0 to 55 ppm, with an average of 9.5 ppm (7). During extensive measurements in the Los Angeles area the highest concentration was 72 ppm (1).

Concentrations higher than this occasionally occur locally in garages, tunnels, behind automobiles, or in the open atmosphere.

For example, maximum instantaneous concentrations of more than 100 ppm were found during several months of observation in Detroit in 1960 (8). Recent measurements in London, on the other hand, suggest that such levels may not be simply sporadic; in Oxford Circus there were frequent periods of more than 100 ppm (8).

There is disagreement as to whether or not carbon monoxide is a threshold pollutant. Some researchers believe that even small amounts of this gas are likely to produce some detectable response (9). Although there may be a difference between a "response" and a "harmful effect," the question is of particular concern because of the increasing number of automobiles in our cities.

Most American scientists believe that carbon monoxide is not a cumulative poison (3); when exposure is discontinued, the carbon monoxide that had combined with hemoglobin is spontaneously released and the blood is cleared of half its carbon monoxide, at least in healthy subjects, in 3 to 4 hours (5). Carbon monoxide can cause acute poisoning as a result of exposure to high air concentrations of the gas, but chronic poisoning does not occur as a result of long-continued exposure to relatively low concentrations. However, some European scientists maintain that chronic carbon monoxide poisoning does occur (6). Some particularly susceptible persons, such as those already afflicted with a disease that involves a decrease in the oxygen capacity of the blood (for example, anemia), or persons with cardiorespiratory disease, may be affected by the carbon monoxide levels reached in city streets (6). People who already have variable amounts of carbon monoxide in their blood from smoking or from exposure in their occupations may be further affected by inhaling an additional amount of the gas from the carbon monoxide–contaminated air in their communities. The question needs further study. In adopting its "serious" level of standards for carbon monoxide in 1960, the California Department of Public Health indicated that exposure to 30 ppm of carbon monoxide for 8 hours, or exposure to 120 ppm for 1 hour, may be a serious risk to the health of sensitive people (10). These levels were based on the assumption that such exposures would result in the inactivation of 5 percent of the body's hemoglobin.

At high levels of concentration, carbon monoxide, more than any other air pollutant, has been identified as a participant in synergistic reactions (3). For example, the combined effect of carbon monoxide in the presence of hydrogen sulfide or nitrogen dioxide is more severe than the sum of the effects of each of the gases. At low levels, synergism has not been established; however, carbon monoxide with other pollutants probably has an additive effect.

Control

Since carbon monoxide results from incomplete combustion of carbonaceous materials, the obvious control measure is more complete combustion. In many cases, this will lead to fuel economy. Combustion of carbon monoxide yields nearly as much heat as the combustion of fuels to carbon monoxide.

In most cities the primary source of this gas is automotive exhaust. Today's automobile engines do not function well on fuel mixtures sufficiently lean to accomplish a major reduction in the carbon monoxide emitted. Recently manufacturers announced modifications of engine design that would guarantee more efficient use of fuel and lower emission. The principal approach to automobile control has been through studies on afterburners. The first goal of the automotive exhaust control program in California is to decrease carbon monoxide emission in Los Angeles to the levels measured in 1940. However, even if this is achieved, the levels would then increase again in proportion to the increase in the number of cars, unless control devices become increasingly effective. (It will also be necessary to safeguard against increases in nitrogen oxide that can accompany the completion of carbon monoxide combustion.)

Global Implications

From a long-range point of view, it is not likely that the accumulation of carbon monoxide will seriously change the composition of the atmosphere. The global emissions of carbon monoxide per year may be somewhat less than twice that of the United States. This would be about 200 million tons which, evenly spread over the lower atmosphere, would result in an increase of 0.03 ppm of carbon monoxide per year if it were not oxidized. It is generally assumed that carbon monoxide is oxidized in the atmosphere, although at a slow rate, and accumulation seems improbable. However, there are no measurements of the rate of conversion of carbon monoxide to carbon dioxide, and it therefore cannot be stated with absolute certainty that there is no increase.

References

1. *Summary of Air Pollution Statistics for Los Angeles County* (Los Angeles County Air Pollution Control District, Los Angeles, 1963).
2. U.S. Department of Health, Education, and Welfare, Public Health Service, Division of Air Pollution, *Motor Vehicles, Air Pollution, and Health—A Report of the Surgeon General to the U.S. Congress in Compliance with Public Law 86-493, the Schenck Act* (Government Printing Office, Washington, D.C., 1962).
3. Stokinger, H. E., "Effects of air pollution on animals," in *Air Pollution,* A. C. Stern, Ed., vol. 1, pp. 282–334 (Academic Press, New York, 1962).
4. American Medical Association, "Threshold limit values for 1956," *AMA Arch. Ind. Health,* **14,** 186–189 (1956).
5. Goldsmith, J. R., "Effects of air pollution on humans," in *Air Pollution,* A. C. Stern, Ed., vol. 1, pp. 335–386 (Academic Press, New York, 1962).
6. Heiman, H., "Effects on human health," in *Air Pollution,* WHO Monograph No. 46, pp. 159–220 (World Health Organization, Geneva, 1961).
7. Katz, M., "Some aspects of the physical and chemical nature of air pollution," *ibid.,* pp. 97–158.
8. Lawther, P. J., B. T. Commins, and M. Henderson, "Carbon monoxide in town air: an interim report," *Ann. Occupational Hyg.,* **5,** 241–248 (1962).
9. Goldsmith, J. R., personal communication, 1963.
10. *Technical Report of California Standards for Ambient Air Quality and Motor Vehicle Exhaust* (California State Department of Public Health, Berkeley, 1960).

3. CARBON DIOXIDE

Carbon dioxide is not normally considered an air pollutant because (i) the uncontaminated atmosphere has a concentration of approximately 300 ppm, (ii) it is essential for animal and plant life, and (iii) there must be at least 5000 ppm in the air before man's respiration is adversely affected (*1*).

Man-Made Sources

However, since about the middle of the 19th century, worldwide atmospheric concentrations of carbon dioxide have been rising steadily because of the increasing dependence of our industrial era on fossil fuels. Huge quantities of carbon dioxide—the main product of combustion—are emitted each day into city air. Carbon dioxide concentrations over heavily industrialized areas are at times as high as 1000 ppm (*2*). At the beginning of the 20th century, the burning of coal produced 3 billion tons of carbon dioxide a year (*3*). Since 1950, the amount produced has averaged about 9 billion tons per year. By the end of the century, as much as 50 billion tons may be released annually into the atmosphere. About 2300 billion tons of carbon dioxide are now present in the atmosphere. Since the beginning of the industrial era, 330 billion tons, or roughly 14 percent of the natural carbon dioxide in the air, have been produced by coal combustion. This is about 42 ppm, and, as calculated in 1960–61, combustion processes are now increasing this amount at a rate of about 1.6 ppm per year (*4*). By the year 2000, this figure of 14 percent will probably have risen to about 50 percent (*3*).

Appraisals made by the United Nations show that, by the first decade of the 21st century, the combustion of fossil fuel could have produced an amount of carbon dioxide equal to 20 percent of the amount now in the atmosphere. They indicate, moreover, that 1700 billion tons, or 73 percent of the original atmospheric carbon dioxide, will probably be the cumulative total that will have been produced since the middle of the 19th century (*5*). In all probability, this figure is two orders of magnitude greater than the usual rate of carbon dioxide production from volcanoes.

Ten times as much carbon dioxide is being emitted into the air from coal fires and metallurgical furnaces alone as from the natural process of breathing (6). As a result, the amount of carbon dioxide in the entire atmosphere would be doubled in the course of about 500 years if there were no compensating influences.

It has been predicted that the known reserves of coal and oil, which amount to about 13×10^{18} grams, will be used up in less than 1000 years, allowance having been made for the growth of industrial activity. If this prediction is fulfilled, nearly 40×10^{18} grams of carbon dioxide will have been added to the atmosphere, 17 times the present amount in the air (7).

Local Effects

The principal undesirable local effect of atmospheric carbon dioxide is deterioration of building stones—in particular, carbonate rock such as limestone. In the presence of moisture, carbon dioxide produces carbonic acid, which converts calcium carbonate to the water-soluble bicarbonate that is then leached away. Carbon dioxide is also responsible in part for the atmospheric corrosion of magnesium, and perhaps of other structural metals.

Global Implications

Scientists are more concerned, however, by the possible future effect on the heat balance, and hence on the climate of the whole earth, of the extra amounts of atmospheric carbon dioxide that are derived from the combustion of fossil fuel. The temperature of the earth is controlled by the balance between energy received from the sun and that lost back into space. Light passes through the atmosphere to the surface of the earth. There some of it is absorbed, heating the ground. This energy is then reradiated as infrared radiation. The atmosphere is kept warm because three substances in its upper layers absorb some of this infrared radiation from the earth. In the order of importance, they are water vapor, carbon dioxide, and ozone. These substances act like the glass in a greenhouse. Human activities have little effect on the amount of water vapor or ozone available, but they have already changed the carbon dioxide concentration. Some scientists believe that the slight rise of average temperature over the entire earth, which has been observed during recent decades, may be the result of the increase in atmospheric carbon dioxide (5).

However, the hypothesis that an increase in carbon dioxide will increase global temperatures is by no means proved. Möller recently examined the best available mathematical analyses of the total heat balance, and he has shown that, depending on the assumed dependence of the atmospheric water content on the temperature, any answer, from an actual temperature decrease to an infinite increase, can be obtained (8).

It is unlikely that the climate has been seriously affected as yet by the small increase in atmospheric carbon dioxide that has taken place since industrial coal combustion began (5). Significant effects may occur in the coming centuries, on the other hand, if the combustion of fossil fuels continues to increase—and it will keep rising if the fuel and power requirements of our worldwide industrial civilization continue to rise exponentially, and if these needs are met only to a limited degree by the development of tidal, solar, and nuclear power.

Both biological and geochemical processes provide a natural disposal, as well as a replenishment, system for carbon dioxide. Green plants use carbon dioxide in photosynthesis, but most of the plant material formed is reoxidized in a few years, thus returning carbon dioxide to the atmosphere. Carbon dioxide is absorbed in the weathering of rocks and is used in the formation of peat, coal, and petroleum, but these are very slow processes. This carbon dioxide is balanced by the amount ejected into the atmosphere by volcanoes and mineral springs, which are probably the greatest natural sources of carbon dioxide. (The decay of dead animals and plants adds a comparatively small amount, and this is carbon that was originally withdrawn from the atmosphere.)

The potential of plant life in the sea and on land to adjust the world carbon dioxide supply is not known, but it may be considerable. The only other real possibility for disposing of the extra amounts of carbon dioxide from the combustion of fossil fuels is through the oceans. However, it could take as long as 10,000 years for all the extra carbon dioxide to be dissolved; the oceans circulate slowly (7). It is not known precisely at what speed such absorption occurs, but it appears that only a small fraction of the extra carbon dioxide can be assimilated by the surface layers of the oceans during a period of several hundred years. It is, therefore, probably true that most of the additional carbon dioxide that is released into the air will remain there for at least several centuries. Keeling estimates that at least 30 percent, and possibly as much as 50 percent, of the carbon dioxide from the combustion of fossil fuels may have remained in the atmosphere (9).

In any case, the fear seems legitimate that an unchecked increase in the rate of combustion of carbon fuels may eventually extend carbon dioxide levels to meteorological and physical significance, and that carbon dioxide concentrations may become great enough to cause climatic changes. If, at the end of this century, the average temperature has continued to rise and, in addition, measurement shows that the amount of atmospheric carbon dioxide has also increased, this will add validity to the idea that carbon dioxide is a determining factor in causing climatic change.

Within a few centuries, man will be returning to the atmosphere and the oceans the concentrated organic carbon that has been stored in sedimentary geologic formations during hundreds of millions of years. If, by so doing, he finds that his climate is being altered in an undesirable way, he may be forced to turn to new sources of energy in order to reestablish a viable carbon dioxide equilibrium.

References

1. Cadle, R. D., and P. L. Magill, "Chemistry of contaminated atmospheres," in *Air Pollution Handbook*, P. L. Magill, R. F. Holden, and C. Ackley, Eds., section 3, pp. 1–27 (McGraw-Hill, New York, 1956).
2. Wayne, L. G., personal communication, 1963.
3. Suess, H. E., "Fuel residuals and climate," *Bull. Atomic Scientists,* **17**, 374–375 (1961).
4. Bolin, B., and C. D. Keeling, "Large-scale atmospheric mixing as deduced from the seasonal and meridianal variations of carbon dioxide," *J. Geophys. Res.* **68**, 3899–3920 (1963).
5. Revelle, R., "Dynamics of the carbon dioxide cycle," in *Proceedings of the Conference on Recent Research in Climatology*, H. Craig, Ed., pp. 93–105 (Committee on Research in Water Resources, University of California, La Jolla, 1957).

6. Lotka, A. J., *Elements of Mathematical Biology* (Dover, New York, 1956).

7. Plass, G. N., "The carbon dioxide theory of climatic change," in *Proceedings of the Conference on Recent Research in Climatology*, H. Craig, Ed., pp. 81–92 (Committee on Research in Water Resources, University of California, La Jolla, 1957).

8. Möller, F., "On the influence of changes in the CO_2 concentration in air on the radiation balance of the earth's surface and on the climate," *J. Geophys. Res.*, **68**, 3877–3886 (1963).

9. Keeling, C. D., "The concentration and isotopic abundances of carbon dioxide in the atmosphere," *Tellus*, **12**, 200–203 (1960).

4. OXIDES OF NITROGEN

Sources and Emissions

Oxides of nitrogen are one of the most important groups of atmospheric contaminants in many communities. They are produced during the high-temperature combustion of coal, oil, gas, or gasoline in power plants and internal combustion engines. The combustion fixes atmospheric nitrogen to produce the oxides. At these temperatures, nitric oxide forms first and in the atmosphere it reacts with oxygen and is converted to nitrogen dioxide. While this oxidation is very rapid at high concentrations, the rate is much slower at low concentrations. In sunlight, especially in the presence of organic material as typified by Los Angeles–type photochemical smog, the conversion of nitric oxide to nitrogen dioxide is greatly accelerated.

The most intensive investigations yet undertaken on the emission of oxides of nitrogen have been carried out in Los Angeles, and detailed data are available on the production of such oxides from various kinds of stationary sources and from the internal combustion engine. In January 1963, the total production from stationary sources during the Rule 62 period (April 15 to November 15, when natural gas was used in place of high sulfur-containing fuels) was 212 tons per day and, during other times of the year, 352 tons per day. Total emissions of nitrogen oxides from moving sources— mostly automobiles, trucks, and buses—were 500 tons per day, approximately 1.5 to 2.3 times the emissions from stationary sources, depending on the time of year (1).

Thus, 0.15 kilogram of nitrogen oxides is produced per person per day. This is a maximum figure, and it reflects a standard of material well-being directly related to the industrial development of the community, the number of automobiles used, and the population density. In less mechanized societies, the figure would be far less.

The increase of oxides of nitrogen is illustrated in Fig. 2. A striking rise in emissions in downtown Los Angeles occurred from January 1957 to September 1961, and then, after a substantial decrease, there was a renewed increase in 1963. The 1963 values amount to 195 percent of the initial 1957 readings.

Fig. 2. Comparison of 12-month moving average trends for carbon monoxide and oxides of nitrogen for downtown Los Angeles, 1957–1963 (parts per hundred million, pphm). [Los Angeles County Air Pollution Control District]

Today there is a trend toward higher combustion-chamber temperature and more efficient combustion. The higher temperature results in a further increase in the production of oxides of nitrogen, especially from automobiles.

Concentrations

Most determinations of oxides of nitrogen combine nitric oxides and nitrogen dioxide, with a typical range of concentrations being 0.02 to 0.9 ppm (2). Separate determinations of these oxides of nitrogen have been made in downtown Los Angeles, and maximum values of 1.73 ppm have been found for nitrogen dioxide, recorded on September 17, 1953, and 3.50 ppm for nitric oxide on January 13, 1961. The Los Angeles Air Pollution Control District has set the first alert level for the direct adverse effect of the oxides of nitrogen at 3.0 ppm.

Effects

The hazards associated with nitrogen oxides are (i) a direct noxious effect on the health and well-being of people and (ii) photochemical oxidation of organic material, which is an indirect effect. In the concentrations normally found in community air pollution, by far the most objectionable consequences of the oxides of nitrogen are those that arise from photochemical reactions.

Of the oxides of nitrogen, nitrogen dioxide is considerably more toxic than nitric oxide, acting as an acutely irritating substance. In equal concentrations, it is more injurious than carbon monoxide. Since the smoke from cigarettes, pipe tobacco, and cigars contains several hundred parts per million of nitrogen dioxide (3), its effects on the respiratory system deserve attention. Chronic lung disease has been produced experimentally by subjecting animals to nitrogen dioxide, and there is some evidence that exposure to the nitrogen dioxide released during the filling of silos has caused a chronic pulmonary condition (4). The Cleveland Clinic fire of May 1929 illustrated the insidious nature of nitrogen dioxide as a poison; a large number of people died after inhaling nitrogen dioxide produced by burning x-ray film (5). However, exposures of this severity are rare. Nitrogen oxides, at levels found in air pollution, are only potentially irritating and potentially related to chronic pulmonary fibrosis (4).

Nitrogen dioxide has received considerable attention as an air pollutant because it is a hazard in numerous industries. The threshold limit (established by the American Conference of Governmental Industrial Hygienists) for an 8-hour working day has been tentatively set at 5 ppm. However, a report that a 3- to 5-year exposure of Russian workmen to concentrations of nitrogen dioxide generally below 2.8 ppm resulted in chronic changes in the lung (3) has contributed to the belief that 5 ppm of nitrogen dioxide may not be safe for daily exposure.

Since nitrogen dioxide can react with the water vapor in the air or with raindrops to produce nitric acid, small concentrations in the atmosphere can cause considerable corrosion to metal surfaces in the immediate vicinity of the source.

Concentrations of 25 ppm near factories handling large amounts of nitric acid have caused injury to plants (6). The concentration of nitrogen oxides in the air of the community, however, is probably always too low to cause plant damage.

In recent years Los Angeles County recorded its first instances of nitrogen oxide concentrations that exceeded the first alert level: 3.17 ppm on December 19, 1960 and 3.93 ppm on January 13, 1961 (7). Because of its limited ventilation, there is reason for concern at the increase of oxides of nitrogen in areas such as Los Angeles. If no steps are taken, Los Angeles will become more crowded, the ventilation will become worse because of the greater number of buildings, and the direct adverse effect may become an important factor in community air pollution.

Nitrogen dioxide is unique among the common pollutants in that it absorbs light in the visible region of the spectrum, mostly in the blue region. It is thus a yellow-brown gas. Because it is visible, substantial concentrations reduce visibility even without the presence of aerosol particles. A concentration of 8 to 10 ppm would probably reduce visibility to about 1 mile (8).

No standards have been set for oxides of nitrogen with regard to their part in the formation of noxious substances in the photochemical oxidation of organic material. The permissible level for this indirect adverse effect is likely to be much lower than for the direct effect—perhaps as low as 0.1 to 0.2 ppm (9). The process by which sunlight reacts with nitrogen dioxide in the presence of organic material to form ozone and other harmful by-products, and the complex reactions and effects produced, are discussed later.

Control

A continued increase in the burning of fuel, both in power plants and in transportation, will result in a corresponding increase in the oxides of nitrogen. The amount of oxides of nitrogen emitted by power plants can be reduced by lowering the peak-flame temperatures in combustion. Control efforts at the power plants may result in an overall reduction of approximately 50 percent (*10*).

In trying to control emissions from automobiles, attention has been given to hydrocarbons and carbon monoxides rather than to the oxides of nitrogen. The goal of present devices to control automobile exhaust emissions is to reduce hydrocarbons by up to 80 percent and carbon monoxide by 60 percent. Little has been done with the oxides of nitrogen (*11*) and extensive engineering research and development are necessary.

Global Implications

If we assume that the worldwide incidence of high-temperature combustion is about twice that of the United States, the total amount of nitrogen oxides formed would be in the order of 30,000 tons per day. If we were to assume that the oxides of nitrogen remain in the air and are evenly distributed globally (in a volume of air of 4.3×10^{21} liters), the increase per year would be only 2.0×10^{-6} ppm. This amount would be insignificant. We know, however, that under the influence of sunlight, oxygen, in contact with and in reaction to particulate matter, forms oxides that are then converted to nitrates which are slowly removed from the atmosphere by precipitation. The formation of nitrogen oxide, while of local significance as a source of air pollution, is probably of no concern globally even from a long-range point of view.

References

1. *Summary of Air Pollution Statistics for Los Angeles County* (Los Angeles County Air Pollution Control District, Los Angeles, 1963).
2. Tebbens, B. D., "Residual pollution products in the atmosphere," in *Air Pollution*, A. C. Stern, Ed., vol. 1, pp. 23–40 (Academic Press, New York, 1962).
3. Stokinger, H. E., "Effects of air pollution on animals," *ibid.*, pp. 282–334.
4. Goldsmith, J. R., "Effects of air pollution on humans," *ibid.*, pp. 335–386.
5. Cadle, R. D., and P. L. Magill, "Chemistry of contaminated atmospheres," in *Air Pollution Handbook*, P. L. Magill, F. R. Holden, and C. Ackley, Eds., section 9, pp. 1–27 (McGraw-Hill, New York, 1956).
6. Thomas, M. D., and R. H. Hendricks, "Effect of air pollution on plants," *ibid.*, pp. 1–44.
7. Brunelle, M. F., and R. G. Holmes, *Study of Oxides of Nitrogen Alerts in*

December 1960 and January 1961 (Los Angeles County Air Pollution Control District, Los Angeles, 1961).

8. Leighton, P. A., personal communication, 1963.
9. Haagen-Smit, A. J., and M. M. Fox, "Automobile exhaust and ozone formation." *SAE Trans. (Soc. Automotive Engrs.)*, **63**, 575–580 (1955); Schuck, E. A., G. J. Doyle, and N. Endow, *A Progress Report on the Photochemistry of Polluted Atmospheres*, Report No. 31, p. 49 (Air Pollution Foundation, San Marino, Calif, 1960).
10. Barnhart, D. H., and E. K. Diehl, "Control of nitrogen oxides in boiler flue gases by two-stage combustion," in *Proceedings of the Fifty-Second Annual Meeting*, pp. 1–15 (Air Pollution Control Association, Los Angeles, 1959).
11. Rose, A. H., "Automotive exhaust emissions," in *Air Pollution*, A. C. Stern, Ed., vol. 2, pp. 40–80 (Academic Press, New York, 1962).

5. PHOTOCHEMICAL AIR POLLUTION

One of the early observations on atmospheric reactions was made by John Aitken, the inventor of the particle counter that bears his name. He described the formation of haze when a water-saturated atmosphere containing sulfur dioxide was exposed to sunlight. In a letter to the Royal Society of London entitled "Phenomena connected with cloudy condensations" (1892) he wrote: "The colours produced by such simple materials as a little dust and a little vapor are as beautiful as anything seen in nature and will repay the trouble of reproducing them" (1). (Aitken's observations have been repeated frequently. Whenever combustion occurs, large numbers of condensation nuclei are produced, leading to the formation of fogs in the presence of air supersaturated with water vapor.)

Aitken's ecstasy is not shared by air pollution control officials. To them the colors described by Aitken represent a definite number of particles per cubic meter, a potential dustfall running into tons per day per square mile, and irritating clouds, toxic to plants, animals, and human beings.

In about 1943, Los Angeles began to experience a new type of air pollution that caused plant damage, eye irritation, cracking of stressed rubber, and a decrease in visibility. The annoying components in this pollution were products formed in a photochemical reaction between oxides of nitrogen and many types of organics in the presence of sunlight. This system can also oxidize sulfur dioxide to sulfur trioxide with the haze formations observed by Aitken.

Photochemical air pollution is commonly referred to as "smog." However, the term *smog* was coined originally to denote pollution by a combination of smoke and fog, so that its use to describe photochemical pollution is etymologically incorrect.

Sources

Among the substances responsible for photochemical air pollution are unsaturated hydrocarbons (faster reactors), saturated hydrocarbons (slower reactors), aromatics, and aldehydes. These are emitted during the incomplete combustion of all fuels (including

89

rubbish and agricultural field wastes), but automobile exhaust is the major source. Hydrocarbons and other organic gases are also expelled during the production, refining, and handling of gasoline and from such manufacturing operations as industrial dryers and ovens, and furnaces used for baking paints, enamels, and printing ink.

After stringent control of these stationary sources in Los Angeles, the present hydrocarbon emissions for the county are estimated to be 1600 tons of organics per day from motor vehicles, 250 tons from various operations of the petroleum industry, and 300 tons from users of organic solvent (2).

The oxides of nitrogen, the other partner in the formation of photochemical smog, are formed during high-temperature combustion, chiefly in automobiles and large power plants. The temperature produced by the explosion of gasoline in the automobile engine causes a few thousand parts per million of nitric oxide to form from the mixture of nitrogen and oxygen in the air. Oxides of nitrogen are formed mainly during cruising and acceleration cycles of automobile operation. The average concentration of oxides of nitrogen produced during all driving cycles amounts to about 1000 ppm. The formation of oxides of nitrogen in power plants is quite similar to that in the automobile engine. Here also a high temperature is reached, followed by rapid cooling. The high temperature causes nitric oxide to form; the rapid cooling prevents the decomposition back to nitrogen and oxygen, which would occur if the cooling were slower. The concentration of the oxides of nitrogen differs greatly from one power plant to another. Recent measurements have established a range of concentrations from a few hundred to more than a thousand parts per million of nitric oxide (3).

Approximately 750 tons of oxides of nitrogen are released in the Los Angeles Basin daily, and of this amount about 500 tons are produced by automobile engines and the remaining 250 tons primarily by power plants. The automobile therefore plays a major role in producing both of the components that are essential to the formation of photochemical smog (2).

The exceptionally high degree of photochemical pollution in Los Angeles County results from the county's phenomenal growth in population and industrial activity, its high consumption of petroleum fuels, its frequently poor ventilation, and its steady sunshine. The mountains that ring three sides of the large county basin reduce winds and impose atmospheric stability. The stagnant air mass accumulates emissions for several days, and the concentrations of pollutants become disturbingly high.

A California health survey made in 1956 showed that 74 percent of the people in Los Angeles were bothered by smog. In the San Francisco Bay Area, which has similar meteorological and topographical conditions but only half the population, and therefore fewer acute pollution episodes, only 24 percent were adversely affected (Fig. 3). Although smog may be less frequent and severe in other cities, many have similar meteorological problems; and the rising population and number of automobiles in most large cities, accompanied by the increased use of fuel for heat and power, predict critical problems elsewhere. All cities have poor ventilation and bright sunshine at least a few days of the year.

Reactions

The naturally occurring ozone that exists in the upper atmosphere limits sunlight radiation at the earth's surface to wavelengths longer than the near ultraviolet at about 2900 angstroms. Even though the part of the solar spectrum that reaches the earth contains energy-rich radiation, it cannot directly affect organic substances such as hydrocarbons. In order to produce a chemical reaction, light must be absorbed; and among the more common pollutants the most important light absorber is nitrogen dioxide.

Nitrogen dioxide is a yellow-brown gas that absorbs light in the blue and near ultraviolet part of the spectrum, and is thereby dissociated into nitric oxide and atomic oxygen. At a concentration of 0.10 ppm, the photolysis rate of nitrogen dioxide by average sunlight amounts to about 2 ppm per hour (4). This reaction is the fastest of all known primary photochemical processes in polluted air and is one of the reasons that nitrogen dioxide has played a dominant role in photochemical smog symptoms. Other contributing reactions are the photochemical decomposition of aldehydes and the formation of excited oxygen molecules. Any one of these

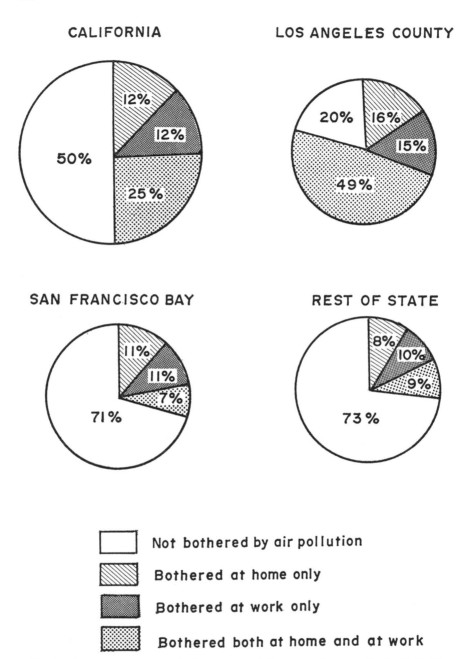

Fig. 3. Impact of air pollution on working population. [*Air Pollution,* A. C. Stern, Ed. (Academic Press, New York, 1962), vol. 1]

agents can attack organic material; the mechanism may involve removal of a hydrogen atom from the hydrocarbon. The alkyl and acyl radicals unite with oxygen to form peroxyl radicals. These in turn can react with oxygen to form ozone, and with nitrogen dioxide to produce plant-damaging peracyl nitrates and numerous, more stable oxidation products such as formaldehyde (which irritates the eye), and polymeric compounds (which reduce visibility). In these reactions, the nitric oxide that results from the photodissociation of nitrogen dioxide is reoxidized by the excess ozone, peroxyl radicals, and other oxidizing materials to nitrogen dioxide, which can thus continue to function as the primary light-energy absorber.

A schematic picture of this complex of reactions is shown in Fig. 4 (3). The oxidant pool consists of the atomic oxygen from the dissociation of nitrogen dioxide, excited oxygen from the irradiation of molecular oxygen, peroxyl radicals from the action of oxidants on hydrocarbons, and ozone formed as a by-product in photochemical reactions. The oxidants react further with the original materials as well as with their reaction products, so that at any time a very complex mixture of intermediate oxidation and reaction products is present.

The rapid conversion of nitric oxide to the dioxide in the presence of free ozone has an important practical consequence: No distinction is made between the two oxides for control purposes. However, the two oxides do have different effects on health (5).

While the same photochemical process that takes place in Los Angeles probably occurs in most urban areas, there is a distinct possibility that, under different circumstances and different patterns of emissions, the dominant role of nitrogen dioxide may be taken over by other primary absorbers—organic compounds of many types as well as inorganic compounds.

Any one of the symptoms of Los Angeles–type smog can be reproduced in a fumigation room by irradiating hydrocarbons in the presence of oxides of nitrogen. However, these experiments are only successful when they are conducted in the range of the low concentrations that prevail in polluted city air. At these low concentrations, reactive substances, such as ozone, sulfur dioxide, and olefins, can coexist for quite some time. For example, mixtures of olefins and ozone that would explode at concentrations of a few percent, react slowly at atmospheric concentrations of a few tenths of a part per million.

Photochemical Pollutants and Their Effects

1) *Plant Damage*

Photochemical pollutants (*6*) are of definite economic significance because of their effects on vegetation. At an early stage in the study of these effects, two distinctly different injury syndromes were identified. The first of these was termed, somewhat misleadingly, "smog injury." Later, another disease, known as "grape stipple" or "weather fleck," depending on the plant species affected, was also shown to be the result of photochemical pollution.

Laboratory studies showed that the latter type of injury could be duplicated by exposing susceptible plants to low concentrations of ozone. A typical symptom is the splotched or stippled appearance of the upper surface of the leaf, with some spots becoming necrotic if the concentration is sufficiently high. Tobacco and grape are among the species most susceptible to *ozone injury.*

So-called *smog injury,* on the other hand, is characterized by the collapse of the cells on the under surface of the leaves of susceptible plants, resulting in a silvered or bronzed appearance. Lower levels of pollution than those that cause irreversible damage will cause parts of the under side of the leaf to temporarily appear water-soaked. High doses may result in the collapse of the cells throughout the leaf. There is considerable evidence that chronic exposure of a variety of plants to concentrations below those that cause irreversible damage adversely affects plant growth (*7*).

At least two laboratory mixtures produce effects that superficially resemble smog injury: (i) A mixture of ozone and a reactive olefin, with the latter in sufficient excess so that no free ozone remains, and (ii) the products of photolysis of a mixture of nitrogen oxides and olefins. In this latter photochemical process, peroxyacetyl nitrate is formed. This was the first pure compound isolated from the photochemical reaction mixtures that was found to produce typical plant damage. Since it also produces eye irritation, peroxyacetyl nitrate is the only compound so far identified that can produce both effects (7). The products of the ozone-olefin reaction primarily attack plant leaves that are significantly older than those attacked by peroxyacetyl nitrate (8), and it seems reasonable to conclude that peroxyacetyl nitrate is the active agent in the photochemical mixture. Present evidence (8) suggests that both types of phytotoxicants may be present in photochemical pollution, since both young and old leaves are affected.

Smog injury to vegetation has been reported in or near a number of cities, including Paris, London, São Paulo, Philadelphia, Baltimore, New York, San Francisco, and Los Angeles (9). It has also been observed in the western and midwestern states of Washington, Utah, Colorado, Missouri, and Illinois, and in the northwest coastal Baja California (10). Although smog injury occurs in many eastern states, ozone damage seems to predominate in Connecticut, New York, New Jersey, Pennsylvania, Delaware, Maryland, District of Columbia, and North Carolina (10). It is not common in California except for especially susceptible plants such as grape, bean, and tobacco. Smog injury is common throughout most urban and adjacent rural areas in California and is responsible for significant damage to agricultural crops, particularly the salad crops, and to rye and annual bluegrass.

Estimates of visible damage to agricultural crops amount annually to about $8 million in California for field and vegetable crops and approximately $18 million along the Atlantic seaboard (9). Tobacco growers in Connecticut, North Carolina, and Mary-

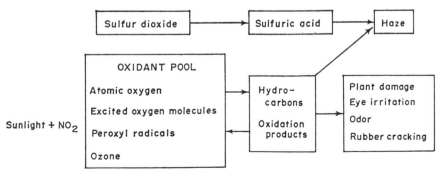

Fig. 4. Complex reactions in photochemical air pollution.

land have sustained heavy losses caused by weather fleck. No estimates have yet been made of the real economic loss caused by sup-
pression of growth, delayed maturity, and the attendant increase in
the cost of crop production and reduction in yields.

2) *Deterioration of Materials*

The high ozone content of the polluted atmosphere in Los
Angeles is responsible for deterioration of materials. One of the
early indications of this type of pollution is the unusually fast
cracking of stretched rubber products. Even the slightest stretching
brings rapid deterioration. This kind of damage is common in Los
Angeles and San Francisco and has been seen in the vicinity of
Honolulu, Phoenix, Washington, D.C., Wilmington, Philadelphia,
Trenton and New Brunswick, New York, Hartford, Boston, and in
rural southern Ontario, Canada (*10*).

Although it has long been known that ozone affects the strength
of fabrics and the colorfastness of dyes, it is only recently that experiments have been conducted to determine the quantitative
effects of ozone on these materials. Preliminary investigation suggests that exposure to photochemical smog conditions causes definite
deterioration of a number of natural and synthetic fabrics, as well as
the fading of dyes (*11*). Awareness and understanding of the many
factors involved are so new that active research is just beginning.

3) *Eye Irritation*

The effects of photochemical air pollution are many and varied,
but the most noticeable and annoying of its nuisance effects are
eye irritation and decreased visibility. Almost three-fourths of the
people in metropolitan areas of southern California say that they
are affected by eye irritation (*12*). Studies by eye specialists have
not indicated that repeated irritation results in any permanent
injury to the eye (*12*), but severe photochemical smog can be highly
distressing and can temporarily hinder normal function. The
precise composition of all the substances responsible for eye irritation has not been definitely determined. Ozone, at observed
levels in photochemical air pollution, does not irritate the eyes or
respiratory membranes. It is possible that the irritant is a mixture

of formaldehyde and acrolein, peroxides of various types, and free radicals. Peroxyacetyl nitrate is a powerful eye irritant at concentrations in the 1-ppm range and some people therefore believe that it is probably responsible, along with acrolein and formaldehyde (8). Since the concentration of known gaseous irritating substances in the photochemical smog mixture has not been considered sufficiently high to account for the effects observed, the question has been raised as to whether irritation of the eyes and respiratory tract may also be associated with the presence of particles in the air. The aerosols that are produced by the oxidation of hydrocarbons by sunlight in the presence of nitrogen oxides and by the oxidation of sulfur dioxide to sulfur trioxide, with the subsequent formation of sulfuric acid aerosols, may intensify the physiological reaction to other pollutants, or may even themselves contribute to the reaction (13).

4) Decrease in Visibility

Visibility is reduced by smoke, by submicron dust and fumes, and by the formation of aerosols from reactions in the atmosphere. Wherever hydrocarbons are oxidized by sunlight in the presence of oxides of nitrogen, aerosols are produced.

There are about 2000 particles above 0.5 micron in diameter per cubic centimeter of air in the photochemical air pollution of Los Angeles (14). Ninety-five percent of the particles in this photochemical smog are below 1 micron in diameter (15). It has been observed that, as visibility decreases in Los Angeles County, the particles in the 0.5- to 0.8-micron range increase more rapidly than in the other size ranges.

The nature of aerosols is not well understood. However, they are probably polymeric oxidation and reaction products of the primary reactants.

5) Health Hazard Being Studied

The high frequency of photochemical smog days in the Los Angeles area has aroused public concern over (i) the possibility that someday a level of air pollution may be reached that will cause severe illness among susceptible people, and (ii) the possibility that continued exposure to local air pollutants may have an effect on health that will not appear until many years later. Efforts by public agencies to respond to these concerns have led to a number of local surveys and studies. These studies showed that there was no obvious relationship between incidence of general sickness and air pollution in Los Angeles. The rate of hospital admissions for respiratory and cardiac diseases did not change significantly during periods of photochemical air pollution, nor was there a marked increase in the number of deaths and transfers to hospitals of nursing home residents (16). Thus, the mixture of pollutants that afflicts Los Angeles has not yet been shown to produce fatalities, nor has acute disease resulted, except possibly in a small minority of asthmatics (12). (The question of allergic reactions is only beginning to be raised.) There is, however, reason to be concerned about the fact that these pollutants might cause chronic disease and that they might produce conditions that will affect the lungs or aggravate chronic respiratory conditions. (12). They have also been suspected of a role in chronic pulmonary disease and lung cancer. The failure to demonstrate these effects may be the result of inadequate methods for detecting them and does not prove that they do not exist.

Ozone, by itself, is known to be a highly toxic substance. Experimental exposure to 1.25 ppm for about 1 hour causes an increased residual lung volume and a decreased breathing capacity (12). Higher levels tend to produce pulmonary edema and hemorrhage, and to impede the transport of gases from the lung alveoli into the blood. In experiments with rats, exposures as low as 1 ppm for 8 hours a day over a year or so have produced bronchitis, fibrosis, and bronchiolitis. Although this suggests the possibility that ozone may have a similar effect in man, there are no data to substantiate it. It is possible that this lack of effect on human beings may be related to the discovery that oil mists, as well as preexposure to lower levels of the gas, tend to protect animals from the acute effects of ozone (17). However, whether they protect man from chronic effects is not known. Further investigation of the effects of exposures to ozone at low levels is urgently needed. It is quite possible that, even if the use of afterburners results in a substantial reduction of hydrocarbon emissions from automobile exhaust, ozone concentrations may not be very greatly reduced (12).

6) *Dynamics of Pollution*

Photochemical air pollution will affect different areas in different ways, according to the makeup of the area and to the highly complex workings of the photochemical syndrome.

The first of these complex factors involves the various rates of decay of the oxidants. (The following figures are true for the movement of pollution over urban areas.) The olefin-ozone reaction components, responsible for some plant damage, decay quite rapidly after emission because the half-life of the phytotoxicant is estimated to be no more than a few minutes (*10*). In this photochemical system, ozone has a half-life of about 1 hour, whereas eye irritants, including peroxyacetyl nitrate, have been shown to persist for more than 24 hours. The aerosols formed in the photochemical processes from hydrocarbons and nitrogen dioxide, and from sulfur dioxide, persist for a considerably longer time. One group of phytotoxicants, therefore, reaches peak concentrations at relatively short distances from the emission source, while ozone, eye irritants, other phytotoxicants, and haze production may remain high some distance from the source. Their concentrations are diminished gradually by atmospheric diffusion.

The second factor is that the precursors produce their products at different rates; saturates and slow-reacting olefins, such as ethylene, are much slower than most olefins. Therefore, ozone, for example, is produced at a far slower rate by saturates although peak concentrations from both precursors may well be of the same magnitude. The smog damage to plants and eye irritation from saturated hydrocarbons has been shown to be much less than that resulting from olefins (*10*).

These factors would explain why, in a well-defined area of pollution, without the addition of other contaminants, medium eye irritation, plant damage, and low oxidant values near the source may be expected at first. After traveling a few hours, the ozone level of the pollution cloud may become high, while eye irritation may remain moderate and plant damage may decrease considerably. After a longer period, and at a greater distance from the source, with low oxidant values, there may be high concentrations of ozone and noticeable eye irritation, but no plant damage of the smog type. This may explain the fact that ozone damage is found on tobacco in Connecticut whereas no smog injury is noticed. The occurrence of smog damage in and around Washington, D.C., and the discovery of ozone injury on tobacco some distance from there, is also explained by the variations in reaction rates and by meteorological phenomena that move the pollution cloud away from the city.

However, in extended urban areas, such as Los Angeles and San Francisco and their surrounding communities, many sources of emission of hydrocarbons, nitrogen oxides, and sulfur dioxide continue to inject new primary pollutants into the moving, dynamic, chemical and photochemical system. Under this situation—a nearly continuous area of pollution from motor vehicles and other sources—plant injury, eye irritation, elevated oxidant, rubber cracking, and haze formation stretch for many miles while the pollution cloud passes through community after community.

Measurement and Monitoring

One frequently used measurement of the concentration of photochemical air pollution is total oxidant. Oxidant is defined operationally as the total of all substances that are capable of oxidizing the iodide ion to iodine under certain specified conditions, or of producing some similar reaction. Oxidant concentration is thus a function of the method used to measure it and is therefore not an absolute quantity. Concentrations are normally reported in terms of the equivalent concentration of ozone that would produce the same effect. However, total oxidant is an index of the intensity of photochemical air pollution only under certain conditions that are not always present in the urban atmosphere. In particular, elevated sulfur dioxide levels can mask the chemical reaction without removing the oxidant, resulting in erroneously low values. It is clear that sound judgment is necessary in selecting the method to be used in a particular case.

The concentration of total oxidant is approximately correlated with the eye-irritating characteristic of West Coast photochemical smog. At an oxidant concentration in Los Angeles of 0.8 to 0.10 ppm, there is a light smog, presumably visible and just noticeable by its typical odor, while at 0.13 to 0.15 ppm slight eye irritation is

Table 1. Percentage of eye irritation to different levels of oxidant, San Francisco Bay Area, September–November 1956 and January–December 1957.

Oxidant (ppm)	Response (%)	Oxidant (ppm)	Response (%)
0.00–0.05	14	0.15–0.20	70
0.05–0.10	26	0.20–0.25	75
0.10–0.15	40		

usually felt (18). The California ambient air quality standards have established 0.15 ppm for 1 hour by the potassium iodide method as the "oxidant index" at which eye irritation, plant damage, and reduced visibility will occur (5).

The standards on which present controls are based do not imply that no effects will be noticed below the levels indicated. There is ample evidence for this in the California State Department of Public Health's technical report on standards (5), which contains many graphs and tables listing severity of symptoms in relation to the concentration of pollutants. These clearly show that there is a gradual decrease in symptoms or complaints as the concentration decreases but that a significant part of the population still experiences discomfort far below the adopted standards.

Table 1 shows the degree of eye irritation caused by different levels of oxidant as measured in the San Francisco Bay Area (5). It is clear that even below 0.15 ppm of oxidant, often used as a standard, a considerable percentage of the population will be adversely affected. The adopted standard of 0.15 ppm of oxidant is therefore not regarded as a level of desirable air quality, but rather as a short-term goal to be lowered as soon as engineering knowledge permits.

The maximum concentration of total oxidant for the Los Angeles area was recorded by the potassium iodide method at 0.75 ppm in 1955 (19). Elevated oxidant values are found in California throughout the southern coastal basin, the San Francisco Bay Area, and in many cities in the San Joaquin and Sacramento valleys (9). Elevated oxidant concentrations have also been recorded in a number of midwestern and eastern cities in the

United States, including St. Louis, Missouri; Whiting-Hammond, Indiana; Washington, D.C.; Cincinnati, Ohio; Charleston, West Virginia; Elizabeth, New Jersey; and Beltsville, Maryland (10). These concentrations are at a lower level than those in Los Angeles, the maximum value measured probably being 0.58 ppm for a brief period in Louisville, Kentucky (20). In New York City, the pollution complex may have a low oxidant concentration either because of the reactions with higher sulfur dioxide or because of the masking effect on the determination.

The diurnal fluctuation of oxidant concentration in Los Angeles has a pattern that is typical for many smogs: A low concentration at night, rarely exceeding 0.05 ppm, increasing to a maximum around noon, and practically disappearing at sunset after a gradual decrease during the afternoon (21).

Ozone concentrations measured by spectrographic and chemical methods agree reasonably well. Ozone often comprises more than three-fourths of the total oxidant, measured by liberating iodine from potassium iodide. In Los Angeles, concentrations of 0.2 to 0.3 ppm have repeatedly been recorded, and monthly maximums for 1962–63 averaged 0.4 ppm (21). These figures exceed the maximum allowable average concentration of 0.1 ppm for an 8-hour work day that has been set for American industry (22). On 41 occasions, from 1955 to 1961, the first alert level for ozone of 0.50 ppm, set by the Los Angeles Air Pollution Control District, has also been exceeded (23). The maximum content of ozone as an urban contaminant in outdoor air was measured as 0.90 ppm during an episode of photochemical air pollution in Los Angeles in 1955. [A recording of 1.00 ppm in 1956 is of doubtful validity since, when it was rechecked 4 minutes later, only 0.70 ppm was reported (19).]

Control of Exhaust from Automobiles

Control of pollutants emitted by motor vehicles has been directed primarily toward hydrocarbons and carbon monoxide.

Currently, California is the only jurisdiction with an active control program. In 1959, the State Board of Public Health, under a directive from the legislature, set emission standards for automobile exhaust at 1.5 percent for carbon monoxide and 275 ppm for hydrocarbons. These values were calculated as necessary in order to "roll back" photochemical pollution in Los Angeles to the 1940 level (so-called pre-smog days), and to prevent carbon monoxide levels in Los Angeles from reaching the state ambient air standard of 30 ppm for 8 hours, at least until 1970 (5). Obviously, areas of the state less populated than Los Angeles were provided even greater protection by having automobile emission standards based on those for Los Angeles.

In order to further control hydrocarbons, a crankcase emission standard was adopted in 1961 which restricted emissions to "0.15 per cent by weight of the supplied fuel" (24).

The actual consequence of the combined crankcase and exhaust emission standards was expected to be an 80-percent reduction of the atmospheric load of hydrocarbons and a 60-percent reduction of carbon monoxide.

Following the adoption of emission standards in California, a State Motor Vehicle Pollution Control Board was appointed to test and to certify control devices that would reduce pollutant emissions to levels required to meet the standards.

By March 1964, 46 crankcase hydrocarbon control devices had been approved for factory installation (new vehicles) and five for installation on used cars. An inspection program has also been set up to insure proper maintenance of the devices.

Beginning with the 1963 models, all American-made motor vehicles, and some foreign cars, have been equipped with crankcase control devices. Inasmuch as crankcase emissions are approximately one-fourth of the total automotive hydrocarbon emissions (25), installation on all motor vehicles should reduce the atmospheric load by this amount.

In June 1964, four devices for the control of exhaust emissions were approved in California by its Motor Vehicle Pollution Control Board. One of the control devices was a direct-flame and three were catalytic afterburners installed in the exhaust line to reduce both hydrocarbons and carbon monoxide to levels required by law. These devices were approved for new cars, and the direct-flame device was approved for used cars. The automobile industry has announced that it will be prepared to meet the California standards by the end of 1966 on the new 1967 cars.

Designers of exhaust control devices are plagued by the wide variations in the flow rate, temperature, and composition of exhaust gas, not only among different vehicles, but also among the various ways of operating a given vehicle. Concern has also been expressed with regard to the initial cost of devices, particularly for old cars, and with respect to maintenance and inspection costs (26). Accordingly, the California Board has specified that approved devices must not impose an undue burden on the motorist and must operate for 12,000 miles (equivalent to an average of 1 year of driving) free of maintenance (27).

Future Control

Because the emissions of both organics and oxides of nitrogen are rapidly increasing, present hydrocarbon standards alone do not provide an acceptable degree of control of photochemical air pollution in Los Angeles County. In practice, control inevitably falls far short of laboratory-attained efficiencies. In order to compensate for this expected deficiency in control, attention is being directed toward a possible simultaneous control of both of the primary components of photochemical smog: oxides of nitrogen and hydrocarbons. At the low concentrations present in photochemical air pollution, it is the product of the concentration of hydrocarbons and oxides of nitrogen that determines the severity of such symptoms as the formation of ozone and eye irritation (28–30). (Deviations from this simple relationship appear at higher concentrations. They are, however, only of theoretical interest because at these higher concentrations the components begin to be objectionable of themselves.) Because of this product relationship there is a distinct advantage in simultaneously controlling both of the primary reactants rather than just one. Control of both would mean that control of either one of the components could be less drastic and therefore less costly and more acceptable to the community. The California Board has shown some concern about emissions of oxides of nitrogen, but neither ambient air standards nor vehicle emission standards have yet been set by the State Board of Public Health. However, reconsideration by the Board of practical, attainable control has led to a suggested new set of standards that takes

Table 2. Hydrocarbon emissions from gasoline-powered motor vehicles in Los Angeles County (uncontrolled).* [Los Angeles County Air Pollution Control District]

Source	Total		Nonreactive†		Reactive	
	Quantity (lb./car/ day)	Weight (%) of supplied fuel‡	Quantity (lb./car/ day)	Total (%)	Quantity (lb./car/ day)	Total (%)
Exhaust	0.77	6.1	0.15	20	0.62	80
Crankcase	0.27	2.1	0.02	8	0.25	92
Fuel tank	0.08	0.6	0.03	40	0.05	60
Carburetor	0.11	0.9	0.01	7	0.10	93
Total	1.23	9.7	0.21	17	1.02	83

* From an air pollution point of view, the weight of the emission (that is, concentration × exhaust volume) per unit distance is important. Workers at the Robert A. Taft Engineering Center, U.S. Department of Health, Education, and Welfare, Cincinnati, have determined the emission weight of the exhaust pollutants per mile of average city driving. Their tables and graphs are useful in calculating the emissions in various cities in areas with different average traffic speed. Some authorities believe caution is needed in the use of the values listed in this table as well as those presented by the Taft Center since especially the hydrocarbon values differ materially in the various studies.   † Nonreactive hydrocarbons include methane, ethane, propane, butane, acetylenes, and benzene.   ‡ Assuming each vehicle uses 12.7 pounds of fuel per day weighing 6.2 pounds per gallon (based on 1964 statistics).

into account the role of oxides of nitrogen in the formation of photochemical smog (31).

Although conditions in Los Angeles have been stressed here, other communities also have photochemical problems that have been created by the increased use of automobiles. Emissions may be estimated by referring to Table 2, which lists the emissions from cars in pounds per day per average vehicle (32). These estimates assume an average daily fuel consumption of 2 gallons, corresponding to an average daily mileage of 30 miles; the figures in Table 2 can readily be converted to emissions per mile or per gallon of gasoline. The nonreactive compounds include methane, ethane, propane, butane, benzene, and acetylene.

By making the same assumptions for fuel consumption, the average vehicular emission of oxides of nitrogen is 120 grams per day

Table 3. Distribution of gasoline losses from several emission points in automobiles.

Emission point	Supplied fuel (%)
Exhaust	6.5
Crankcase	2.1
Fuel tank	0.6
Carburetor	0.9
Total	10.1

per vehicle. Power plants produce about 50 grams of oxides of nitrogen per gallon of oil per day [calculations made from reference (3)]. The carbon monoxide emission in automobile exhaust is 3 kilograms per car per day (32). The distribution of the gasoline losses from the several emission points is shown in Table 3 (31).

The concentration of the exhaust pollutants is: hydrocarbons (hexane), 950 ppm; carbon monoxide, 35,000 ppm (3.5 percent); and oxides of nitrogen, 1050 ppm (32). Frequency distribution of exhaust concentrations show a tremendous spread: 10 percent of the cars have an exhaust concentration of hydrocarbons of less than 300 ppm, while 10 percent show more than 1500 ppm (32). In order to properly evaluate the contribution of individual cars and groups of cars, the differences in flow rates must be considered.

Global Implications

The accumulation of products from photochemical air pollution is not likely to be important for a number of years. The oxidation of organic material of low molecular weight is completed in the upper atmosphere and eventually water and carbon dioxide will be the main products. The objectionable substances are products of the first steps in the oxidative destruction of the primary pollutants. However, the carbon chain of the organic compounds will oxidize gradually, and it is possible that the more resistant substances, such as methane, will persist for a very long time. The ozone formed does not accumulate, and the high level observed during the daytime returns to normal during the night.

References

1. Aitken, J., "On some phenomena connected with cloudy condensation," *Proc. Roy. Soc. London,* **51**, 408–439 (1892).
2. *Summary of Air Pollution Statistics for Los Angeles County* (Los Angeles County Air Pollution Control District, Los Angeles, 1963).
3. Haagen-Smit, A. J., "Reactions of sulfur dioxide and other air contaminants in the atmosphere," in *Proceedings of Power Conference* (Illinois Institute of Technology, Chicago, in press).
4. Leighton, P. A., *Photochemistry of Air Pollution* (Academic Press, New York, 1961).
5. *Technical Report of California Standards for Ambient Air Quality and Motor Vehicle Exhaust* (California State Department of Public Health, Berkeley, 1960).
6. Extensive reviews of the effects of photochemical pollution are found in the World Health Organization's Monograph No. 46 entitled *Air Pollution* (1961), and in volume 1 of *Air Pollution,* edited by A. C. Stern (1962). The chapter by M. D. Thomas in the WHO volume, "Effects of air pollution on plants," contains many colored pictures of typical photochemical smog damage.
7. Middleton, J. T., "Photochemical air pollution damage to plants," *Ann. Rev. Plant Physiol.,* **12**, 431–448 (1961).
8. Stephens, E. R., E. F. Darley, O. C. Taylor, and W. E. Scott, "Photochemical reaction products in air pollution," *Intern. J. Air Water Pollution,* **4**, 79–100 (1961).
9. Thomas, M. D., and R. H. Hendricks, "Effect of air pollution on plants," in *Air Pollution Handbook,* P. L. Magill, F. R. Holden, and C. Ackley, Eds., section 9, pp. 1–44 (McGraw-Hill, New York, 1956).
10. Middleton, J. T., and A. J. Haagen-Smit, "The occurrence, distribution, and significance of photochemical air pollution in the United States, Canada, and Mexico," *J. Air Pollution Control Assoc.,* **11**, 129–134. (1961).
11. Yocum, J. E., "Effects of air pollution on materials," in *Air Pollution,* A. C. Stern, Ed., vol. 1, pp. 199–219 (Academic Press, New York, 1962).
12. Goldsmith, J. R., "Effects of air pollution on humans," *ibid.,* pp. 335–386.
13. Haagen-Smit, A. J., "Reactions in the atmosphere," *ibid.,* pp. 41–64.
14. Cadle, R. D., and P. L. Magill, "Chemistry of contaminated atmospheres," in *Air Pollution Handbook,* P. L. Magill, F. R. Holden, and C. Ackley, Eds., section 3, pp. 1–27 (McGraw-Hill, New York, 1956).
15. Steffens, C., "Visibility and air pollution," *ibid.,* section 6, pp. 1–43.
16. Heiman, H., "Effects on human health," in *Air Pollution,* WHO Monograph No. 46, pp. 159–200 (World Health Organization, Geneva, 1961).
17. Stokinger, H. E., "Effects of air pollution on animals," in *Air Pollution,* A. C. Stern, Ed., vol. 1, pp. 282–334 (Academic Press, New York, 1962).
18. Haagen-Smit, A. J., "Present status of the smog problem," *J. Appl. Nutr.,* **6**, 298–299 (1953).
19. *Biannual Summary: Meteorology, Air Pollution Effects and Contaminant Maxima Fiscal Year 1962–63* (Los Angeles County Air Pollution Control District, Los Angeles, 1963).
20. Yocum, J. E., J. M. Saslaw, S. Chapman, and R. L. Richardson, *Summary*

Report on Research Investigations of Air Pollution in the Vicinity of Louisville, Kentucky, report to Rubbertown Industrial Group (Battelle Memorial Institute, Columbus, Ohio. July 1954).

21. Tebbens, B. D., "Residual pollution products in the atmosphere," in *Air Pollution*, A. C. Stern, Ed., vol. 1, pp. 23–40 (Academic Press, New York, 1962).

22. "Threshold limits values for 1956," *AMA Arch. Ind. Health*, **14**, 186–189 (1956).

23. *Contaminant Concentrations Equal to or Greater than First Alert Levels in Los Angeles and Durations of Alerts Called During Existence of Regulation VII*, Air Quality Report No. 39 (Los Angeles County Air Pollution Control District, Los Angeles, 1961).

24. *Technical Report of California Standards for Ambient Air Quality and Motor Vehicle Exhaust—Supplement No. 1, Crankcase Emission Standard* (California State Department of Public Health, Berkeley, 1960).

25. U.S. Department of Health, Education, and Welfare, Public Health Service, Division of Air Pollution, *Motor Vehicles, Air Pollution, and Health—A Report of the Surgeon General to the U.S. Congress in Compliance with Public Law 86-493, the Schenck Act* (Government Printing Office, Washington, D.C., 1962).

26. Faith, W. L., "Automobile exhaust control devices," *J. Air Pollution Control Assoc.*, **13**, 33–35, 39 (1963).

27. Middleton, J. T., "Criteria for certification of motor vehicle pollution control devices in California," *ibid.*, pp. 78–80.

28. Korth, M. W., A. H. Rose, and R. C. Stahman, "Effects of hydrocarbon to oxides of nitrogen ratios on irradiated auto exhaust," in abstracts, annual meeting papers, Paper 63-19 (Air Pollution Control Association, Detroit, 1963).

29. Haagen-Smit, A. J., "The control of air pollution," *Sci. Am.*, **210**, No. 1, 2–9 (1964).

30. —— and M. M. Fox, "Automobile exhaust and ozone formation," *SAE Trans. (Soc. Automotive Engrs.)*, **63**, 575–580 (1955).

31. *Summary Report of Proposed Motor Vehicle Emission Standard* (California State Department of Public Health, Berkeley, 1964).

32. Air Pollution Control District, County of Los Angeles, December 18, 1964.

6. PARTICULATE MATTER

In addition to a variety of gaseous pollutants, air may contain liquid or solid particles. The larger particles are usually solids—fly ash, coarse dirt, and dirt particles larger than 10 microns in diameter —and normally settle out of the air rapidly. They are composed of a variety of materials, some soluble in water, some not. In heavily polluted areas, the soluble part is usually high in sulfate and is relatively acidic.

Fume or smoke particles, ranging in size from 5 microns to 0.1 micron or smaller, may be liquid or solid. They may form mechanically stable suspensions in the air. The smaller particles, generally less than 1 micron, are readily transported by wind and currents and have motions similar to the surrounding gases, and, in fact, may be treated as such. These very fine particles may often be found in metal oxide fumes such as those of lead, zinc, arsenic, cadmium, and beryllium.

Figure 5 gives a birdseye view of the nature and sizes of particles and permits a comparison with natural aerosols such as pollens and rain drops. Viruses are between 0.01 and 0.1 micron in size, and bacteria are between 1.0 and 25 microns (1, 2).

Particles may be complex in their chemical composition. The inorganic fraction of collected samples of airborne particles usually contains a few dozen metallic elements in addition to carbon or soot and tarry organic material. The most frequent metallic elements are silicon, calcium, aluminum, and iron; relatively high quantities of magnesium, lead, copper, zinc, sodium, and manganese may also be found. The organic fraction of collected samples of particles is usually even more complex and may contain a large number of aliphatic and aromatic hydrocarbons, acids, bases, phenols, and many other compounds.

Sources

Both organic and inorganic particles emanate from a number of sources: industrial operations, modern transportation facilities, and domestic combustion processes. Major sources of dust include coal- and oil-burning power plants, iron and steel mills, cement mills,

DIAM. OF PARTICLES IN MICRONS	U.S. STD MESH	SCALE OF ATMOSPHERIC IMPURITIES	RATE OF SETTLING IN F.P.M. FOR SPHERES SPEC.GRAV.1 AT 70°F.	DUST PARTICLES CONTAINED IN 1 CUB. FT. OF AIR (See Foot Note) NUMBER	SURFACE AREA IN SQ. IN.	LAWS OF SETTLING IN RELATION TO PARTICLE SIZE (Lines of Demarcation approx.)
8000 6000 4000	1/4"		1750			**PARTICLES FALL WITH INCREASING VELOCITY**
2000	10	1/8"				
1000 800 600 400	20	1/16" 1/32"	790 / 555	.075 / .6	.000365 / .00073	
200	60	1/64" 1/128"				
100 80 60 40	100 150 200 250 325 500		59.2 / 14.8	75 / 600	.00365 / .0073	**STOKES LAW**
20	1000					
10 8 6 4 2			.592 / .148	75000 / 600,000	.0365 / .073	FOR AIR AT 70°F.
1 .8 .6 .4 .2			.007 = 5" PER HR. / .002 = 1.4" PER HR.	75 X 10^6 / 60 X 10^7	.365 / .73	CUNNINGHAM'S FACTOR
.1			.00007 = ⅜" PER HR.	75 X 10^9 / 60 X 10^10	3.65 / 7.3	**PARTICLES MOVE LIKE GAS MOLECULES**
.01			0	75 X 10^12 / 60 X 10^13	36.5 / 73.0	BROWNIAN MOVEMENT
.001			0	75 X 10^15	365 / 2.53 SQ.FT.	

Scale of atmospheric impurities labels: RAIN, HEAVY INDUSTRIAL DUST, MIST, DRIZZLE, FOG, DUSTS, TEMPORARY ATMOSPHERIC IMPURITIES, PARTICLES LARGER THAN 10 MICRONS SEEN WITH NAKED EYE, POLLENS CAUSING HAY FEVER, DUST CAUSING LUNG DAMAGE, MICROSCOPE, PERMANENT ATMOSPHERIC IMPURITIES, SMOKES, AVERAGE SIZE OF TOBACCO SMOKE, ULTRA MICROSCOPE, MEAN FREE SPACE BETWEEN GAS MOLECULES, CYCLONE SEPARATORS, WATER SPRAY, DYNAMIC PRECIPITATOR WITH WATER SPRAY, DYNAMIC PRECIPITATOR + ATMOSPHERIC DUST, AIR FILTERS + ATMOSPHERIC DUST, ELECTRICAL PRECIPITATORS, QUIET ATMOSPHERE, DISTURBED ATMOSPHERE, INDUSTRIAL PLANTS, FUMES, SIZE OF DUST PARTICLES IN SUSPENSION, PARTICLES SMALLER THAN .1 MICRON SELDOM OF PRACTICAL IMPORTANCE.

Equations (Laws of Settling column):

$$C = \sqrt{\frac{2gds_1}{3Ks_2}}$$

$$C = 24.9\sqrt{Ds_1}$$

Stokes Law:

$$C = \frac{2r^2}{9}g\frac{s_1 - s_2}{\eta}$$

For air at 70°F.:

$$C = 300{,}460\, s_1 d^2$$
$$C = .00592\, s\, D^2$$

Cunningham's Factor:

$$c = c'\left(1 + K\frac{\lambda}{r}\right)$$

c' = C of Stokes Law   K = .8 to .86

Brownian Movement:

$$A = \sqrt{\frac{RT}{N}\cdot\frac{t}{3\pi\eta r}}$$

Legend:
- C = Velocity cm./sec.
- C = Velocity ft./min.
- d = Diam. of particle in cm.
- D = Diam. of particle in Microns
- r = Radius of particle in cm.
- g = 981 cm./sec.² acceleration
- s = Density of particle
- s_2 = Density of Air (Very small relative to s_1)
- η = Viscosity of air in poises = 1814 X 10⁻⁷ for air at 70°F.
- λ = 10⁻⁵ cm. (Mean free path of gas molecules)
- A = Distance of motion in time t
- R = Gas constant = 8.316 X 10⁷
- T = Absolute Temperature
- N = Number of Gas molecules in one mol = 6.06 X 10¹¹
- PARTICLES SETTLE WITH CONSTANT VELOCITY

Fig. 5. Size and characteristics of airborne solids. It is assumed that the particles are of uniform spherical shape, having specific gravity 1, and that the dust concentration is 0.6 grain per 1000 cubic feet of air, the average of metropolitan districts. [Compiled by W. G. Frank; © American Air Filter Company, Inc., Louisville, Kentucky]

and oil refineries. In addition, small sources, such as automobiles and incinerators, contribute significantly to the dust load of the atmosphere because they are so numerous. Smoke (dust and droplets) is produced during combustion or destructive distillation, and fume (dust) is formed by high-temperature volatilization or by chemical reaction.

A large number of extremely fine particles are emitted from automobile exhaust systems, with approximately 70 percent in the size range of 0.02 to 0.06 micron (3). These particles consist of both inorganic and organic compounds of high molecular weight. The quantity of solid and droplet material produced in the exhaust amounts to a few milligrams per gram of gasoline burned (3). For a car population such as that of Los Angeles, the latest estimate of aerosol emission from gasoline-powered vehicles, made by the County of Los Angeles Air Pollution Control District, is 40 tons per day (4).

Most modern gasolines contain additives. One of these provides the antiknock characteristics that are required by present-day high compression engines. The most common additives contain tetraethyl lead or tetramethyl lead together with organic chlorides and bromides, and the resulting lead compounds comprise some of the exhaust particles. Thus, distribution of lead in the air of some cities is usually correlated with the density of vehicular traffic (5). (Another source of lead pollutants is the melting of scrap metals in foundries.)

Highly refined liquid fuels do not ordinarily contain appreciable amounts of dust-forming ash except when additives are blended to improve quality. Nevertheless, poor combustion of any fuel produces soot and tars, and heavy heating oils also contain some metals as well as substantial amounts of sulfur.

Measurements

Large particles are measured in dustfall pans, in cyclone collectors, and by filtration. For the smaller particles, impactors and centrifugal and electrostatic collectors are used. Light-scattering instruments that give a continuous record of the quantity of particles as well as an approximation of their size distribution have been developed. For submicroscopic particles, nuclei counters that are based on the principle of the Wilson cloud chamber have been developed (6).

Deposited matter has been measured in dustfall containers in Great Britain and the United States since the early 1900's, thus providing an index of the trend of pollution from sources of larger particulate matter. In some of the thickly populated industrial areas in Great Britain, the amount of solid matter deposited is between 500 and 2000 tons per square mile per year, in comparison with between 10 and 100 tons in rural areas and small country towns (7). A systematic survey of air pollution in New Haven, Connecticut, shows that individual measurements of dustfall within the city limits ranged from a low of 5 tons to a maximum of 62 tons per square mile per month (8). In the most contaminated districts of the larger, more heavily polluted cities, where large quantities of coal are burned, 50 to 100 or more tons per square mile per month of dustfall have been recorded (5). In Pittsburgh, the maximum dustfall measured was 291 tons per square mile per month (8).

The concentration of suspended particles per unit volume in a polluted atmosphere may be extremely large, although the mass concentration may be low in comparison with that of gaseous contaminants. Even in relatively clean air, nearly 1000 million aerosol particles per cubic meter may be present. In conditions of photochemical smog, 100,000 million particles per cubic meter may be reached (5). The concentration of particles greater than 0.5 micron in diameter in Los Angeles smog is estimated at about 1500 million per cubic meter.

Some heavily industralized areas show figures a good deal higher than Los Angeles for weight concentration of suspended matter. For example, during the years 1957–1962, Charleston, West Virginia, had an average of 228 micrograms per cubic meter, and a maximum (in 1960) of 958, whereas the average for Los Angeles during the same years was 182 micrograms per cubic meter with a maximum (in 1959) of 594 (9). It is reported that, during the winter, in thickly populated industrial towns in Great Britain, air pollution by smoke and soot reaches more than 1000 micrograms per cubic meter (7).

Figures from the National Air Sampling Network serve to confirm the qualitative observation that the concentration of suspended particles in the air over a community is, very broadly, related to the number of people contributing to the pollution. The average total particulate loading between the years 1957 and 1961 for a group of cities with populations of 400,000 to 700,000 was 129 micrograms per cubic meter. On the other hand, the corresponding loading for two cities of 3 million or more people was 189 micrograms per cubic meter, or about 50 percent more than for smaller cities (9).

Variations in the concentration of smoke and other fine particulate matter is closely related to meteorological conditions and human habits. There is a daily cycle that is nearly the same for widely separated locations, such as England, the east and west coasts of the United States, and Japan (8). Particulate pollution is at a minimum at night; it reaches its maximum levels twice during the hours of major activity: in the early morning (except in areas of 24-hour industry and poor night ventilation, where there may be increases after 2:00 to 3:00 A.M.) and in the late afternoon or evening. London, New York, and Tokyo have a daily maximum near 8:00 A.M., while Berkeley, California, shows a peak near noon. The difference seems to be due to the fact that the first three cities are coal-burning communities, whereas the major fuels in Berkeley are gaseous and liquid. The daily fluctuation reflects the influence of solar heating and cooling, turbulence, industrial activity, automobile traffic, and other factors. Concentrations are also considerably less on weekends than on weekdays, and the average is two to three times higher during the winter months than in summer in communities that use coal or petroleum fuels.

Reactions

When a liquid or solid is dispersed to form a cloud or smoke, many of its properties are considerably altered. For example, its surface area is greatly increased, and the nature of the surface will influence the behavior of the material in many ways. Particles may absorb reacting gases and thereby catalyze their reaction. They also absorb free radicals and destroy them, thus decreasing the rate of free radical chain reactions.

Dusts and aerosols will speed up the rate of oxidation of gases. For example, the oxidation of sulfur dioxide is normally very slow. However, aqueous droplets, which may be present in great quantity in contaminated atmospheres, dissolve sulfur dioxide, and the sulfurous acid formed is quickly oxidized to sulfuric acid when heavy metal salts are in the solution. Organic particles, such as those from heated fats and oils, may produce similar reactions of organic substances. It is possible, too, that many natural particles are complex combinations of organic and aqueous materials. There is evidence that some particles are aqueous droplets surrounded by an organic surface layer that is relatively insoluble in water (10).

Thermal radiation effects become much more pronounced if suspended solid or liquid particles are present in the air (5). Such particles absorb radiation and conduct heat rapidly to the surrounding gas molecules, which may be quite transparent to the radiant energy.

Generally vapors must be greatly supersaturated before condensation will occur in the absence of foreign particles. However, if the vapor contains particles that can act as nuclei, little supersaturation is required since these nuclei facilitate the condensation of water vapor upon them, and thus promote and prolong the formation of fogs and ground mists. Without them, condensation would occur mainly on walls of buildings and on other exposed surfaces.

Most of these nuclei range in size from about 0.001 to 0.1 micron. Enormous quantities are often produced by a single source; for example, an average grass fire extending over 1 acre produced some 2×10^{22} nuclei (11). The number of nuclei in the atmosphere usually exceeds the number of dust particles by a factor of several thousandfold.

Effects

Smaller particles of suspended matter, less than 5 microns in size, have a greater effect than coarse material in reducing visibility, in soiling, and in impairing human health.

One of the most important consequences of pollution of the air by fine particles is the reduction of visibility. There is a critical size for each chemical and physical type of particle at which loss of visibility is at a maximum for any given set of conditions. It can be shown that, for a given mass concentration of particles, the loss in visibility will be greatest if the particle size is in the range from 0.3 to 0.6 micron, assuming that the particles are transparent spheres (5). The behavior of opaque particles will be qualitatively similar, although quantitatively different, since these particles both absorb and scatter light.

Meteorological conditions will greatly affect the reduced visibility that results from a given rate of emission of particulate pollutants. With very low wind speeds and low turbulence, high concentrations accumulate near the source, thereby reducing visibility. Very substantially higher wind velocities will also cause low visibility if surface dust and debris are picked up from vacant lots and streets. The wind velocity that will give the greatest visibility during continuous emission of man-made pollutants will depend, therefore, not only upon atmospheric stability and other factors relating to pollutant dispersal, but also upon soil moisture, vegetation cover, and other surface characteristics in the immediate vicinity.

A portion of the particles in urban atmospheres collects substantial quantities of sorbed water at humidities well below water saturation (12). Examples are sulfuric acid droplets and sea-salt particles. These hygroscopic particles (those that readily absorb moisture) will then increase in size by picking up water and, as they enlarge, the amount of light transmitted through them will be reduced, thereby decreasing visibility. If sufficient moisture is available, these particles will grow until they become large enough to settle.

The California Department of Public Health has established a standard for particulate matter at the "adverse" level: "Sufficient to reduce visibility to less than three miles when relative humidity is less than 70 percent" (13). This standard, however, is based primarily on Federal Visual Flight Regulation limits. It is not necessarily one that the community would find acceptable. A case could easily be made, for example, for a 30-mile visibility as a standard.

Particulate matter damages materials (such as a tablecloth, a white marble column of a building, or a polished mahogany table) by soiling, either directly or when the dirt is being removed. It is frequently difficult to distinguish between the soiling caused by droplets and that caused by small solid particles.

Particulate matter appears to be an important factor in the corrosion of metals, especially in the presence of pollutant gases of an acidic nature. The exteriors of buildings are affected by the tarry components of carbonaceous materials that accumulate on their surfaces; these materials result from the poor combustion of coal, oil, rubbish, or scrap metal on which there are grease coatings. Expensive sandblasting is needed to remove these corrosive, sooty layers since, because of their stickiness and acidity, they are not flushed off by rain (14). This same type of particle can produce holes in canvas awnings. Dust collecting on electrical insulators in high-tension power lines can cause short circuits when damp. Asphalt roofs near restaurant exhaust fans can be seriously damaged by droplets of cooking oils and greases settling on them.

Many houses in urban areas, as well as newly painted automobiles, require repainting because discoloring particles accumulate on their surfaces. These particles are the result of thermal, electrostatic, and mechanical forces. Although these same mechanisms soil fabrics, fabrics deteriorate mainly from repeated attempts to clean them. Sulfuric acid aerosols, on the other hand, are directly destructive to many fabrics, such as stretched filaments of silk, cotton, or nylon.

Acid aerosols that are associated with fog have been found to produce a "pock mark" type of injury on plants, particularly on the upper surfaces of table beets and Swiss chard (15). The fog droplets apparently contain enough acid, and perhaps other toxicants as well, to damage the leaf. Injury appears after moisture evaporates. However, further critical study of this type of damage is needed.

The effect of particles on human health is determined not only by their chemical composition but also by their size. The particle size determines the location of any toxic effect. Small particles will penetrate deep into the respiratory system while coarse ones have a tendency to remain in the upper respiratory tract or on the skin. There are, however, no sharply defined areas of action.

Community air pollution produces more eye irritation than can be accounted for by the additive effects of its known gaseous components; this suggests that particulate matter may also play a role.

This may be explained by the way in which particles concentrate material on their surfaces and in their interstices and thus tend to produce a locally high concentration of an otherwise very dilute substance (10). However, there is some evidence that mechanical filtration of particles down to 0.05 micron does not reduce eye irritation, whereas activated carbon filtration of gas does (16).

During times of heavy pollution, the average individual breathes about 1 milligram of suspended matter per day (7). The largest particles lodge only in the nostrils. Particles slightly smaller, but above 5 microns, are probably collected by the mucous lining of the upper airway. If these particles are insoluble, they are carried by ciliary action to the throat and are swallowed. Particles smaller than about 2 to 3 microns usually reach the deeper structures of the lung where no mucous blanket exists. There they produce their effects directly or, if sufficiently insoluble, they may be absorbed by the phagocytic cells in the lung parenchyma and be deposited in the lymph glands. The mucous and ciliary lining of the airway is found in the bronchi and above, but this defensive system is absent in the alveolar ducts and alveoli.

Because the air in the respiratory tract usually has a higher temperature than the inspired air and is virtually saturated with water vapor, an inhaled particle that can absorb water increases in size as it progresses down the respiratory tract. This complex relationship needs further study since it is not quite certain whether the particles grow rapidly enough to prevent submicron hygroscopic particles from reaching deeper portions of the lung (10).

It has been suggested that particles carry biologically active energy in the form of free radicals. If free radicals are present within the interstices of a particle, it is possible that they may be incorporated into the cell. Radiation effects are thought to be mediated by the formation of free radicals within cells. Thus, pollutant particles could possibly induce mutagenic effects similar to those caused by radiation (10).

Particles may also modify the response to simultaneously inhaled gases. The combination of gases with particles has been shown to cause toxicity changes in rodents, respiratory resistance in air flow, and bactericidal action (17). Such synergism may arise in several ways. A water-soluble gas might be carried by adsorption on small penetrating particles past the region of scrubbing action in the upper tract and deeper into the lungs. It has also been suggested that there may be local, statistically higher, gas concentrations immediately around an aerosol particle, even in the absence of strong adsorptive forces. If this is so, there should be an increased local tissue dose at the point of particle contact.

Sulfur dioxide, in concentrations of about 1 ppm, increases the airway resistance of guinea pigs when it is inhaled simultaneously with a sodium chloride aerosol, which, of itself, has no effect (18). Airway resistance increases in human beings when they are exposed to a number of so-called inert particles (10). This also includes the particles in cigarette smoke.

In Great Britain, it has been known for many years that smoke and the smaller soot particles aggravate the symptoms of those who have chronic bronchitis. The high porosity of these carbon particles tends to make them avid adsorbers of gases and vapors. Furthermore, most soots are generated in the same combustion processes that generate the complex polycyclic hydrocarbons (such as benzo[a]pyrene) that are known to produce cancer in animals experimentally. It has also been found experimentally that benzo-[a]pyrene is tightly bound to associated small soot particles and cannot be eluted by human serum or gastric juice. Larger soot particles give up the sorbed organics more easily (10). No disease has, as yet, been clearly related to community exposure to soot alone. However, the action of soot as a carrier of pollutants into the deeper portions of the lung seems to have been established. One of the first occupational cancers to have been described was cancer of the scrotum in chimney sweeps. The combination of polynuclear carcinogens with soot was clearly indicated to have had a causal relationship.

The effects of sulfuric acid mist and of such deleterious metals as lead and beryllium will be discussed later.

Control

There is wide familiarity with methods to reduce or minimize the emission of dust into the atmosphere. Reliable devices are available for removing particles from many types of combustion gases.

Three approaches to the control of particles from coal combustion are (i) reducing the ash content of the coal before it enters the furnace, (ii) installing dust control devices in the effluent stream from the furnace, and (iii) replacing the coal with other fuel. Fly ash, a waste produce of coal combustion, is partially replacing cement in concrete mixes, and tests, as well as construction experience, show that fly ash concrete is stronger, more durable, more waterproof, and easier to handle than conventional concrete (19). In addition, it is also less expensive, and so a former total liability has been turned into a lesser liability. Some of the disposal costs have also been saved.

During the past 20 to 30 years, soot and dustfall averages have been markedly reduced in several cities, reflecting a change in the use of fuel, improved technology, enforcement programs by control agencies, and other factors. For example, measures instituted in Los Angeles for controlling atmospheric particles, such as regulations for industry, the elimination of open-burning dumps in 1947, and the later abolishment of open-burning and single-chamber incinerators, seem to be primarily responsible for reducing dustfall during the period 1947–1960 (Fig. 6).

The effective control of foundry dusts and fumes requires equipment that can capture the extremely fine particles that are usually more difficult to handle. Burners are used to complete the combustion of evaporated greases from scrap metal prior to the final cleaning by other control equipment. Many types of foundries have found it profitable to change their melting equipment to nonpolluting types with improved quality and production control.

Global Implications

Scientists can identify the mechanisms that remove fine particles from the atmosphere, but they have no quantitatively satisfactory understanding of them as yet. Junge (20) has estimated that the mean life of particles in the troposphere is of the order of a few days. However, this is a long-term average and any process that injects particles at levels higher than the tropopause will give much longer lifetimes to these particles, in some cases of the order of a few years.

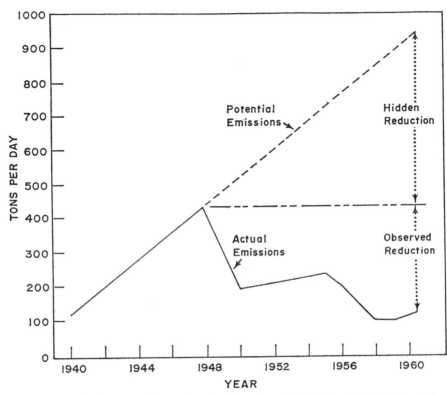

Fig. 6. Particulate emissions in the Los Angeles Basin, 1940–1960 (*21*).

There are four mechanisms that seem to be responsible for removing particles from tropospheric air. The first of these is gravitational settling, which prevents the very large particles of fly ash and soil from traveling great distances. Somewhat smaller particles are brought near the ground by gravity, where they may be removed by the second mechanism, impacting on the surface of obstacles, such as vegetation and buildings. However, studies by Twomey (*22*) and Byers *et al.* (*23*) strongly suggest that these effects are of consequence only in the very low layers of the atmosphere. Neither of these studies showed any decrease in the concentration of the largest particles of marine aerosol (larger than 10 microns) after traveling as much as 3 days from the sea. Turbulent diffusion was apparently sufficient to offset sedimentation effects for extended periods of time.

However, if clouds form and it rains, the higher layers of the atmosphere are cleansed quite efficiently. This is the third mechanism for removing particles; clouds are formed on small particles and appear to gather substantial quantities of still finer aerosols to them. Once precipitation has begun, these particles are brought to the surface. Even in the case of those cloud droplets that subsequently evaporate instead of becoming a part of the precipitation, substantial coagulation has been effected.

In the layers below the cloud, still another cleansing mechanism occurs. The precipitation intercepts some of the larger particles in the air underneath the cloud and also carries them to the surface of the earth in what is called a "wash-out." This mechanism is ineffective for particles smaller than 2 microns in diameter. However, a typical soluble particle, such as sea salt, increases its diameter by nearly an order of magnitude when the relative humidity is raised from 50 percent to 99 percent.

While particles may remain airborne for only a few days on the average, under certain circumstances they may remain in the air for a longer period and may be transported great distances. If a particular source is very large or intense—for example, an erupting volcano, a forest fire, or a large metropolitan area—international and intercontinental transport of aerosols can be expected. It is well known that dust from major volcanic eruptions, such as Krakatoa and Agung, have covered the entire earth. Particles from nuclear explosions that enter the stratosphere may remain airborne for some years.

A layer of aerosol, sufficiently dense and covering a large area, could affect the world's weather and climate by changing the earth's albedo and the altitude at which heat is released in the atmosphere.

References

1. These bioaerosols will not be discussed; however, a review is available in the chapter, "Natural sources of air pollution," by A. R. Jacobson, in *Air Pollution*, A. C. Stern, Ed., vol. 2 (Academic Press, New York, 1962).
2. Munger, H. P., "The spectrum of particle size and its relation to air pollution," in *Air Pollution: Proceedings of the United States Technical Conference on Air Pollution*, L. C. McCabe, Ed., pp. 129–166 (McGraw-Hill, New York, 1952).

3. Rose, A. H., "Automotive exhaust emissions," in *Air Pollution*, A. C. Stern, Ed., vol. 2, pp. 40–80 (Academic Press, New York, 1962).

4. *Summary of Air Pollution Statistics for Los Angeles County* (Los Angeles County Air Pollution Control District, Los Angeles, 1963).

5. Katz, M., "Some aspects of the physical and chemical nature of air pollution," in *Air Pollution*, WHO Monograph No. 46, pp. 97–158 (World Health Organization, Geneva, 1961).

6. For a review of these methods, reference is made to the chapters on sampling procedures in *Air Pollution Handbook*, P. L. Magill, F. R. Holden, and C. Ackley, Eds. (McGraw-Hill, New York, 1956), and the chapter, "Air sampling," by E. R. Hendrickson in *Air Pollution*, A. C. Stern, Ed. (Academic Press, New York, 1962).

7. Haagen-Smit, A. J., Workshop I, Appendix I, in *Proceedings of the First Workshop Conference on Lung Cancer Research*, pp. 56–71 (American Cancer Society, New York, 1957).

8. Tebbens, B. D., "Residual pollution products in the atmosphere," in *Air Pollution*, A. C. Stern, Ed., vol. 1, pp. 23–40 (Academic Press, New York, 1962).

9. U.S. Department of Health, Education, and Welfare, Public Health Service, *Air Pollution Measurements of the National Air Sampling Network—Analyses of Suspended Particulates, 1957–61* (Government Printing Office, Washington, D.C., 1962); *National Air Sampling Network, Air Quality Data, 1962* (U.S. Public Health Service, Cincinnati, 1962).

10. Goldsmith, J. R., "Effects of air pollution on humans," in *Air Pollution*, A. C. Stern, Ed., vol. 1, pp. 335–386 (Academic Press, New York, 1962).

11. Cadle, R. D., and P. L. Magill, "Chemistry of contaminated atmospheres," in *Air Pollution Handbook*, P. L. Magill, F. R. Holden, and C. Ackley, Eds., section 3, pp. 1–27 (McGraw-Hill, New York, 1956).

12. Robinson, E., "Effects of air pollution on visibility," in *Air Pollution*, A. C. Stern, Ed., vol. 1, pp. 220–254 (Academic Press, New York, 1962).

13. *Technical Report of California Standards for Ambient Air Quality and Motor Vehicle Exhaust* (California State Department of Public Health, Berkeley, 1960).

14. Yocum, J. E., "Effects of air pollution on materials," in *Air Pollution*, A. C. Stern, Ed., vol. 1, pp. 199–219 (Academic Press, New York, 1962).

15. Thomas, M. D., "Effects on plants," in *Air Pollution*, WHO Monograph No. 46, pp. 233–278 (World Health Organization, Geneva, 1961).

16. Richardson, N. A., and W. C. Middleton, *Evaluation of Filters for Removing Irritants from Polluted Air*, Report No. 57-43 (Department of Engineering, University of California, Los Angeles, 1957).

17. *Air Pollution Manual*, part 1 (American Industrial Hygiene Association, Detroit, 1960).

18. Amdur, M. O., "The effect of aerosols on the response to irritant gases," in *Inhaled Particles and Vapours, Proceedings of an International Symposium Organized by the British Occupational Hygiene Society*, C. N. Davies, Ed., pp. 281–292 (Pergamon Press, London, 1961).

19. Rupp, W. H., "Air pollution sources and their control," in *Air Pollution Handbook*, P. L. Magill, F. R. Holden, C. Ackley, Eds., section 1, pp. 1–58 (McGraw-Hill, New York, 1956).

20. Junge, C. E., *Air Chemistry and Radioactivity* (Academic Press, New York, 1963).
21. J. B. Taylor, "Dust fall trends in the Los Angeles Basin, 1947–60" (Los Angeles County Air Pollution Control District, Los Angeles, 1961).
22. Twomey, S., "The distribution of sea-salt nuclei over land," *J. Meteorol.*, **12**, 81–86. (1955).
23. Byers, H. R., J. R. Sievers, and B. J. Tufts, "Distribution in the atmosphere of certain particles capable of serving as condensation nuclei," in *Artificial Stimulation of Rain*, W. Weickmann, and W. E. Smith, Eds., pp. 47–70 (Pergamon Press, London, 1957).

7. LEAD AND OTHER DELETERIOUS METALS

Of the nonferrous metals, lead is one of the most widely used in industry and everyday life. In 1962, more than a million tons were consumed in the United States; of this amount 40 percent (*1*) was used in such chemical compounds as white lead, red lead, black oxides, lead silicates, and tetraethyl lead; this last compound accounted for the largest amount in this form, 172,000 tons. The remaining 60 percent of the lead was used either as pure lead or as an alloy, some of the more important products being grids for storage batteries, cable sheathing, ammunition, pipes, sheet metal, solder, and type metal for printing. The storage battery industry was the largest consumer, using 387,000 tons.

Sources

Lead occurs naturally and is found in soils, rocks, water, and food; it contributes only a small fraction to air pollution. The average concentration of lead in rocks is about 16 ppm (*2*). The lead content of soils ranges from 0.04 ppm in alluvial and virgin soils to more than 1000 ppm in arable soils. In some industrial areas, for example, near sites of distillation or burning of coal, soils have had a lead concentration as high as 12,340 ppm (*2*). Drinking water has been reported to contain 0.001 to 0.04 ppm (*2*).

The amount of lead in food varies with the kind of food, the way in which it is prepared, and where it was grown. The importance of food as a source of lead is reflected in the fact that 0.3 milligram is the estimated average daily intake (*3*), an amount that is substantially greater than the intake of lead from air pollution. However, only a small portion of the ingested lead is retained by the body.

Lead is emitted into the atmosphere from smelters that recover primary lead from ores and secondary lead from scrap. Emissions of lead also result from the combustion of certain fuels, such as coal, which may contain as much as 54 ppm (*4*). Dusts and sprays that contain lead arsenate can also contribute to levels of atmospheric lead; so also may the attrition of lead paint on buildings. Although the combustion of products that contain large amounts of lead, such as storage battery dividers and heavily painted wood scrap, may produce high amounts of atmospheric lead locally, such combustion is not likely to be a widespread problem.

In urban areas with a large number of motor vehicles, the most important source of atmospheric lead is probably exhaust emissions. Tetraethyl lead and the more recently introduced tetramethyl lead are used in most gasolines to slow down the combustion of gasoline vapor in the engine.

Of the tetraethyl lead added to gasoline, only a small amount is released as organic material, the most harmful form as far as health is concerned. A recent study reported that only about 0.023 percent of the lead additive in fuel was exhausted in an organic form (5). Some may evaporate from the gasoline. On exposure to heat, the remaining lead decomposes to an inorganic form either in the combustion chamber or in the crankcase or carburetor. From one-quarter to one-half of the inorganic lead is emitted to the atmosphere as lead bromides, chlorides, and so forth. It is this lead that is of major concern in studying community air pollution. The remaining portion deposits on the moving surfaces of the engine.

Some of the lead particles are large enough to fall out as street dust. This is reflected in the concentration of lead in the street dirt of New York City, which, in 1924, averaged 1190 ppm and in 1934 averaged 1760 ppm (6). By 1953, the average had risen to 2650 ppm (7). Tetraethyl lead was introduced early in 1923 as a motor fuel additive.

Levels of Atmospheric Lead

The level of atmospheric lead varies directly with the size of the community. Los Angeles has the highest concentration of the communities studied, with a mean of approximately 5 micrograms of lead per cubic meter of air (8). Other urban communities with a population greater than 2 million have values of about 2.5 micrograms. Communities that are smaller than a million have a mean atmospheric concentration of about 2 micrograms, and cities with a population of less than 100,000 have a mean concentration of about 1.7 micrograms per cubic meter.

Just as traffic fluctuates with the time of day, so does the concentration of lead in the air of many urban areas. The concentration is higher in commercial and industrial areas than it is in the peripheral residential sections (when these are upwind of commercial and heavily traveled portions of the community), and the concentration tends to be high during periods of low atmospheric winds and low turbulence. There is some evidence (8) that the concentration in Cincinnati decreased (somewhat erratically) between 1941 and 1961 from a mean of about 5 to a mean of about 1.5. This occurred during a period in which there was a change over from the use of coal for space heating to natural gas and oil and a shift in transportation to motor vehicles with an increased consumption of tetraethyl lead in their fuel. Thus, the increase in lead from motor fuel has apparently not yet overcome the decrease that is associated with cessation of coal-burning.

Effects of Lead on Farm Animals

Over a period of many years, chronic and acute lead poisoning has been observed in farm animals grazing near smelters, lead mines, and in orchards that had been sprayed. In 1955, it was reported from Germany that lead poisoning afflicted cattle and horses grazing within a radius of 5 kilometers of two lead and zinc factories. It was thought that, in this particular case, the poisoning was not caused by lead alone but by its combination with another toxic agent, presumably zinc (9).

Effects of Lead on Human Health

Intoxication by inorganic lead is one of the oldest and is still one of the most common of occupational hazards. Its symptoms are neurological in extreme cases, gastrointestinal in less severe cases, and, in mild cases, the red blood cells and the formation of hemoglobin are affected. There is evidence that long-term exposure to lead can result in chronic kidney disease and an increased likelihood of death from cerebrovascular disorders (10).

In addition to disease, an excess accumulation of lead produces biochemical changes in the appearance of stained red cells, in the fragility of the red cell, and in the metabolism of porphyrins, particularly the excretion of coproporphyrin III. There is also the question of whether lead affects enzymes and in what way (*11*).

As a community air pollutant, lead has a particle size that is likely to be retained in the lung. Data from Los Angeles show that, with atmospheric concentrations of 10 micrograms, 60 percent of the total particle mass consisted of particles below 0.45 micron, 75 percent below 0.9 micron, and 90 percent smaller than 1.6 microns (*12*). Particles of approximately 1 micron or smaller will probably be retained by the lung.

Of the lead that is ingested by mouth, 5 to 10 percent may be absorbed into the blood and the rest is excreted. However, of the lead that is inhaled with a particle size of less than or about 1 micron, up to 50 percent may be retained in the body, the remaining portion being carried to the expired air (*13*). Particles larger than 2 microns impinge on the mucous lining of the airways, are swallowed and excreted, and, in effect, are handled as though ingested by mouth. The fact that a higher proportion of very small particles is retained by the body makes the particle-size distribution of atmospheric lead considerably important in evaluating its possible health hazard. The small particle size cited as characteristic of community air pollution does not necessarily apply to occupational exposures to lead. Here lead is usually retained to a lesser degree because of its particle size.

Probably the most conservative estimate of the amount of lead that might be a public health hazard is the amount which leads to an increased storage in the body. Under metabolic stress, stored lead is mobilized. Unfortunately, there have been very few studies on the amount of lead that can be stored in the body. However, a rough estimate can be obtained by examining the lead content of blood. Table 4 shows that, in some recent studies, the lowest values were observed in people who lived and worked in rural or suburban areas. There is a tendency toward a gradual increase from rural to city populations and there is a more striking increase associated with occupations having greater exposure to automobile exhaust. These increases appear to be associated with exposure to atmospheric lead. Even though there was a 100-percent difference in the atmospheric levels for several of the urban areas studied, and within these areas there was another sizable spectrum of different environmental exposures, the general population in large urban areas all tended to have approximately the same amount of lead in their blood. There were differences between cigarette smokers and nonsmokers in most groups, and between men and women, the former having higher levels of lead in their blood.

With respect to the actual burden of lead on the body, Schroeder reports that the concentration of lead in kidneys, liver, and lungs

Table 4. Mean lead levels of population groups in relation to probable atmospheric exposures. [*Air Pollution*, A. C. Stern, Ed., vol. 1 (Academic Press, New York, 1962)]

Type of population	Estimated atmospheric exposure (μg/m³)	Males		Females	
		Smokers	Non-smokers	Smokers	Non-smokers
		(μg/100 ml of blood)		(μg/100 ml of blood)	
Remote mountain California counties	0.12	12		9	
Composite rural U.S.	0.3	16		10	
Suburban Philadelphia	1.0	13	9	19	10
Composite urban U.S.	1.4	21		16	
Culver City, Calif., aircraft workers	1.9	22	16	16	14
Pasadena, Calif., city employees	2.0	20	17	11	12
Downtown Philadelphia	2.0	25	20	24	18
Los Angeles policemen	3.0	22	20		
Philadelphia policemen	3.0	26	24		
Cincinnati traffic policemen	4.6	30			
Cincinnati auto test lane inspector	14.0	30			
Cincinnati garage workers	21.0	38			
Boston Sumner Tunnel employees	44.5	30			

is higher in the United States than in other parts of the world (11).
Butt et al. have observed that the differences between smokers and
nonsmokers and between men and women can also be detected in
serum (most of the blood lead is in the red cells), although in
most cases the differences are small (14).

More work is needed before the physiological effects of lead can
be accurately evaluated. There are no data to indicate that the
high ambient air concentrations in urban areas can be associated
with definite disease conditions. It is not certain whether urban
residents who have levels of blood lead higher than those of rural
residents necessarily show this gradient because of gradients in the
atmospheric air. Other factors include differences in diet, water
supply, and occupation.

The reasons for the effects of smoking are of some interest. Lead
is present in cigarette tobacco in approximately the same proportion as the arsenic in lead arsenate sprays. Although these sprays
are no longer used for tobacco in the United States and have not
been used for many years, the soils in which the tobacco is grown
were heavily contaminated many years ago and the tobacco still
shows evidence of this contamination and continues to transmit
some of it to smokers. This phenomenon provides a most instructive prototype of the long-term effects of the pesticides used in
agriculture.

Other Possibly Deleterious Metals

Beryllium can produce chronic beryllium intoxication in people
who live in the vicinity of plants that process this metal (15). This
commonly includes diffuse infiltration of the lungs. As a result of
this finding, the occupational health standards of the American
Conference of Governmental Industrial Hygienists contain a single
ambient air standard which states, "The average daily concentrations of beryllium in the vicinity of a plant producing and processing beryllium should be limited to 0.001 micrograms per cubic
meter" (16). The use of beryllium as an ingredient in rocket
fuels has raised another question of possible community exposures.

Studies are just beginning with regard to the effects of exposure to such metals as vanadium, arsenic, nickel, manganese, and

chromium and their role as possible air pollutants in metropolitan areas (*17–19*); however, there is no evidence as yet on which to evaluate the possibility of hazards. Analysis of trace metal in the organs of persons whose deaths were unexpected could provide a valuable point of reference for further work (*14*).

In small towns adjacent to major extracting or smelting plants, emissions may be sufficient to pose a hazard to community health. Such was the case, for example, with an outbreak of epidemic dermatitis as a result of atmospheric arsenic in the vicinity of a Nevada smelter (*20*).

Control of Atmospheric Lead Pollution

There is no systematic approach to the control of community air pollution from lead. The Ethyl Corporation and the duPont Corporation, which manufacture and distribute the bulk of leaded motor fuel additives, have set certain limits to the concentration of additives in the motor fuel marketed by their customers. There are no air quality standards for lead in the United States, although the Soviet Union has them. Neither the U.S. Public Health Service nor the states have any regulations to control the lead concentrations in motor fuel or in the community's atmosphere. This is in contrast to the control of the workroom atmosphere for which there are standards [200 micrograms per cubic meter of air (*21*)].

One of the reasons for the lack of community standards is that no adequate predictive evidence is available upon which to base them. Much of the medical research on the effects of lead has been directed toward occupational problems. This has made the evaluation of conclusions with respect to air pollution somewhat difficult. Representatives of the Ethyl and the duPont corporations and public health agencies agreed to combine their efforts to study air pollution from lead and their findings have recently been published (*22*).

A new phase of the problem was raised by the need, recognized in California, for controlling hydrocarbons in motor vehicle emissions. Nearly all the proposed devices were adversely affected by lead compounds in the exhaust, whether they coated the parts mechanically or "poisoned" the catalyst. It is claimed that present devices are not so seriously affected; however, the fact remains that an effective catalytic device could have been developed sooner if leaded fuels were not used. It must also be recognized that lead deposited in an afterburner is not emitted into the atmosphere. Use of these exhaust devices may cause some reduction in atmospheric lead.

Global Pollution from Lead

The study of lead isotopes and of their distribution in various sediments and other materials in the earth's crust has been used as a basis for determining the age of the earth and the approximate dates for various events that have marked its history. In conjunction with these methods, an accurate and sensitive way to estimate very low concentrations of lead by means of isotopic dilution techniques has been developed. These techniques have been the subject of two reports (23, 24).

The first observation in this series of studies was of a relatively high concentration of lead in surface waters of the ocean; that is, these values were high in comparison with the concentrations in the lower strata of the ocean where it is thought that the waters reflect a much earlier phase of the earth's history. This gradient was particularly marked in the Mediterranean Sea and the Pacific Ocean; it was somewhat less so in the Atlantic Ocean. Data were also obtained from river water that drained relatively industrialized areas as well as relatively primitive parts of the earth. The data were supplemented by analyzing levels of lead in the snow at the Lassen Volcanic National Park in California, a site which is distant from vehicular traffic. These data have led Chow and Patterson (23) to conclude that "Man is perturbing the marine geochemical cycle." This determination is indicated by the estimated increase of lead input to the oceans during the last 40 years of from 1×10^{10} grams per year to 40×10^{10} per year.

It is theorized that the sedimentation rate of lead in the ocean reflects its incorporation in marine animal life (24). It is thus possible that the increase in the lead in ocean waters may introduce increased amounts of lead into the metabolism of some marine biota. However, the concentrations involved are still minute and it is possible that they will have no effect. However, it does seem clear that the washout of atmospheric lead into rivers and oceans is sufficient to have distorted the previously existing equilibrium.

The fact that there are no standards to control emissions of lead is largely the result of a lack of data for developing them. Without this information, it is reasonable to suspect that atmospheric exposure would indicate some risk of chronic intoxication. Indeed, there are areas in the world where, up to 1947 at least, the use of lead in motor fuel was not permitted, the constraints being based on hygienic considerations (25).

References

1. Ziegfeld, R. L., "Importance and uses of lead," *Arch. Environ. Health* (Frank Princi Memorial Issue, Symposium on Lead), **8**, 202–212 (1964).
2. de Treville, R. T. P., "Natural occurrence of lead," *ibid.*, pp. 212–221.
3. Kehoe, R. A., "Normal metabolism of lead," *ibid.*, pp. 232–235.
4. Phillips, P. H., "The effects of air pollution on farm animals," in *Air Pollution Handbook*, P. L. Magill, F. R. Holden, and C. Ackley, Eds., section 8, pp. 1–12 (McGraw-Hill, New York, 1956).
5. Hirschler, D. A., and L. F. Gilbert, "Nature of lead in automobile exhaust gas," *Arch. Environ. Health*, **8**, 297–313 (1964).
6. Kaye, S., and P. Reznikoff, "A comparative study of the lead content of street dirts in New York City in 1924 and 1934," *J. Ind. Hyg.*, **29**, 178–179 (1947).
7. New York City Department of Air Pollution Control, unpublished data, 1958.
8. Cholak, J., "Further investigations of atmospheric concentration of lead," *Arch. Environ. Health*, **8**, 314–324 (1964).
9. Stokinger, H. E., "Effects of air pollution on animals," in *Air Pollution*, A. C. Stern, Ed., vol. 1, pp. 282–334 (Academic Press, New York, 1962).
10. Lane, R. E., "Health control in inorganic lead," *Arch. Environ. Health*, **8**, 243–250 (1964).
11. Schroeder, H. A., and J. J. Balassa, "Abnormal trace metals in man: lead," *J. Chronic Diseases*, **14**, 408–425 (1961).
12. Robinson, E., F. L. Ludwig, J. E. DeVries, and T. E. Hopkins, *Variations of Atmospheric Lead Concentrations and Type with Particle Size*, SRI Project No. PA-4211 (Stanford Research Institute, Menlo Park, Calif.).
13. Kehoe, R. A., "Metabolism of lead under abnormal conditions," *Arch. Environ. Health*, **8**, 235–243 (1964).
14. Butt, E. M., R. E. Nusbaum, T. C. Gilmour, S. L. Didio, and Sister Mariano, "Trace metal levels in human serum and blood," *ibid.*, pp. 52–57.
15. Hardy, H., "Beryllium case registry progress report: 1962," *ibid.*, **5**, 265–268 (1962).

16. Eisenbud, M., *et al.*, "Nonoccupational berylliosis: Summary," *J. Ind. Hyg. Toxicol.*, **31**, No. 5, p. 294 (1949), as quoted in *Technical Report of California Standards for Ambient Air Quality and Motor Vehicle Exhaust*, p. 24 (California State Department of Public Health, Berkeley, 1960).

17. Tipton, I. H., and J. J. Shafer, "Statistical analysis of lung trace element levels," *Arch. Environ. Health*, **8**, 58–67 (1964).

18. *Clean Air for California*, initial report (California State Department of Public Health, San Francisco, 1955).

19. Nusbaum, R. E., E. M. Butt, T. C. Gilmour, and S. L. Didio, "Trace metal studies of bone in relationship to air pollution exposure," presented at the Seventh Annual Air Pollution Medical Research Conference, Los Angeles (California State Department of Public Health, Berkeley, 1964; to be published in *Arch. Environ. Health*).

20. Goldsmith, J. R., *Air pollution medical studies*, (California State Department of Public Health, Berkeley, 1964); personal communication.

21. American Conference of Governmental Hygienists, "Threshold limit values for 1963," *Arch. Environ. Health*, **7**, 592–599 (1963).

22. Working Group on Lead, *Survey on Lead in the Atmosphere of Three Urban Communities*, Publ. 999 AP12 (U.S. Public Health Service, Washington, D.C., 1965).

23. Chow, T. J., and C. C. Patterson, "The occurrence and significance of lead isotopes in pelagic sediments," *Geochim. Cosmochim. Acta*, **26**, 263–308 (1962).

24. Tatsumoto, M., and C. C. Patterson, "The concentration of common lead in sea water," in *Nuclear Geophysics*, proceedings of a conference, Woods Hole, Massachusetts, June 7–9, 1962, Publication 1075 (National Academy of Sciences–National Research Council, Washington, D.C., 1963).

25. Eidgenossische Bleibenzin-Kommission, Bericht der Eidg. Bleibenzin-Kommission an den Bundesrat über ihre Tatigkeit im Zeitraum 1947–1960. Aus den *Mitteilungen aus dem Geiete der Lebensmitteluntersuchung und Hygiene* (Eidg. Gesundheitsamt, Bern, Switzerland, 1961).

8. FLUORIDES

Sources

Fluorine is never found as an element in nature, but as a fluoride it occurs in vegetation and in various minerals. It may be found in small or large amounts in most ores, coals, clays, and soils. Fluoride has been found in the natural dusts from soil in certain localities; some topsoil in Idaho contained up to 1640 ppm (1), and in many soils it may range as high as 2000 ppm.

Fluorides may be released into the atmosphere in both gaseous and solid form by certain industrial processes, such as the reduction of phosphate fertilizers, the reduction of aluminum, the smelting of iron and nonferrous ores, and the manufacture of such clay products as ceramics. Small amounts of fluorides are also liberated during the combustion of coal, from fluxing agents that are used in making foundry iron, and in miscellaneous cupola and blast furnace operations.

Some of the fluorides in ambient air are relatively soluble in body fluids while others are virtually insoluble; some, like hydrogen fluoride, are irritants and are corrosive while others are relatively nonreactive.

The fluorides in raw materials are the principal source of the fluorides in air pollution. However, the electrolytic aluminum process, which involves a molten cryolite bath, produces some silicon tetrafluoride and cryolite fumes. Treating rock phosphate with acid liberates hydrogen fluoride from the fluoride impurities that are always present in phosphate rock. The high-temperature reactions of the ceramic and metal industries may liberate silicon tetrafluoride and hydrogen fluoride. Although silicon tetrafluoride is an important effluent from many industrial processes, it is possible that moisture in the air hydrolyzes it to hydrogen fluoride, the most common of the fluorides found in industrial waste gases. Some fluosilicic acid may also be evolved or formed from the tetrafluoride.

In nonferrous smelting, there is only a small fluoride output and this is discharged through tall stacks. In the ceramics industry the units are small and the fluoride output is limited so that only the immediate area is affected. The aluminum and fertilizer industries, however, have had chronic fluoride problems from the beginning.

Effects

Airborne fluorides damage sensitive plants and are harmful to farm animals that have eaten contaminated forage. The concentration of fluorides in the ambient air is usually too low to cause damage by inhalation. The effect on plants and animals is the result of the remarkable ability of some of them to concentrate fluorides.

Some plants are injured by extremely low concentrations in the atmosphere and/or in the tissue, while others can withstand more than a hundredfold as much. Even within a species the variation is great, and the reason for this enormous range of tolerance is not clear.

Generally, concentrations in the range of 50 to 200 ppm will cause necrosis in susceptible plants. In resistant species, levels can be above 500 ppm without producing injury. Fluoride levels can be extremely low and still injure such sensitive plants as gladiolus, prune, apricot, and peach. Hydrogen fluoride and silicon tetrafluoride are toxic to some plants in concentrations as low as 0.0001 ppm. Gladiolus fumigated at 0.0001 ppm for 5 weeks, for example, developed necrosis over 1 inch of the leaf blade and had a leaf concentration of 150 ppm (2).

Young leaves are the most sensitive. The young needles of pines and other conifers are very sensitive to hydrogen fluoride, whereas the old needles are very resistant. The growth of young needles will be stunted and they will be shed in fewer years than normal.

The susceptibility of some plants to hydrogen fluoride and the resistance of others appear to be the result of several factors. In varieties of some species, such as gladiolus, differences in susceptibility to necrosis at equal exposures may be related, in part, to the rate of absorption. In other cases, resistance seems to be inherent in the leaf. Inactivity because of the formation of insoluble compounds may be a factor in special cases.

Part of the hydrogen fluoride that attacks foliage may be adsorbed on the exterior of the leaf, but it is uncertain whether the apparent surface fluoride is a true absorption. In the case of forages, the question is academic.

Fluoride enters the leaf through the stomata and moves to the edges and tip of the leaf with the normal flow of water. The body of the leaf, where the absorption takes place, may remain at a low level of concentration while the lethal concentrations that cause marginal necrosis build up at the edges. Gradients of 2 or 3:1 and up to 100:1 have been observed from the tip or edges to the body of the leaf (3). With time and continued exposure, however, the necrosis usually progresses inward from the edge and tip.

The most common effect of toxic concentrations of fluoride is plasmolysis and the collapse of the internal cells of the leaf. The cells dry out and generally turn tan to deep brown, resulting in a characteristic burned appearance. A narrow, dark, reddish-brown line of dead tissue distinctly separates the healthy tissue from the necrotic.

If exposure is discontinued, there is a gradual but extensive lowering of the fluoride content of the leaves. While this effect may be partly the result of movement and of dilution by growth, careful examination suggests that some of the fluoride is lost by volatilization.

The fluoride does not move from the leaf to other parts of the plant. The roots, stems, flowers, and seed generally remain very low in fluoride content even when the leaves have high concentrations. All agricultural soils contain appreciable amounts of fluoride; concentrations of 100 to 500 ppm are frequent and concentrations of up to 25,000 ppm have been noted (4). However, plants show little tendency to take it up, even from soils with very high concentrations. Therefore, when a plant contains more than a few parts per million of fluoride, atmospheric contamination is normally indicated.

The effect of hydrogen fluoride on plants may be contrasted with that of sulfur dioxide. With most species of plants, the fluoride causes lesions and interferes with photosynthesis at much lower concentrations. Although both fluoride and sulfite interfere with photosynthesis when they are accumulated in cells in sublethal amounts, the sulfite is deactivated by simple oxidation to sulfate, whereas the fluoride can be removed only by translocation, by volatilization, or by an obscure chemical reaction that permits a much slower recovery of plant function.

Gaseous fluoride compounds are responsible for most of the fluoride injury to plants. It is unlikely that solid fluorine compounds (except perhaps soluble compounds like sodium fluoride or even, in some cases, the slightly soluble cryolite) deposited on the surface of leaves would injure vegetation. It is well known that cryolite has been extensively used as an insecticide, particularly in apple orchards, without causing damage to leaves. However, peaches and corn are injured by these sprays.

Indirect injury to livestock as a result of ingesting fluorides in forage poses a problem that often has greater economic significance than the direct plant-damaging effects of fluorides.

Fluorides at low levels of ingestion are beneficial to bone and teeth in man and animals. An example is the approximately 1.0 ppm (milligram per liter) that is normally used in fluoridated public water supplies. At this level, no adverse effects have been observed in human beings. However, at higher levels and after long-continued ingestion, fluorides cause an increase in brittleness and density in bones.

Livestock fluorosis first appeared in the United States about the time the aluminum and fertilizer industries were developing. The fluoride-containing effluents from these industries, particles as well as gases, may be accumulated by forage crops, which are subsequently eaten by cattle or sheep, the animals most susceptible to fluorine toxicosis. Such contaminated forage may cause fluorosis because of the affinity of fluorine for calcium. In areas where the air is not contaminated by fluorides, for example, forage may contain as little as 2 to 40 ppm. In areas where fluoride is present as a pollutant, as much as 500 to 1000 ppm are sometimes found in forage (5).

Symptoms of fluoride injury first appear in the teeth. While a minimum of 2 to 3 ppm of fluoride is to be expected in most animal diets, approximately 20 ppm (dry-weight basis) of soluble fluoride is needed to faintly mottle the teeth of cattle (6). Two to three times this amount of soluble fluorine—some authorities cite figures of 30, 40, and 50 ppm (3, 7)—may cause cattle to lose weight and may reduce milk production and retard growth. A greater amount may produce a crippling overgrowth of bony spurs. It is possible that the size of the particle taken into the system is a factor in the assimilation of fluorine compounds (8). If feed that contains fluorides is removed when the first symptoms appear on the teeth, the animal will recover and may show no further signs of fluorosis. However, when ingestion of the contaminants has already caused overgrowth in bones and knee joints, accompanied by lameness and loss of weight, the cattle will not recover.

The toxicity of fluorine appears to be greater in forage contaminated with gaseous effluents rather than with rock phosphate. Whereas 30 to 50 ppm (by weight) of soluble fluoride compounds in the total diet of dairy cattle may cause deleterious effects, it takes 60 to 100 ppm of insoluble fluorides to produce the same effects (9).

Fluorides that are highly reactive chemically will be irritating to exposed areas of the human body (skin and some membranes) when they are present in the air in sufficient concentration. However, exposures to such highly reactive fluorides is extremely rare and is limited to occupational exposure.

Less is known about the effects on human beings of inhaled fluorides that are not surface irritants and whose action, if any, depends upon their absorption from the lungs by the blood.

The fact that animals grazing in the vicinity of factories that were discharging fluorides into the air have had adverse health effects does not mean that people living in the same area will be similarly affected. The grazing animal obtains most of its fluoride from the great amount concentrated in the forage and from grossly contaminated water rather than from the air.

The amount of fluoride inhaled in community air pollution appears to be far lower than the optimum that has been estimated as beneficial to human beings. [An optimum ingestion for the control of caries in children has been estimated at from 1.0 to 1.2 milligrams per day (7).]

The mean concentration of fluoride that has been found in the air of a number of communities ranged from 0.003 ppm in Charleston to 0.018 ppm in the industrial area of Baltimore (10). The maximum concentration in most cities is about 0.025 ppm, with the highest, 0.08 ppm, reported from Baltimore. Even values from the limited number of air analyses that have been reported in the literature for fluoride in the vicinity of plants (3) are lower than the optimum level from breathing alone: 0 to 0.29 ppm near a superphosphate plant, and 0.009 to 0.140 ppm at Fort William, Scotland, between 100 yards and 1 mile downwind of an aluminum plant, both reported in 1949; and an average 8-hour concentration of 0.005 to 0.018 ppm at 12 stations measured near an aluminum plant outside Spokane, Washington, in 1949–1950, with maximum concentrations of 0.011 to 0.147 ppm. (This area was resampled a year later and maximums of only 0.020 and 0.030 ppm were measured.)

The total intake of fluorides from daily ingestion of food, from drinking fluoridated water, and from inhalation does not normally exceed the safe amount desired for caries control.

The toxicity of fluorides for man depends to a great extent on the metabolism and storage of this substance in his body. Fluoride in almost any form is efficiently absorbed from the gastrointestinal tract, and approximately half of the amount administered experimentally is promptly excreted in the urine. Experimental inhalation of hydrogen fluoride gas in concentrations ranging from 1 to almost 5 ppm resulted in a prompt excretion of a sizable portion of the inhaled dose (11). Irritation of the nasal passages was reported in all exposures, and hyperemia and superficial desquamation of the face were noted with concentrations in excess of 2 ppm. Prompt absorption and excretion also occur if fluoride is experimentally inhaled in the form of finely divided rock phosphate (11).

No bone changes have been observed when the urinary concentration of fluorides is less than 5 milligrams per liter (12). It is unlikely that such a level of excretion will occur as a result of exposures to fluoride in ambient air.

On the basis of these facts, it is unlikely that fluorides, as an atmospheric pollutant, will cause any adverse effects to human health (7).

Control

In areas where there has been damage to plants and livestock as a result of industrial contamination with fluorides, mechanical equipment has frequently been introduced to control the effluent. Most of the aluminum and fertilizer plants remove at least 85 to 90 percent of the gaseous fluoride by scrubbing their waste gases with water. Many serious problems have thereby been solved or minimized. Other problems remain. For example, the ceramics industry would be hard pressed if it were required to process its stack gases to remove the small amount of fluoride emitted. Further, coal may contain 85 to 295 ppm of fluoride (*3*), which is largely emitted on combustion and adds to the contamination of urban atmospheres.

References

1. Catcott, E. J., "Effects of air pollution on animals," in *Air Pollution,* WHO Monograph No. 46, pp. 221–231 (World Health Organization, Geneva, 1961).
2. Brandt, C. S., "Effects of air pollution on plants," in *Air Pollution,* A. C. Stern, Ed., vol. 1, pp. 255–281 (Academic Press, New York, 1962).
3. Thomas, M. D., "Effects of air pollution on plants," in *Air Pollution,* WHO Monograph No. 46, pp. 233–278 (World Health Organization, Geneva, 1961).
4. —— and R. H. Hendricks, "Effect of air pollution on plants," in *Air Pollution Handbook,* P. L. Magill, F. R. Holden, and C. Ackley, Eds., section 9, pp. 1–44 (McGraw-Hill, New York, 1956).
5. Heiman, H., "Effects on human health," in *Air Pollution,* WHO Monograph No. 46, pp. 159–220 (World Health Organization, Geneva, 1961).
6. Phillips, P. H., "The effects of air pollutants on farm animals," in *Air Pollution Handbook,* P. L. Magill, F. R. Holden, and C. Ackley, Eds., section 8, pp. 1–12 (McGraw-Hill, New York, 1956).
7. *Technical Report of California Standards for Ambient Air Quality and Motor Vehicle Exhaust,* supplement No. 2 (California State Department of Public Health, Berkeley, 1962).
8. McCabe, L. C., "The identification of the air pollution problem," in *Air Pollution,* WHO Monograph No. 46, pp. 39–47 (World Health Organization, Geneva, 1961).
9. *The Fluorosis Problem in Livestock Production,* a report of the Committee on Animal Nutrition, National Research Council Publication 824 (National Academy of Sciences, Washington, D.C., 1960).
10. Cholak, J., "The nature of atmospheric pollution in a number of industrial communities," in *Proceedings of the Second National Air Pollution Symposium,* May 5–6, 1952, Pasadena, pp. 6–15; ——, "Current information on the quantities of fluoride found in air, food, and water," *AMA Arch. Ind. Health,* **21,** 312–315 (1960).
11. Largent, E. J., "The metabolism of fluorides in man," *AMA Arch. Ind. Health,* **21,** 318–323 (1960).
12. Hodge, H. C., "Notes on the effects of fluorides in man," *ibid.,* pp. 350–352.

9. AIR POLLUTION AS A FACTOR IN ENVIRONMENTAL CARCINOGENESIS

Air pollution is only one of many factors in environmental carcinogenesis; others include industrial processes, cigarette smoking, and smoked and dried foods. A great deal of information about these factors has been gathered over the years, and the progress that has been made in the study of air pollution as related to cancer will be described here.

The combined roles of epidemiology, biological testing, and chemical examination in identifying the impact, source, and modification of environmental carcinogens are well illustrated by the case of aromatic hydrocarbon carcinogens in chimney soot. In 1775, the British surgeon, Percivall Pott, published a report that described "The Cancer of the Scrotum," and attributed its occurrence to the exposure of chimney sweeps to soot (1).

The carcinogenicity of coal tar was established by Yamagiwa and Ichikawa (2) who produced carcinomas by painting coal tar on the inner surface of the ears of domestic rabbits. Later Kennaway showed that the pyrolysis of a number of organic substances produced carcinogenic tars, and he isolated the first pure carcinogenic chemical, dibenz [a,h] anthracene (3, 4). Cook and his co-workers tested the carcinogenicity of a number of polynuclear aromatic hydrocarbons (5) and it was shown that benzo[a]pyrene and related hydrocarbons are produced by incomplete combustion of organic compounds.

Epidemiological and Statistical Studies

Much of our recent knowledge of environmental carcinogenesis is based on epidemiological studies, and a variety of factors, including organic chemicals, metals, and physical agents, such as ultraviolet light and ionizing radiation, have been incriminated.

Epidemiological evidence is usually the first indication of the presence of environmental carcinogens. The study of the epidemiological relationship between lung cancer and exposure to air pollutants is difficult because of (i) the long period of latency between exposure to a carcinogen and a recognizable tumor, (ii) population mobility that results in a change of exposure and loss of contact with the subjects, and (iii) difficulty in obtaining accurate occupational and personal histories. The problem is further complicated by cigarette smoking, which, through its prevalence, tends to mask other factors (6).

Studies in this country and abroad have shown that the rates of lung cancer in metropolitan areas are higher than in rural areas, and in small towns they are intermediate (7). These differences suggest that there is a possible correlation between lung cancer and air pollution. In studies made on smokers and nonsmokers, the lung cancer rate was higher in urban than in the rural populations (8, 9).

Other studies involved persons who migrated from one area to another. Recently Dean (10) reported that, although white South Africans are the world's heaviest smokers, their incidence of lung cancer is less than half that of Great Britain. British immigrants to South Africa had a lung cancer rate 44 percent higher than the South African rate; as a group they had smoked less than the South Africans before emigrating, but thereafter they had increased their smoking to the higher level customary in South Africa. Eastcott (11) has reported similar findings from New Zealand. Although there is heavy smoking among the native born, the rate of lung cancer is considerably lower than that of British immigrants. Earlier exposure of the immigrants to air pollutants may have been responsible for their increased incidence of lung cancer.

Haenszel and Shimkin (12) related mortality from lung cancer in white males to residence and smoking histories and showed that persons who moved from rural to urban areas experienced an increase in the rate of lung cancer that was greater than could be explained by smoking histories alone, which again suggests that some factor associated with urban living was responsible.

Laboratory Studies of Biological Effects

Studies have shown that atmospheric pollutants can induce several types of cancer in experimental animals. In 1942 (13), tars collected in a number of American cities produced subcutaneous sarcomata in mice. More recently, an extensive survey of the biological activity of extracts of particulate air pollutants showed that they could produce cancer in experimental animals (14). These and other studies (15) show that air pollutants contain biologically active tumor factors.

The foregoing experiments did not involve inhalation exposure of the animals and relatively little work has been done along these lines. This is partly due to the fact that techniques for studying experimental bronchogenic lung cancer need further development. However, polynuclear hydrocarbons readily produce bronchogenic lung cancer when they are implanted in the lungs of mice and rats (16); from these and other studies, it seems very clear that lung cancer can be caused by a number of factors, probably including tissue irritation and injury, and possibly cocarcinogenic factors (17).

Early studies on the induction of pulmonary tumors by inhalation were made by Campbell (18), who exposed mice in dust chambers to asphalt road sweepings; benign lung tumors were produced. Kotin and Falk (19) produced malignant lung tumors in mice that were exposed to both influenza virus and carcinogenic hydrocarbons, a finding consistent with the concept that lung cancer generally involves the interaction of several factors.

In summary, the biological examination of air pollutants in the laboratory clearly shows the presence of carcinogenic materials.

Sources and Types of Atmospheric Pollutants

Numerous investigators have examined urban atmospheres (20, 21), gasoline and diesel engine exhaust (22, 23), and other combustion effluents, such as incineration and open-dump burning (24), for carcinogens.

A significant portion of the airborne aromatic hydrocarbons and other organic pollutants are often adsorbed on soot particles in the atmosphere. The size of the soot particles has an important bearing on their entry into and retention in the lung and on the degree of elution of harmful materials by body fluids within the bronchus and pulmonary area (25).

Incomplete combustion of organic materials is a primary source of airborne carcinogenic aromatic hydrocarbons. The airborne carcinogens that have been identified are mostly polynuclear aromatic hydrocarbons. Some 40 aromatic hydrocarbons have been identified in polluted atmospheres, including benzo[a]pyrene, which is a potent carcinogen, and approximately five other compounds that are classed as weakly carcinogenic. However, there are still many aromatic hydrocarbons that have not been tested for carcinogenic activity. In general, compounds that have fewer than three, or more than six, condensed benzene rings do not exhibit carcinogenic activity, but there are exceptions, such as the methylphenanthrenes. Efforts have been made to relate structure to carcinogenic activity (26) for aromatic hydrocarbons and heterocyclics. Although there is some correlation in terms of active K regions and inactive L regions, some carcinogenic materials have recently been described that are not expected (from Pullman's criteria) to be carcinogenic, notably the benzofluoranthenes and tricycloquinazoline.

The tars and asphalt used in road surfacing are another source of aromatic hydrocarbons, but, because of their low vapor pressure and relatively limited dust production, this source is probably minor.

Although several carcinogenic heterocyclic nitrogen-containing compounds have been identified in cigarette smoke (27), they have not been reported in urban polluted atmospheres or in engine exhausts. Nitrogen is fixed in the form of oxides from gaseous nitrogen during combustion, in particular during combustion in gasoline and diesel engines. However, it is not fixed to any measurable extent in the form of nitrogenous airborne carcinogens, with the possible exception of nitroso compounds, some of which are carcinogenic.

It has been found that a composite organic residue from particulate pollution (aromatic pollutants have been removed from the organic fractions of atmospheric samples) can produce tumors in laboratory animals, which indicates airborne tumorigens of a different class. Kotin (28) has postulated the presence of oxygenated compounds that are formed by the oxidation of the olefinic hydrocarbons known to be among atmospheric pollutants. However, the verification of this theory demonstrates a frequent problem in air pollution research since it is not certain whether the suspected carcinogens are actually present in the atmosphere, or whether they are being produced by primary pollutants during sampling and analysis. Conversely, some carcinogens may be destroyed during fractionation and examination of air pollutant mixtures. Kotin and Falk presented indirect evidence for the presence of oxygenated tumor agents by using ozonized gasoline to produce pulmonary tumors in mice (29).

Work has been done on determining the carcinogenic activity of various oxygenated compounds, including epoxides, hydroperoxides, peroxides, and lactones (30, 31). The results suggest the need for a more thorough examination since the concentration of olefins, from which these compounds may be derived, is relatively high in a polluted atmosphere.

Benzene extracts of the particulate phase of air pollutants, obtained from eight cities in the United States, were each resolved into three fractions: aromatic hydrocarbons, aliphatic hydrocarbons, and oxygenated compounds. These fractions, as well as the benzene extracts themselves, all exhibited carcinogenic activity to varying degrees (14). This finding emphasizes the fact that it is very difficult to reduce atmospheric samples to single pure compounds or to definitive mixtures because of the large number of components and their low concentrations.

Many unknown compounds have been separated from atmospheric extracts. These compounds show fine structure in their ultraviolet-visible absorption spectra and show single spots on paper chromatograms, and are therefore probably pure materials. However, these unidentified compounds are not available in sufficient quantity for bioassay.

Industrial sources of air pollutants for which there is either experimental or industrial evidence for carcinogenicity include chromates, nickel, asbestos, beryllium, arsenic, selenium, and cobalt (32). They are normally present only in trace amounts as outside air contaminants, and there is no clear evidence to indicate that they contribute to cancer incidence.

It has been postulated that free radicals may play a role in causing lung cancer (33). The relatively high concentration of free radicals in the atmosphere suggests that a closer evaluation is needed.

Concentrations of Airborne Carcinogens

Considerable progress has been made in developing analytical techniques, including sampling, storage, extraction, and analysis of atmospheric pollutants. However, at present there is no standardization of techniques (34–36).

The amount of carcinogens to which urban dwellers are exposed is a significant factor in determining the potential dangers of air pollutants. The U.S. Public Health Service measured the concentration of aromatic hydrocarbons per 1000 cubic meters of atmosphere over 14 American cities (20). The total amount ranged in various locations from 146 micrograms down to approximately 5 micrograms. Benzo[a]pyrene, a potent airborne carcinogen, ranged in concentration from 31 micrograms to 0.25 micrograms. It is difficult to estimate the possible carcinogenic effect on human beings of continually inhaling these minute quantities. In Great Britain there have been regional differences and seasonal trends in connection with variation in fuel consumption (21).

Fate of Airborne Carcinogens

The degradation of aromatic hydrocarbons in the solid state and in dilute solutions has been investigated in the presence of air with and without ultraviolet irradiation (37, 38). The degradation involves a number of complex chemical reactions, including oxidation and dimerization of the hydrocarbons. Additional work is needed in order to determine the persistence time of aromatic hydrocarbon carcinogens in the air.

Control

The relevant issues relate to the control of effluents from the incomplete combustion of fuels and irritants, and these are covered elsewhere.

Summary

Investigations over a number of years have shown that carcinogenic materials are present in the air of large urban and industrial centers, and the sources of many of these materials have been clearly established. Epidemiological investigations are consistent with these findings and it may be concluded that general air pollutants (compared to cigarette smoking) have a significant, although minor, role in the incidence of lung cancer. The number of other factors makes it impossible to attribute the higher cancer rate in urban areas to any specific source.

References

1. Pott, P., *Chirurgical Observations* (London, 1775).
2. Yamagiwa, K., and K. Ichikawa, *J. Cancer Res.,* **3**, 1 (1918).
3. Kennaway, E., *Brit. Med. J.,* **2**, 1 (1925).
4. ———, *Biochem. J.,* **24**, 497 (1930).
5. Cook, J. W., I. Hieger, E. Kennaway, and W. V. Mayncord, *Proc. Roy. Soc. London Ser. B.,* **111**, 455 (1932).
6. *Smoking and Health: Report of the Advisory Committee to the Surgeon General of the Public Health Service, U.S. Department of Health, Education and Welfare* (Government Printing Office, Washington, D.C., 1964).
7. Hueper, W. C., *Public Health Service Monograph No. 36* (Government Printing Office, Washington, D.C., 1955).
8. Hammond, E. C., and D. Horn, *J. Am. Med. Assoc.,* **166**, 1159, 1294 (1958).
9. Stocks, P., and J. M. Campbell, *Brit. Med. J.,* **2**, 923 (1955).
10. Dean, G., *ibid.,* **1959-II**, 852 (1959).
11. Eastcott, D. F., *Lancet,* **1956-I**, 37 (1956).
12. Haenszel, W., and M. Shimkin, *Acta Unio Intern. Contra Cancrum,* **15**, 493 (1959).
13. Leiter, J., M. B. Shimkin, and M. J. Shear, *J. Natl. Cancer Inst.,* **3**, 155 (1942); J. Leiter and M. J. Shear, *ibid.,* p. 167.
14. Hueper, W. C., P. Kotin, E. C. Tabor, W. W. Payne, H. L. Falk, and E. Sawicki, *Arch. Pathol.,* **74**, 89 (1962).
15. *Motor Vehicles, Air Pollution and Health, A Report of the Surgeon General to the U.S. Congress, U.S. Department of Health, Education and Welfare, Public Health Service* (Government Printing Office, Washington, D.C., 1962).
16. Kuschner, M., S. Laskin, E. Cristofano, and N. Nelson, *Third Natl. Cancer Conf.,* p. 485 (American Cancer Society, New York, 1957).
17. Nelson, N., *Arch. Environ. Health,* **8**, 100 (1964).
18. Campbell, J. A., *Brit J. Exptl. Pathol,* **15**, 287 (1934).
19. Kotin, P., and H. L. Falk, *Proc. Natl. Conf. on Air Pollution,* USPHS Publication No. 1022, p. 140 (Government Printing Office, Washington, D.C., 1963).
20. Sawicki, E., T. R. Hauser, W. C. Elbert, F. T. Fox, and J. E. Meeker, *Am. Ind. Hyg. Assoc. J.,* **23**, 137 (1962).
21. Waller, R. E., *Brit. J. Cancer,* **6**, 8 (1952).
22. Kotin, P., H. L. Falk, and M. Thomas, *AMA Arch. Ind. Hyg.,* **9**, 164 (1954).

23. ———, *ibid.*, **11**, 113 (1955).
24. Kennaway, E., and A. J. Lindsey, *Brit. Med. Bull.*, **14**, 124 (1958).
25. Falk, H. L., and P. Kotin, *Natl. Cancer Inst. Monogr. No. 9*, p. 81 (1962).
26. Pullman, A., and B. Pullman, *Advan. Cancer Res.*, **3**, 117 (1955).
27. Van Duuren, B. L., J. A. Bilbao, and C. A. Joseph, *J. Natl. Cancer Inst.*, **25**, 53 (1960).
28. Kotin, P., *Cancer Res.*, **16**, 375 (1956).
29. ——— and H. L. Falk, *Cancer,* **9**, 910 (1956).
30. Van Duuren, B. L., N. Nelson, L. Orris, E. D. Palmes, and F. L. Schmitt, *J. Natl. Cancer Inst.*, **31**, 41 (1963).
31. Hendry, J. A., R. F. Homer, F. L. Rose, and A. L. Walpole, *Brit. J. Pharmacol.*, **6**, 235 (1951).
32. Haddow, A., *Brit. Med. Bull.*, **14**, 79 (1958).
33. Lyons, M. J., and J. B. Spence, *Brit. J. Cancer,* **14**, 703 (1960).
34. Payne, W. W., *Natl. Cancer Inst. Monogr. No. 9,* p. 75 (1962).
35. Moore, G. E., J. L. Monkman, and M. Katz, *ibid.*, p. 153.
36. Commins, B. T., *ibid.*, p. 225.
37. Falk, H. L., I. Markal, and P. Kotin, *AMA Arch. Ind. Health,* **13**, 13 (1956).
38. Kuratsune, M., and T. Hirohata, *Natl. Cancer Inst. Monogr. No. 9,* p. 117 (1962).

10. ECONOMIC POISONS AS AIR POLLUTANTS

Economic poisons are all those materials that are toxic to man and desirable life, but are used by him to control some pest in his environment. As generally used, the term refers to the pesticides: insecticides, fungicides, herbicides, rodenticides, arachnicides, and nematocides. Economic poisons may also include other agriculturally important chemicals such as regulators of plant growth, defoliants, and desiccants (1). Some materials that are not normally considered economic poisons become so under the law when they are specifically prepared, formulated, labeled, or marketed for use as pesticides. Kerosene, sulfur, copper sulfate, and cyanides are common commercial items that are considered economic poisons when used as pesticides.

Because of the very nature of their intended use, the economic poisons must be considered toxic. Yet the classification of a material as an economic poison makes it no more toxic than it would be otherwise. Sulfur sold for the production of sulfuric acid is a common item of commerce. The same sulfur sold in a garden store as a fungicide is an economic poison. When coumarin and its derivatives are marketed as bait, they are highly effective rodenticides; when they are prescribed by a doctor, they are highly useful drugs. At present, parathion is used only as an insecticide, and all parathion is considered an economic poison, but additional uses obviously would not change its toxicity. The question of concern is not only how toxic, but also how hazardous.

Hazard involves length of exposure, concentration, and all the factors that affect individual sensitivity, in addition to the toxicity of the material. On the basis of these factors, together with consideration of opportunity for exposure, the risk can be evaluated. In this section degrees of toxicity will not be covered nor will opportunity for exposure be evaluated. We will attempt only to outline the possible routes of economic poisons into the air, and to summarize what we know of possible concentrations.

Our use of economic poisons is frequently questioned in specific cases, but it is accepted as necessary in agriculture, forestry, and public health (2, 3). In 1910 we could do little more about malaria than feed quinine to the patient. Today, through the use of economic poisons, we have nearly eliminated the disease by controlling the mosquito.

Agricultural Uses

In 1910, a little more than 90 million people were fed from 330 million acres of land; in 1962 about twice as many people were fed from the same acreage (4). Part of this gain is the result of using pesticides. In spite of their wide use, however, it is estimated that, because of pests, we are losing the production from 88 million acres before harvest and from 32 million acres after harvest (2).

Because of the economic gain that results, we are using about 225 million pounds of insecticides per year (5), and their use is increasing (6). Although the demonstrable hazard to man is minimal, our policy and procedures in pest control must be under continual review (3, 7). The possibility of air pollution from economic poisons is just one aspect of our need to give careful and foresighted consideration to the total impact of our ever-increasing and highly successful technology upon the simple, essential, and limited elements of our environment (8).

After an effective agent has been found for controlling a pest, the major problem is to deliver the material from its container to the target (the pest) in a manner that is efficient, safe, and effective. The methods used vary with the nature of the target as well as with the pesticide, and they include spraying, dusting, baiting, drenching, dipping, and painting as well as generating smokes and vapors for fumigating closed spaces.

Spraying, dusting, and fumigating involve the air directly in the transport to the target. While the air is not directly involved with other types of application, accidents in use or subsequent reentrainment could result in some of the materials being introduced into the open air.

Aerial Application

Sprays and dusts account for most of the insecticides used. Although no accurate national figure is available, application by aircraft is a major method. In California about 60 percent of the pesticides used are applied from the air (6).

In all aerial applications, part of the material ejected does not reach the target. Rollins (9), who summarized much of the work, indicates that 5 to 70 percent of the sprays and 40 to 80 percent of the dusts may drift off target. Methods for determining spray patterns and for estimating target efficiencies for application to open ground are well described by Isler and Yuill (10) and Akesson and Yates (11).

Some of the problems that are involved in determining these factors under actual field conditions are evident, if not directly evaluated, in several reports (12–16). Maksymuik (12) indicates that efficiency is greater over forested areas than over open ground.

Even with the best designed equipment and with the most efficient application, the weather, and all this term implies, becomes the overriding factor that affects the drifting of spray (12–16). Rather obviously, stable conditions are ideal, with practically no turbulence or vertical motion, so that the spray or dust will settle quickly. A slight crosswind might be desirable, however, to help smooth out irregularities in the distribution across spray swaths (13).

As a result of ground-based radiation inversions during the growing season, conditions are stable for an hour or two after dawn on more than 20 to 30 percent of the days (17). These inversions usually do not last long after sun up. We do not know how much of the aerial application is carried out under these optimum conditions nor how much of it is performed under definitely unfavorable conditions. Since, in order to be effective, pesticides must reach their target, strict management efficiency argues against applying them under unfavorable conditions.

Ground Application

In the case of crop spraying and dusting from the ground, we have less definite information regarding drift, although studies have been made on a ground spray test (14), on ground rigs (9, 15), and on cover dusts (18, 19). The limited data available indicate that there is greater efficiency in reaching the target when well-designed and properly operated ground equipment is used under optimum weather conditions. The optimum weather for spraying from the ground is the same as for spraying from the air. While there are no data available on the amount of spray that is applied from the ground under nonideal conditions, it is probably somewhat more than from the air. Because of the short transport path from equipment to target, however, the efficiency of ground spraying is generally not as greatly affected by adverse weather.

Nonagricultural Uses

Sprays and dusts of economic poisons are used on more than forests and crop plants. Some 20 percent or more (5) are used in the home and garden and by public authorities in buildings, parks, street plantings, and so forth. Commercial establishments and industry use something less than 5 percent.

We can only speculate on how much of these insecticides drift out of the target area. In the case of industry and commercial establishments, target efficiency is probably high since most of this use is within confined areas. Public authorities generally use insecticides in the open air and this is accompanied by all the uncertainties of crop and forest treatment. For this reason the operation should be supervised by people who are well informed of the hazards and adequately trained to minimize them.

Use of insecticides by the householder is another matter. Any large garden supply owner can probably give you the name of a customer who sprayed the Japanese beetles on his roses with 2-4D instead of DDT; he will probably add a joking comment that starving the poor "beasties" to death is too cruel. And one would not have to search very long to find a mother, concerned about bacteria, who regularly uses an aerosol can to kill the flies over the table while her children are eating. The householder is probably just as careless in his use of economic poisons as he is in his use of drugs, power lawn mowers, paint thinners, stepladders, and kitchen knives. Undoubtedly, much of the spray he uses outdoors sometimes drifts far beyond the target. How much, how frequently, and how far, we do not know. Most of his applications are at low levels with low-pressure equipment, which argues against a great deal of drift. But, he also probably does not pay much attention to wind speed.

The successful use of a fumigant requires that a definite concentration of vapor or aerosol be uniformly dispersed within a confined space for a specific length of time. In the case of greenhouses, grain silos, holds of ships, and so forth, the structure defines the space. The fumigant is released into the structure by various methods so that there will be a uniform distribution throughout the area without exchange with the atmosphere. After fumigation, the structure is opened and ventilated, and at this time any residue is released to the atmosphere.

This is not as hazardous as it sounds. Generally, the concentration within the structure has been reduced considerably by reaction, absorption, or settling. In some cases, efforts are made to remove the fumigant during ventilation. In practically all cases, however, some of the fumigant is released into the atmosphere. How much and how significant a factor this may be is not known.

Soil fumigation is also practiced. The fumigant may be injected under the soil surface with or without some cover to reduce exchange with the atmosphere. Here again, effectiveness depends on the ability of the system to prevent exchange or loss from the soil. Usually, no attempt is made to ventilate the volume of treated soil after fumigation. In this use, the loss to the atmosphere is probably very low, but again we have no information on which to base estimates.

Economic poisons are also used in animal dips and drenches, paints, baits, waxes, and cleaning compounds. However, loss to the air is probably minimal. Although the purpose and effectiveness of these uses argue for keeping the material in a well-defined area, there is still opportunity for volatilization or entrainment into the atmosphere as dust.

The problem of entrainment has not been well evaluated. Rachel Carson (20) cites a case in Long Island where schools were closed because of dust from potato fields and cites the concern of health officials over the possibility that arsenic and other insecticides might be entrained in the dust. Such a possibility was very real.

Volatilization and, in the case of DDT, codistillation (21) are also routes by which economic poisons may escape into the atmosphere. These materials may be released through manufacturing, handling, and waste disposal. In manufacturing and handling, con-

trols should be practicable and, in most cases, are probably in effect. In the case of waste disposal, however, entrainment or volatilization is probably possible, but it is not known whether it has a significant effect.

Pesticides or economic poisons in general are getting into areas
of our environment where they are not desired. That the problem
is a complex one and has at least two sides (22) is well recognized.
That the problem is not going to solve itself or allow us to ignore
it in the hope that it will become simpler is becoming more
obvious (23). That air transport, or air contamination if you wish,
is a factor in this overall problem of economic poisons in the environment should also be obvious.

Concentrations

Of what significance are economic poisons to air contamination?
The statement that more than 20 percent of the spray from a plane
missed the target may or may not be significant because nothing
was said about what happened to that material. If it settled out
just beyond the target area, it may have been of benefit in controlling the target pest or it may have been highly undesirable because it contaminated a crop (16). Some probably went farther,
and we ought to know how much went how far.

There are very few air analyses available for pesticides. In a
pilot study conducted during the summer of 1963, the Air Quality
Section of the Division of Air Pollution, U.S. Public Health Service, attempted to gain some preliminary information on this subject
(24). It set up a high-volume air sampler (25) in the center of a
cotton-growing community and sampled for several days immediately
following a rain. During this same period after the rain, cotton
and other crops in the surrounding area had been heavily sprayed.
Twenty-four-hour samples were taken and the filters were analyzed
for DDT and related compounds by a method based on one devised
by Coulson, Cavanagh, and Stuart (26). On the 5 days from June 20
to 24, the samplers gave 23, 34, 12, 7.4, and 7.4 nanograms of DDT
per cubic meter of air. The limit of detectability of the method is approximately 0.5 nanogram of DDT per cubic meter.

These data may not represent the worst possible period for a similar area, but the timing was chosen to provide some of the heaviest possible loadings on the filters. Other samples in the same area at other times indicated less than the detection limit. This study did little more than demonstrate that the sampling method is probably adequate and that measurable quantities of DDT and its related compounds are on occasion present in the air of a community in the center of large-scale spraying operations. The scarcity of data of this sort is more important than these specific values. Many more studies must be made before we can adequately evaluate the significance of the observed increase in pesticides in the air.

Control

Another question arises: If we cannot adequately evaluate air contamination as a vector in the spread of economic poisons now, are we taking sufficient precautions to insure minimum spread? Thirty-six states have some type of law to govern the sale and use of pesticides for agricultural purposes. Thirty-one have some restriction on spraying from the air. Perhaps all the states should have specific laws on pesticides, perhaps some of the laws should be more stringent, and perhaps some should be better enforced; but the mechanism for control exists in the areas of greatest use. Regardless of how stringent or how well enforced, a law cannot prevent ignorance, carelessness, or willful negligence. The federal regulations are certainly not perfect, but for the most part they are keeping pace with developments and needs. Legal mechanics are just one element in the control process.

Our methods of using economic poisons can undoubtedly be improved. Our knowledge of the best time to apply pesticides to control pests with a minimum of time, effort, and hazard is increasing. New materials and new concepts of pest control are being developed and, as long as we have pests, this will continue. Better methods, better materials, better forecasting, and more complete knowledge constitute important elements in the process of controlling economic poisons in the air and in our environment.

Yet laws and knowledge are of no value if the individual is irresponsible and ignorant. We need better information for the user as much as we need better, more complete, overall knowledge.

Generally, large-scale users—mostly in agriculture—are fairly well informed of the environmental hazards. Accidents are few, but they can happen (27). Perhaps these incidents should be more thoroughly discussed if this would demonstrate the hazard rather than just frighten the public. Newspaper accounts should have made the small user, the householder, aware that pesticides can be harmful. However, some will argue for controls, whether practical or not; some will read and take care; some will read and forget; and some will be sure their use is of no concern.

All users, whether they are acquainted with the hazards of pesticides or not, must realize that their use of economic poisons is of concern to everyone. Based on what we know, there is no reason to ban all aerial spraying or all household insect bombs, but there is evidence that we cannot afford to be careless and that all uses should be reviewed continuously.

References

1. Federal Insecticide, Fungicide and Rodenticide Act, 62 Statute 163; 7 U.S. Code 135–135k. c.f. amended definition in Fed. Register, Title 7, Chapt. III, Pt. 362, April 28, 1961 and Oct. 6, 1962.
2. Aldrich, D. G., *NAC News and Pesticide Rev.*, **21**, 3–6 (1963).
3. President's Science Advisory Committee, *Report on Use of Pesticides,* Washington, D.C., May 15, 1963.
4. *U.S. Dept. Agr. Statist. Bull. No. 233 Rev.* (1963).
5. Hall, D. C., *Bull. Entomol. Soc. Am.*, **8**, 90–92 (1962).
6. *The Pesticide Situation for 1961–1962,* ASCS (U.S. Department of Agriculture, Washington, D.C., 1962).
7. Publications 920B (1962) and 920C (1963) (National Academy of Sciences–National Research Council, Washington, D.C.).
8. Commoner, B., *Proc. Natl. Conf. Air Pollution,* PHS Publ. No. 1022, pp. 18–24 (1963).
9. Rollins, R. J., *Calif. Dept. Agr. Bull. 49* (1960).
10. Isler, D. A., and J. S. Yuill, *U.S. Dept. Agr. ARS 42–82* (1963).
11. Akesson, N. B., and W. E. Yates, *Calif. Agr.,* **15**, 4–7 (1961).
12. Maksymuik, B. J., *J. Forestry,* **61**, 143–144 (1963).
13. Yuill, J. S., and D. A. Isler, *ibid.,* **57**, 263–266 (1959).
14. "Pesticide drift," *Texas Agr. Exp. Sta. MP-620* (1962).
15. Brooks, F. A., *Agr. Eng.,* **28**, 233–239, 244 (1947).
16. Huddleston, E. W., G. G. Gyrisco, and D. J. Lisk, *J. Econ. Entomol.,* **533**, 1019–1021 (1960).
17. Hosler, C. R., *Monthly Weather Rev.,* **89**, 319–339 (1961).

18. Bowen, H. D., W. M. Carleton, and P. Hebblethwaite, *Agr. Eng.*, **33**, 347–350 (1952).
19. Brittain, R. W., R. D. Brazee, and W. M. Carleton, *ibid.*, **36**, 319–320 (1955).
20. Statement to Subcommittee on Reorganization and International Organizations, Committee on Government Operations, June 4, 1963.
21. Acree, F., Jr., M. Beroza, and M. C. Bowman, *Agr. Food Chem.*, **11**, 278–280 (1962).
22. Baldwin, I. L., *Science*, **137**, 1042–1043 (1962); T. H. Jukes, *Am. Scientist*, **51**, 355–362 (1963); F. E. Egler, *ibid.*, **52**, 11–36 (1964).
23. Langer, E., *Science*, **144**, 35–37 (1964).
24. Tabor, E. C., personal communication, 1964.
25. Robson, C. D., and K. E. Foster, *Am. Ind. Hyg. Assoc. J.*, **23**, 404–410 (1962).
26. Coulson, D. M., L. A. Cavanagh, and J. Stuart, *Agr. Food. Chem.*, **7**, 250–252 (1959).
27. Associated Press, story date line, Toppenish, Wash., Aug. 12, 1963.

11. RADIOACTIVE POLLUTION OF THE ATMOSPHERE

Until about 70 years ago, exposure to ionizing radiation was due exclusively to nature. Today, radioactivity in the atmosphere comes from both natural sources and human activities. Natural radioactivity is either of terrestrial origin, consisting mainly of radioactive gases, such as radon and thoron, which are released from soils and rocks, or it is produced by the interaction of cosmic radiation with atmospheric constituents. Radioactive pollution of the atmosphere may be defined as man's contribution to airborne radioactivity beyond the levels that occur in nature as the result of his use of naturally occurring or artificially produced radioactive substances.

Sources of Radioactive Contamination

Radioactive contamination of the atmosphere results from (i) the reactor-fuel cycle; (ii) the use of nuclear energy as a source of propulsive power; (iii) the use of radioisotopes in industry, agriculture, medicine, and scientific research; and (iv) most of all, from nuclear weapons testing.

Reactor-Fuel Cycle

The first part of the reactor-fuel cycle, the production of nuclear fuel, involves mining, milling, and refining the uranium or thorium ore; chemical separation of uranium and thorium from their daughter products and later from each other; possibly isotopic separation; and the manufacture of fuel elements. Some atmospheric pollution may occur during these operations as the result of the release of radioactive gases or dusts (1). However, the air pollution problems of the uranium industry up to the point of reactor operation are minimal and would be of concern primarily from the standpoint of occupational exposure.

Once the fuels obtained have been introduced into nuclear reactors, the second part of the reactor-fuel cycle takes place. Radioactive wastes that are formed during the operation of reactors include fission products, which normally remain incorporated in the fuel, and extraneous activation products that are found mainly in coolants. Both the fuel elements and coolants are thus potential sources of radioactive atmospheric pollution. Such pollution can be caused by the release of the radioactive gases produced by fission, such as iodine, xenon, and krypton, into the atmosphere; by the induced activity of atmospheric argon; by the formation of radioactive aerosols that contain primary or secondary fuels (uranium, thorium, and plutonium); or by the release of fission products, such as strontium-90, cerium-44, barium-140, and zirconium-95 (1).

Some carbon-14 may also be produced in a reactor by neutron irradiation of the graphite moderator or of the carbon dioxide used as a coolant, and by irradiation of nitrogen.

During the normal operation of all reactors, a small amount of gaseous radioactive pollutants is released into the atmosphere. Of the several types of reactors, research and test reactors often tend to release more radioactive materials than power reactors, and training reactors release the least. Most reactors are water-cooled. Some are air-cooled, however, and the use of air for cooling purposes makes the reactor a more abundant source of radioactive air pollutants. Research reactors at Brookhaven National Laboratory and at Oak Ridge National Laboratory, for example, which utilize this cooling method, routinely emit large quantities of argon-41 produced by neutron capture of the argon-40 that is normally present in the cooling air (2). Brookhaven discharges into the atmosphere as much as 750 curies of argon-41 per hour. However, meteorological dilution from a 400-foot stack and limits of radioactive decay (the half-life of this isotope is 1.8 hours) control exposure beyond the perimeter of the plant site. Also, plant officials can and often do reduce the power level of the reactor whenever unfavorable meteorological conditions develop. Inert dust contained in the cooling air of these reactors may become activated and particles of fission products, caused by defective cladding of the fuel, may be released. These results, however, can be largely prevented by filtration.

Of all the operations that are involved in the reactor-fuel cycle, chemical reprocessing plants, to which the irradiated, spent reactor fuel is taken, present the most important potential source of air pollution. The fuel must be dissolved and the solutions processed in order to separate the unfissioned uranium and plutonium from the radioactive waste products. Because of the large amount of radioactivity, the processes of chemical separation and dissolution present substantial potential hazards which have been overcome by the development of a highly specialized technology to enable the plants to operate safely. Nevertheless, during processing, fission-product gases are released into the atmosphere, including krypton-85, xenon-133, and iodine-131 (3). Although most of the iodine is removed by various processes, some of it does escape. To date, three chemical reprocessing plants have been able to meet the needs of the United States. As the civilian reactor industry grows, however, convenience and economy will make additional installations necessary.

Although little quantitative information on the amount of radioactivity that is discharged in gaseous wastes has been published, some data relating to atomic energy installations in the United Kingdom and the United States are available (see Table 5).

It is not the routine operation of the reactors and reprocessing plants that can cause the most drastic atmospheric radioactive contamination but rather accidents. The International Atomic Energy Agency lists 71 reactor incidents, involving the exposure of about 123 people, which took place from 1945 to 1961 (4). The Agency reported that four of these incidents involved one or more fatalities due to radiation, each of which was brought about by criticality and power excursions of the reactor. (Six persons died in the four incidents.) Ten incidents, in which there was high contamination of people (irradiation above the 13-week permissable dose of 3.9 rem), were described as serious; 25 or more persons received an exposure of from 25 rem to 850 rad.

The Agency report does not indicate whether any of these reactor incidents resulted in emissions of significant amounts of radioactive material to the atmosphere beyond the plant site. However, other sources record cases in which such emissions occurred: The NRX reactor at Chalk River, Canada, on December 12, 1952, released material that, due to the wind direction, "fortunately . . . was spread over a large, uninhabited area" (5); the S1-1 reactor at the National Reactor Testing Station in Idaho on January 3, 1961, emitted materials that, although resulting in iodine-131 levels low enough to provide little off-site hazard, nevertheless extended about 100 miles southwest of the plant site (6).

The only reactor accident that has resulted in significant contamination of the environs occurred at Windscale, England, in 1957 (2). The fission products were carried across the surrounding countryside to the channel and from there across much of Europe. The radioactivity was detectable for great distances. The levels of contamination were high enough to require precautionary procedures downwind in a coastal strip about 30 miles long and 6 to 10 miles wide. In this area, airborne radioactive iodine deposited on foliage and was consumed by dairy cattle. The milk from these

Table 5. Some examples of releases of gaseous waste from atomic energy plants (3, p. 370); c, curie; mc, millicurie.

Site	Amount of waste and radioactive content
United Kingdom	
Springfields (feed material production plant)	Approximately 1 c/yr, alpha
Capenhurst (gaseous diffusion plant)	Approximately 0.1 c/yr, alpha (uranium)
Calder Hall (nuclear power station)	10 c/hr, argon-41
Chapelcross (nuclear power station)	10 c/hr, argon-41
Dounreay (reactor research center)	0.5 mc/hr, argon-41
Harwell (nuclear research center)	30 mc/yr, beta; 1 mc/yr, alpha; 50 c/hr, argon-41
Amersham (isotope production plant)	15 mc/wk, iodine-131
Aldermaston (nuclear weapon research center)	20 mc/yr, beta; 3 mc/yr, alpha
United States of America	
Hanford (plutonium production plant)	1 c/day, iodine-131
Idaho (reactor testing station)	100,000 c/yr, beta, mainly very short half-life, and noble gases
Oak Ridge National Laboratory (reactor development and chemical processing laboratory)	0.25 c/yr, alpha (uranium)
Brookhaven National Laboratory (nuclear research center)	700 c/hr, argon-41

Table 6. Estimates of radioactivity released in Windscale accident (3).

Radioisotope	Curies
Iodine-131	20,000
Tellurium-132	12,000
Cesium-137	600
Strontium-89	80
Strontium-90	2

cattle had such a high iodine content that it was withheld from public consumption for several weeks.

The amount of radioactivity released from the Windscale accident is not known precisely, but the estimates are shown in Table 6 (3).

The highest level of iodine-131 recorded in milk was 1.4 microcuries per liter: 1,400,000 picocuries per liter (3). Continuous consumption of 1 liter of such milk per day for a year would result in a total thyroid dose of about 9000 rad to a 2-gram thyroid, assuming a 30-percent uptake of iodine-131 by this gland (7). Since the iodine-131 in Windscale milk decreased with a half-reduction time of about 5 days, the total dose to the thyroid of a 1-year-old child who consumed 1 liter of milk per day from the location with the highest initial levels in milk would have been about 240 rad (7). However, Windscale milk was not used for human consumption after the iodine levels exceeded 100,000 picocuries of iodine-131 per liter (8). The thyroid dose to infants who continuously consumed milk that reached this maximum value was estimated by Knapp to be about 17 rad (7); scientists from the United Kingdom, using somewhat different assumptions, estimated 25 rad (9).

It is worth noting that most of the strontium-90 and other of the longer-lived nuclides did not escape with the iodine-131; the ratio of strontium-90 to calcium in milk increased only from 44 picocuries to 115 picocuries per gram of calcium.

The amount of radioactive air pollution from the entire reactor-fuel cycle has been small so far. However, a sizeable increase in the use of nuclear energy for peaceful purposes may be expected, primarily in the production of electric power. It has been estimated that the thermal power produced by atomic plants will reach 700,000 megawatts by the year 2000 (3). This greater use may mean an increase in the fission products that are dispersed into the environment during routine operations (especially from fuel reprocessing plants) and as a result of accidents.

Use of Nuclear Energy as a Source of Propulsive Power

Nuclear energy is currently being used as a source of propulsive power for submarines and a few surface vessels. Nuclear-powered rockets will be used for space exploration. In addition, power for measurement and communications systems in space satellites will be obtained to an increasing degree from nuclear sources, either from isotopes, such as plutonium-238, or from reactors (10).

In March 1963, plutonium-238 was the only radionuclide being used in the space program (orbiting the earth in Transit 4A and Transit 4B) and it was being considered for many other space programs (11). However, at that time the Atomic Energy Commission was planning production of a new isotope, curium-244, in quantities that would be large enough, in combination with plutonium-238, to satisfy the sizeable requirements newly projected by the National Aeronautics and Space Administration. These two isotopes are the most desirable for space-power applications because of their long half-lives and excellent power densities, and because they are alpha emitters, which means they do not have to be shielded during launching operations. These isotopes, together with two other alpha emitters—curium-242 and polonium-210—were, in March 1963, the only fuels definitely committed to space missions.

Plutonium-238 and curium-244 are also considered desirable for space-power applications because they do not have to be shielded against the significant radiation hazard on reentry into the atmosphere. However, this assumes either burnup of the capsule upon reentry, with uniform dispersal of the radionuclide in space or in the upper air, or intact contact of the capsule with the earth's surface. The validity of these assumptions is open to question; partial burnup, followed by dispersal of the radionuclide in the lower air or on some surface area, might occur and this would result in a hazard.

In April 1964, 2.2 pounds of plutonium-238 were lost somewhere in the upper atmosphere. The radionuclide was part of the power supply on board a transit navigational satellite that, because of a launching error, did not go into orbit. Because radar contact was lost after the first part of the trajectory in the western Pacific, it is not known whether the accident occurred just before the vehicle achieved orbital velocity or during reentry into the atmosphere (*12*). If the former (thought to be the most critical safety problem to be analyzed for isotope-fueled systems), aerodynamic heating for a narrow band of suborbital velocities would have been enough to damage the fuel-capsule container but insufficient to cause complete burnup and wide dispersal of radioactive debris at high altitudes (*13*). A failure at this point in the launching could result, therefore, in radioactive fuel landing on the earth in marble-sized chunks. If the accident occurred during reentry into the atmosphere, at orbital velocities air-friction heating would have caused the complete burnup and dispersal of the satellite into the upper atmosphere, with the plutonium-238 filtering to the earth over a period of years from a wide band around the earth at above 100,000 feet, much like the fallout from nuclear bomb testing.

The Division of Isotope Development of the Atomic Energy Commission, however, is actively considering the use of four fission-product nuclides in space-power applications—strontium-90, cerium-144, promethium-147, and cesium-137—once the shielding and safeguard obstacles to the use of fission products have been overcome (*11*). Strontium-90 would be the most advantageous because of its long half-life and fairly high power density. This isotope is currently being used in terrestrial power units developed for such applications as remote weather stations, navigation lights, and ocean-bottom sonar signals. In space, strontium-90 is being considered for the military communications satellite system.

As of June 30, 1963, the Division of Reactor Development of the Atomic Energy Commission had 50 naval propulsion reactors in use, plus one in space and one for export (*14*). In the process of being built were 45 naval propulsion reactors and three to be tested for space. Six propulsion reactors for space, as well as a number expected to be tested, were being planned.

The use of nuclear energy for propulsive power presents the same problems of radioactive contamination as were described for nuclear reactors, but with the added complication of a mobile source of contamination. This mobility means that people not located near stationary reactors and other terrestrial systems, such as isotope-powered weather stations and lighthouses, can be exposed.

Use of Radioisotopes in Medicine and Scientific Research

In many universities, hospitals, and research laboratories throughout the country, radioactive isotopes are being used in laboratory research as tracers and for medical diagnosis and treatment. The radioactive wastes that result may occasionally contaminate the air, especially where radioactive wastes are incinerated or gases are evolved. The pollutants are usually in the form of suspended fine particles and are mostly beta-gamma emitters that have a short or medium half-life. Although the releases of radioactivity into the atmosphere from any one installation are usually small, some of the isotopes used and planned, such as strontium-90, are highly radiotoxic, and the total from many installations in a given area must be considered.

The Atomic Energy Commission has established standards for protection against radiation hazards arising out of these activities, and in 1954 it set up a licensing procedure. The Commission estimated that from February 10, 1956 to November 30, 1962 there were 5874 AEC radioscope licensees using radioactive isotopes in the United States (15). These included medical institutions and physicians (2283), colleges and universities (312), industrial firms (1777), federal and state laboratories (1410), foundations and institutes (48), and miscellaneous (44). In addition, during the same period, 1108 physicians in private practice, 398 firms in industrial radiography, and 1141 federal and state laboratories in civil defense were using radioactive isotopes.

Table 7 shows the number of shipments and the radioactivity of ten radioisotopes distributed by Oak Ridge National Laboratory between August 2, 1946 and November 30, 1962. The total of 2,080,864 curies in 169,052 shipments does not include several thousand curies of radioisotopes produced and distributed directly from other AEC facilities or from reactors owned by private industrial firms and universities. Nor does the total include radioisotopes made in other countries and imported. It is estimated that, outside of the radioisotopes used at the AEC installations, about 50 percent of the radioisotopes now used in the United States are imported (16). No detailed data on such shipments are available from organizations other than the Atomic Energy Commission.

Nuclear Weapons Tests

Fallout from nuclear weapons tests is a source of radioactive pollution that is of far greater magnitude and is subject to far less control than those already mentioned. The lack of control is evident after a nuclear detonation larger than a few kilotons of TNT in explosive equivalence; fission products are detectable in the atmosphere thousands of miles away.

In a surface nuclear detonation, fission products volatilized by the intense heat produce a mass of luminescent gas that cools as it

Table 7. Radioisotope distribution by Oak Ridge National Laboratory (includes project transfers, subsidy payments, and so forth) (15). This table does not include several thousand curies of radioisotopes produced and distributed directly from other facilities of the Atomic Energy Commission, such as Mound Laboratory, nor from reactors owned by private industrial firms and universities. Radioisotopes made in other countries and imported into the United States are also not included.

Radiosotopes	August 2, 1946 to December 31, 1961		January 1 to November 30, 1962		Total to November 30, 1962	
	Activity (curies)	Ship-ments	Activity (curies)	Ship-ments	Activity (curies)	Ship-ments
Carbon-14	150	3,782	29	201	179	3,983
Cesium-137	182,711	1,745	120,589	223	303,300	1,968
Cobalt-60	1,058,817	2,344	64,685	117	1,123,502	2,461
Hydrogen-3	146,093	1,361	59.037	202	205,130	1,563
Iodine-131	7,305	48,495	140	1,634	7,445	50,129
Iridium-192	46,905	982	5,047	82	51,952	1,064
Krypton-85	14,805	585	3,928	148	18,733	733
Phosphorus-32	1,945	30,624	97	1,901	2,042	32,525
Promethium-147	4,594	490	2,665	110	7,259	600
Strontium-90	99,246	971	256,488	91	355,734	1,062
All others	2,656	65,697	2,932	7,267	5,588	72,964
Total	1,565,227	157,076	515,637	11,976	2,080,864	169,052

rises, sucking dust from the ground into itself by convection. Some of this dust vaporizes when it reaches the fireball and mixes with the original fission products; the dust particles that are sucked into the fireball at more advanced stages of cooling act as nuclei on which fireball vapors condense as a radioactive coating. These particles of dust fumes constitute the fallout that ultimately returns to the earth.

There are three types of fallout from a nuclear detonation. Relatively large particles of radioactivity (mostly larger than 50 microns) are deposited in several days within a few hundred miles downwind from the point of detonation. This local fallout is intensely radioactive because of the high concentration of short-lived radioactive products that are deposited over a limited surface area.

A second portion of the radioactive debris enters the troposphere. Tropospheric fallout is usually hemispherically contained and is normally confined to a relatively narrow zone within a hemisphere. Some of this debris is carried around the world several times, and a large part of it falls to the earth within a few weeks. Surface and atmospheric shots in Nevada, as well as those underground tests that have vented, have been responsible for high levels of close-in, tropospheric fallout up to several hundred miles beyond the Nevada Test Site (7). This fallout is important because of its relatively large burden of short-lived nuclides, such as iodine-131.

The remainder of the debris enters the stratosphere. If the size of the detonation is large enough or if the height of the burst is far enough above the ground, as was the case in many of the tests since 1954, the stratosphere receives most of the radioactive debris. Stratospheric fallout depends on time of injection, weapon yield, and latitude. It may take one to several years or longer for the bulk of the stratospheric fallout to be deposited on the ground. Since 1952, when tests began on nuclear weapons with much higher explosive yields, stratospheric fallout has been continuous.

It is estimated that, of the total fission products (90 megatons) created by weapons tests conducted in the atmosphere by the United States, the United Kingdom, and the Soviet Union during the period from 1945 to the end of 1958 (determined by taking an inventory of strontium-90), approximately one-third fell out in the

immediate vicinity of the test site (2). Of the remaining 60 megatons, many believe that as much as 90 percent may have been injected
into the stratosphere, with about 10 percent remaining in the troposphere. Some scientists believe the ratio to be 99 percent to 1 percent for individual megaton-yield range shots (17). There is great
difference of opinion with regard to the exact distribution of debris
among the three types of fallout, and figures are very uncertain because it is impossible to measure local fallout over large ocean areas.

It is predominantly in the temperate or polar regions of the
earth's atmosphere that stratospheric-tropospheric exchange takes
place (18). Thus, most of the fallout should be recorded in these
two regions. Since the amount of precipitation decreases toward the
poles, and since rainfall seems to be the primary mechanism for
removing fallout, it follows that fallout should be higher in the
temperate zones. Since most of the nuclear tests have been conducted in the Northern Hemisphere, one would expect to find
more fallout in the North than in the South Temperate Zone. It
has been confirmed experimentally, in fact, that levels of fallout in
the Southern Hemisphere are lower by an order of magnitude or
more than the levels in the Northern Hemisphere for tests conducted above the equator (19).

This explains why debris from a polar source (such as testing
carried out by the U.S.S.R.) falls out faster and is less widely distributed than that from an equatorial source (such as United States
testing). By the end of 1959, the strontium-90 deposited from the
1958 Soviet tests had reached about 80 percent of the total produced,
whereas only about 50 percent of the strontium-90 produced by
our 1958 Pacific tests had been deposited during 1959 (18).

During the years 1945 through 1962, a total of 423 nuclear detonations (20) were announced by nuclear powers: the United States
(271, including those from the Nevada Test Site), the United Kingdom (23), France (5), and the U.S.S.R. (124). The approximate
total yield from these tests, exclusive of those carried out at the
Nevada Test Site, was 511 megatons (406 megatons from atmospheric shots and 105 megatons from surface shots) (21). The approximate total fission yield was 193 megatons (139 megatons, atmospheric; 54 megatons, surface). It is estimated that from 1952
to 1958, when testing stopped temporarily, 66.5 megatons of fission

yield were injected into the stratosphere (22). When testing started again in 1961, and until it ceased aboveground in 1962, about 96 megatons of fission yield were injected into the stratosphere (57 megatons into the lower stratosphere and 39 megatons into the upper stratosphere) (21).

During the period from September 15, 1961 to December 12, 1962, the Atomic Energy Commission reports that there were 59 underground nuclear detonations at the Nevada Test Site and that three tests were performed slightly aboveground (July 7, 14, and 17, 1962) (23). All of these tests were of low yield (20 kilotons to 1 megaton). Of the underground shots, 12 of them released small quantities of steam and/or a gaseous cloud that contained small quantities of radioactivity, but no activity was detected off-site. The same was true of one of the shots aboveground. However, some activity from a release or venting was detected off-site in the case of 13 other underground shots and two that were detonated aboveground. Of these, seven underground and all three aboveground detonations produced a radioactive cloud.

Effects on Man

The radionuclides that are present in the radioactive debris from fallout and that have the greatest significance in terms of their effects on man are (i) strontium-90 and strontium-89, which are beta emitters and principally irradiate the skeleton; (ii) cesium-137, which is a beta-gamma emitter and concentrates in soft tissues, resulting in internal whole-body irradiation; (iii) carbon-14, a beta-gamma emitter, which accumulates in the body and delivers whole-body irradiation; (iv) iodine-131, a beta-gamma emitter, which concentrates in the thyroid gland; and (v) a number of short-lived fission products that produce external whole-body irradiation when deposited on the ground.

Radiation Effects through the Food Chain

Strontium-90 is abundantly formed in the fission process (about 5 percent of the total atoms produced in fission), it has a long life (half-life of about 28 years), and it is chemically similar to calcium, therefore readily absorbed by living things. Thus it may pass easily through the food chain to man by depositing on soil, from which it is absorbed by roots, and by depositing directly on vegetation. When man eats the vegetation or drinks the milk from animals that have eaten it, the strontium-90 is deposited in the skeleton.

Some scientists had thought that strontium-90 and strontium-89 were not a genetic hazard. But recently a report indicated that strontium-90 may, after all, have significant genetic effects (24). C. L. Dunham of the Atomic Energy Commission's Division of Biology and Medicine, however, has commented that, "Unfortunately, the authors have provided no information on the actual radiation exposure to the germ cells from the strontium-90 as it circulated in the blood stream and from that deposited in the bones" (16).

The potential somatic hazard of strontium-90 and strontium-89 is primarily to the bone and bone marrow. Experiments have shown that, when deposited in sufficient amounts in the bones of animals, these isotopes will produce leukemia, bone cancer, and other skeletal effects. However, the amount that would be required to produce bone disease in man is not known. Because of its short half-life (51 days), strontium-89 contributes to the bone dose during only the first year or two after weapons testing and does not accumulate appreciably in the ecological cycle. Strontium-90, on the other hand, with its long physical and biological half-lives, can contribute to skeletal radiation throughout a lifetime. The early years of childhood are particularly important, since it is during this period that most of the calcium in the diet is used to form the skeleton. Even strontium-89, during its short dose-giving period, is an important hazard to infants and children, who are the most sensitive.

The food-chain process operates in the same way for the other nuclides, with the exception of those short-lived fission products that produce only external radiation.

Cesium-137, which irradiates the body externally and internally, is formed in slightly greater amounts than strontium-90 (about 6.2 percent) and has a half-life of about 27 years. It differs, however, from strontium-90 in that it does not become fixed in the body. Its principal significance for man is that it is a gamma emitter and as such it is a major contributor of long-lived gamma activity. The potential hazard from cesium-137 is primarily genetic from irradiation of gonadal tissue.

The capture of escaping neutrons by atmospheric nitrogen produces carbon-14, which has a physical half-life of 5760 years. It emits weak beta rays. However, because carbon is a basic element of all living matter, it is readily taken into the body and is deposited equally throughout, resulting in whole-body radiation; it is both a potential genetic and a somatic hazard. Nuclear detonations produce carbon-14 in relatively significant amounts in comparison with the carbon-14 inventory normally present in nature. In the summer of 1962, the carbon-14 content of the atmosphere was estimated to have increased 37 percent since testing began (25). However, more recent figures show an increase far greater, amounting to 80 percent by the summer of 1963 (26). Ninety-five percent of the carbon-14 is unavailable to the biosphere because of diffusion into the ocean reservoir, with a half-time rather uncertainly estimated at about 20 years. Most of the increase in the population dose is delivered before equilibrium is established with the ocean reservoir and hence carbon-14 presents the greatest hazard to the first generation after a weapons test. The 5 percent remaining in biospheric equilibrium can, however, continue to contribute to the population exposure for a mean time estimated at 8000 years (27).

Iodine-131, at the other end of the scale, is a very short-lived nuclide, with a half-life of 8 days. It irradiates the body as an internal and external emitter. It is produced fairly abundantly in fission since about 3 percent of the fissioning atoms give an iodine-131 atom as one of the two atoms that result from the split uranium atom. Within 2 to 4 days after it is deposited on pasture and consumed by dairy cattle, levels of iodine-131 in the milk reach a maximum. When this milk is consumed, the iodine finds its way into the thyroid glands. This is particularly important for infants (whose main diet is usually milk) and children because the iodine is deposited in a gland that is only one-tenth as large as that of an adult (2 grams in weight as against 20 grams), and therefore much more vulnerable. The total radiation dose to the gland is proportional to the concentration of iodine-131 per gram of thyroid. The adult thyroid can receive at least 4000 rad of iodine-131 with no demonstrable ill effects (3). However, evidence from young children who were given 200 rad of x-ray to the neck suggests that this dose may produce cancer of the thyroid in about 3 percent of the cases (3). The Federal Radiation Council notes that cancer of the thyroid occurred in children after exposures as low as approximately 150 rem (28).

The elusive characteristics of iodine-131, which are just beginning to be understood, also determine the population dose. The most pronounced difference between fallout of iodine-131 and that of the longer-studied strontium-90 is that, while surface deposits of strontium-90 vary by, at most, a factor of 3 or 4 and change relatively little from year to year, surface concentrations of iodine-131 may vary from place to place by a factor of 1000 and by an equally large factor at the same place from time to time.

Recently there has been increased concern over the role played by iodine-131 in nuclear weapons tests. It is now recognized that, in various parts of the United States, there were undoubtedly much higher levels of iodine-131 in milk during the few weeks after weapons tests than had previously been measured (7). The highest levels have resulted from atmospheric detonations in Nevada, but high levels have also resulted in the path of the fallout cloud from vented underground Nevada tests.

Radiation Effects from the Ground

The gamma-ray dose from short-lived fission products deposited on the ground may constitute the major source of external whole-body radiation during the testing of nuclear weapons in the atmosphere and for some months thereafter. The principal nuclides and their radiological half-lives are given in Table 8 (27). Because these nuclides emit penetrating gamma rays that produce whole-body exposure, they constitute both a potential genetic and a somatic hazard.

Radiation Effects through Inhalation

Radioactive nuclides also enter the body through inhalation. This is generally the most important route of entry for some short-

Table 8. Principal nuclides and radiological half-lives.

Isotope	Half-life (days)
Zirconium-95	65
Niobium-95	35
Ruthenium-103	40
Ruthenium-106	369
Cerium-141	33
Cerium-144/praseodymium-144	285
Barium-140/lanthanum-140	14

lived radionuclides and for insoluble radioactive materials. Inhalation of radioactive nuclides creates three potential problems: (i) absorption into the systemic circulation and subsequent deposition in a critical tissue or organ, (ii) irradiation of the lungs themselves from materials deposited on respiratory surfaces and picked up by bronchial lymph nodes, and (iii) ingestion.

When particles are inhaled into the lungs, some are exhaled again, and some are swallowed and enter the gastrointestinal tract. Of the particles that remain in the lungs, the finer ones may be retained in the lung tissue for considerable periods of time. Knowledge of their movement within the lungs, however, is very limited. Tissues in contact with these particles receive relatively high doses because of the small range of beta rays and the abundant ionization they produce.

The average dose to the lungs from concentrations of short-lived cerium-141, cerium-144, and zirconium-95, inhaled and measured daily from March to June 1958, has been estimated as 0.14, 2.6, and 0.7 millirem per year, respectively (3). From the world average of strontium-90 in ground-level air, the annual dose rate would be about 1 millirem per year. A dose rate to the lungs of 5 millirem per year may occur during periods of testing. However, additional information is needed in order to obtain the average dose over prolonged periods of time (3).

We need to learn more about the effects on man of inhaling radionuclides, but it seems likely that nuclides absorbed within the food chain have more far-reaching effects than those inhaled. An exception might be the inhalation of nuclides by radiation workers.

Ingestion is important, of course, only for those nuclides that can be absorbed, and primarily for those that are radioisotopes of elements required by the body or of elements chemically similar to a required element. Thus, gastrointestinal absorption is the most important route of uptake for strontium-90, iodine-131, and carbon-14.

Biological Effects

Exposure of the body to radiation may cause a variety of biological effects, both somatic and genetic. Such effects may be brought about by either acute (high, short-term) exposure or chronic (low, long-term) exposure. Acute exposure might involve total or substantial whole-body exposure to radiation, such as could be experienced in nuclear warfare or in nuclear reactor accidents involving direct exposure to radiation, or it might involve exposure of a limited yet substantial body area in which radiation is given either as a single dose or is fractionated over a few days or weeks, as in therapeutic radiation. Radioactive pollution of the ambient air is of concern, however, primarily because of the possibility of chronic or long-term exposure to radiation over months or years.

One characteristic of the effects of chronic, low-level exposure (as well as of certain acute radiation doses) is that there is usually a long latent period before the onset of clinically observable symptoms. Latent effects may include shortening of the life span, production of cancers, effects on growth and development, and genetic mutations. With regard to carcinogenic effects, for example, several years or decades may elapse between the time of exposure and the appearance of cancer. A delayed effect is even more marked in genetics where defects involving dominant genes may appear in the first generation and those involving recessive genes may be spread over scores of generations. Although the principal latent effects are known, the possibility cannot be excluded of other effects, notably in the fetus.

Another characteristic of the effects of low-level chronic exposure is the difficulty of associating damage with radioactivity. The biological effects of radiation are masked in that they are not unique or necessarily assignable to radiation injury, but may be smothered in effects of nonradiogenic origin. One is, therefore, obliged to look for statistically significant fluctuations in order to relate cause and effects.

It must also be noted that cancerous changes and genetic mutations are usually irreversible, and that the defects associated with gene mutations are transmissible.

Very little is actually known about what dose of radiation will produce what long-term effects in man. A dose of 100 rem to the total body approximately doubles the natural rate of leukemia, but there is no observed effect for much smaller doses (29). Although many experiments have attempted to relate low-level chronic exposure to changes in the life span, the results have given us no cause for concern. Scientists generally agree that, in most cases, radiation exposures, no matter how small, have an associated biological risk, that is, an associated degree of likelihood of harmful biological effect.

The importance and complexity of the effects of low-level radiation are therefore underlined by their irreversibility and transmissibility, a prolonged latent period, a masking effect, and the possible absence of a threshold dose.

Control of Radioactive Pollution

No really effective therapy is known for preventing or curing the harmful effects of internal contamination by radioactive nuclides. The radioactivity of a substance cannot be modified by any practical, known technique. Thus, reliance for health protection must be placed mainly on measures for insuring that radioactive pollution of the atmosphere is adequately controlled.

Radiation Standards and Preventive Measures

An obvious beginning was the development of maximum permissible limits, standards, and guides. Such levels, which would limit the dose of allowable radiation to specific organs and to the whole body of individuals and exposed population groups, have been recommended by the United States National Committee on Radiation Protection and Measurements, by the International Commission on Radiological Protection, and, most recently, by the

Federal Radiation Council. The Radiation Protection Guides (RPG) established by the Federal Radiation Council for normal peacetime operations are shown in Table 9 (*30*).

It is extremely difficult to develop standards that have any real meaning, both because of our lack of knowledge of the relationship between dose and effect in human beings, and because of scientific agreement to assume that, in the absence of evidence to the contrary, there is no threshold below which there are no effects, and therefore that any amount of radiation may cause injury. Experts have tried to make estimates based on both the risk of injury and the benefits to be derived from radiation. However, it is important to note that, on the basis of new evidence, radiation limits have been lowered continually from 1902 to the present day. Table 10 shows the changes made over the years in the occupational permissible limit to the total body from external radiation sources (*31*).

Some perspective may be gained by comparing the recommendations of the Radiation Protection Guides (Table 9) with exposure to natural radiation. The United Nations Scientific Committee on the Effects of Atomic Radiation gives the following figures for natural background radiation: 125 millirem per year to the whole body and gonads; 137 millirem per year to bone; and 122 millirem per year to bone marrow (*3*). Doses to other organs, such as the thyroid gland, may be estimated to be about the same as that for the whole body. A comparison of these figures with those shown in Table 9 for the whole body, gonads, and bone marrow, for the average of a sample of the exposed population, indicates that the latter are approximately one and one-third times that of natural radiation; about three and two-thirds times for bone; and about four times for the thyroid.

Radiation Protection Guides are recommended to, but not binding on, federal agencies. Thus, although the Federal Radiation Council recommends not more than 0.17 rem of whole-body radiation annually for a "suitable sample of the exposed population," and 0.5 rem for individuals, the Atomic Energy Commission uses 3.9 rem per year as the guide for the population in the vicinity of the Nevada Test Site (*32*).

With these standards and guides as a basis, certain preventive measures have been taken. Nuclear reactors, chemical reprocessing plants, and uranium mines have been limited in the amount of

Table 9. Radiation Protection Guides (RPG) of the Federal Radiation Council.

Tissue or organ	RPG for individuals	RPG for average of suitable sample of exposed population group
Whole body	0.5 rem/year	0.17 rem/year
Gonads		5 rem/30 year
Thyroid	1.5 rem/year	0.5 rem/year
Bone marrow	0.5 rem/year	0.17 rem/year
Bone	1.5 rem/year	0.5 rem/year

radioactive pollutants that they are allowed to release to the environment. This is achieved in the design and planning of the installations as well as in the techniques to be used in carrying out particular operations. In the case of nuclear reactors, for example, the reactor can be designed with many safety devices built in and the risk of pollution can be reduced by using closed-cycle coolant systems to completely contain the polluted air. Emission of radioactive particles of a given size can be controlled by filtration. In the chemical and metallurgical industries, handling of the radioactive substances in gaseous and powder forms can be kept to a minimum.

However, even with these preventive measures, it still may not be possible to reduce radioactive pollution below the maximum permissible limits or guides. In nuclear reactors, the short-lived radioactive contaminants may then be held and allowed to decay,

Table 10. Changes made in occupational permissible limits (OPL).

Year	OPL (rem/year)	Year	OPL (rem/year)
1902	2500	1936	25
1925	100	1948	15
1931	50	1956	5*

* The dose rate is based actually on accumulated exposures received. The maximum absorbed dose to total body that could be accumulated from occupational exposure was set at 5 (A-18) in which A is the age in years. This limit on accumulated exposure amounts to an average dose rate of about 5 rem per year.

but, in the case of the longer-lived pollutants, the excess radioactivity must be dispersed from tall stacks so that, by taking advantage of the differing local meteorological conditions, the pollution is spread through a sufficiently large volume of air to reduce the risk to the surrounding population to acceptable limits.

Monitoring Systems

In order to make certain that the standards and guides are not exceeded, a rigorous monitoring system is required to determine the nature and the level of radioactive contamination. The various monitoring systems that make up the total surveillance activities for the United States, as well as for some other countries, are too numerous to discuss here. Programs carried out by the Health and Safety Laboratory and other laboratories of the Atomic Energy Commission, the U.S. Public Health Service, the Food and Drug Administration, and other agencies include the monitoring of radioactivity in air, milk, water, diet, and the human body.

The Health and Safety Laboratory began fallout monitoring operations in 1951 with a network of stations throughout the United States. This was modified at the end of 1952 to include a number of overseas stations. The sampling consisted of collecting settled dust on a gummed film that was then ashed and measured for total beta activity. The number of stations varied with the testing program from about a dozen to as many as 150.

As the testing program continued, the information obtained from gummed-film measurements became inadequate. The technique could determine only the time of arrival and the relative amount of radioactivity in the geographic pattern. Thus, in 1954, monthly collections were begun for radiochemical analysis for strontium-90 and other radionuclides. This network has gradually expanded so that there were about 130 stations at the end of 1963.

By measuring monthly fallout samples, the rate of deposition, geographical distribution, and seasonal effects can be estimated. These data are supplemented by collecting and analyzing soil samples from about 150 sites every 2 or 3 years. Soil analyses give a good measure of the accumulated deposits of the individual nuclides.

The U.S. Public Health Service Radiation Surveillance Network was established in 1956, in cooperation with the Atomic Energy Commission, to provide a supplemental means of promptly determining increases in levels of radioactivity in the air and precipitation. Prior to September 1961, the Network consisted of 45 stations and tested one sample per month at each of these stations, taking daily samples during and after testing periods. Following the resumption of testing by the U.S.S.R. in September 1961, the Network was expanded over a period of several months to 66 stations and began continuous collection of air samples. It now comprises 72 sampling stations. The gross beta activity of particles in surface air is measured and the results provide one of the earliest indications of increased activity in the environment, thus serving as an "alert" system. However, a direct evaluation of biological risk is not possible from these data alone, principally because direct human exposure from airborne radioactivity is small when compared to exposure from contaminated food.

In 1954 the Health and Safety Laboratory began sampling milk at a few sites. These measurements have continued but the practice was never expanded because of the adequate coverage by the Public Health Service.

In 1957 the Public Health Service began to test raw milk in five cities in order to determine the amount and kind of fission products that were in the diet and to develop sampling and radiochemical analytical proficiencies. The program was expanded to include five additional cities and it still continues in nine cities on a monthly basis.

However, in 1960, there was a shift in emphasis from the sampling of raw milk to a program of sampling pasteurized milk. The surveillance program for pasteurized milk began with 46 stations, now comprises 62, and is operated in cooperation with the state and local health and milk sanitation agencies. Most stations had been operating on a monthly basis, but since September 1961 they have been taking weekly samples. Measurements are made of iodine-131, cesium-137, barium-140, strontium-90, strontium-89, and of other radionuclides of concern to public health agencies. Results of iodine-131 analyses are available within a few days, whereas analyses of strontium-90 and strontium-89 are not determined for 2 to 4 months.

Since exposure to internal radiation is fundamentally related to total intake, studies of the amounts of specific radionuclides in the total diet give important and comprehensive data. The total-diet studies of the Consumers Union (33) examined the diets, including food and drink intake, of teenagers, who have relatively high nutritional needs as compared with other age groups and who are still building bone rapidly. The teenagers were from middle- and low-income families located in 30 cities throughout the United States. The diets of some infant and adult groups were also examined. The amounts of strontium-90, strontium-89, cesium-137, cerium-144, radium-226, zinc-65, potassium-40, and stable calcium in the total diets were determined. In its institutional diet study, the Division of Radiological Health of the U.S. Public Health Service (33) analyzed samples of a number of radionuclides: the two strontiums, iodine-131, cesium-137, barium-140, and radium-226, as well as calcium and phosphorus compounds. Twenty-one boarding schools and other institutions, such as orphanages, in 21 states were included in the study.

The Food and Drug Administration and the Health and Safety Laboratory of the Atomic Energy Commission each operates a diet study in which samples are analyzed for strontium-90 alone (34). The former covers the diets of teenagers in five cities, and the latter the average diet of individuals living in three cities. The program of the Health and Safety Laboratory in New York, Chicago, and San Francisco involves the purchase of a large number of diet components based on statistics provided by the Department of Agriculture. These are then combined into 18 groups for analysis. In contrast to other total-diet measurements, this system gives the contribution of various types of foods to the dietary intake of strontium-90. This type of study is of particular value in predicting future levels of strontium-90 in man.

A few studies are being undertaken on the amount of radioisotopes actually within the bodies of human beings. One example is the sampling of human bone at autopsy that has been carried out by the Health and Safety Laboratory in New York, Chicago, and San Francisco since 1961 (35). The sampling allows correlation with the corresponding dietary intakes measured for the same cities. In another example, the Greater St. Louis Citizens' Committee for Nuclear Information, with the help of the Washington

University and the St. Louis University Schools of Dentistry, has collected more than 100,000 baby teeth in an attempt to discover the amount of strontium-90 being absorbed in the bones of children (36). The present generation of children, born between 1949 and 1957, is the first to have been exposed to fallout. Preliminary studies showed that the analysis of baby teeth provides a reliable indication of the amount of strontium-90 in the bones of children.

The statistics compiled from total-diet studies on fallout levels, distribution patterns, and trends are the most basic data available. However, they are helpful primarily in long-range terms, because they comprise information for the recent past and for as far back as data are available.

The High Altitude Sampling Program of the Defense Atomic Support Agency was initiated in 1957 for the purpose of providing direct measurement of the concentrations of strontium-90, cesium-137, and other potentially hazardous components of radioactive fallout in the stratosphere and in order to provide data from which the rates and mechanisms of diffusion of this debris through and out of the stratosphere might be deduced. In order to predict the future hazards from radioactive fallout from past and future tests of nuclear weapons, estimates must be available on the amount of debris that is held in the stratosphere and its rate of release to the troposphere and then to the ground. Indirect estimates of the stratospheric burden of fallout had been made by using surface measurements of fallout rates and estimates of stratospheric injection of debris, but the results had frequently been inconclusive or mutually contradictory.

In November 1957, sampling was begun along a meridian network in the Northern Hemisphere, and, in September 1958, the sampling network was extended into the Southern Hemisphere. A more intensive sampling of the Northern Hemisphere was begun in September 1959, and in May and June 1960, the sampling program was completed with a brief resampling of the stratosphere of the Southern Hemisphere.

The High Altitude Sampling Program undertook direct measurement of stratospheric concentrations by radiochemical analysis of filter samples of stratospheric dust that were collected by Lockheed U-2 aircraft. The radiochemical data, together with other data that were gathered during the program, have been studied in the light of the known properties of nuclear debris and of stratospheric meteorology. Estimates have been prepared of the stratospheric burden of strontium-90, cesium-137, plutonium, and other radio-nuclides and stratospheric residence times of such debris have been calculated (37).

In 1963 the Health and Safety Laboratory took over the 80th Meridian Network formerly operated by the Naval Research Laboratory. Weekly air samples, representing about 10,000 cubic meters, are measured for gamma activity and are analyzed radiochemically. Corresponding measurements of deposits are made at the same sites. During 1963 six additional stations, corresponding to the 80th Meridian Network, were set up in the United States. These stations were to supply data on the relationship between airborne and deposited radioactive material as well as on geographical and meteorological correlations.

Unsolved Problems in Monitoring for Fallout

Although in most cases the monitoring systems for nuclear fallout are extensive and effective, they still require expansion, research, and development, particularly for the short-lived activities that vary greatly in surface concentration from place to place and from time to time.

Of special concern is the fallout of iodine-131 in the fallout patterns from Nevada tests, which extend up to a few hundred miles beyond the Nevada Test Site (7). In these close-in patterns, where milk measurements have not been systematically taken, there is now reason to believe that concentrations of iodine-131 as high as or higher than those noted in Windscale may have occurred without detection on numerous occasions during the years 1952–58 (38). Two separate retroactive calculations, based on the Atomic Energy Commission's measurements of gamma and beta radiation, have shown that the thyroid glands of infants might possibly have been exposed to iodine-131 for each of 189 different readings at various locations following 31 different nuclear test shots conducted at the Nevada Test Site during the period 1952–58 (38). One estimate

(based on evidence from the Windscale experience) indicated thyroid doses that ranged up to 555 rad. The other estimate (based on
experiments by R. J. Garner, British radiobiologist) indicated
doses that ranged from 4 to 3260 rad. On May 19, 1953, for
instance, in the whole of Washington County, Utah, gamma readings
from the 32-kiloton shot "Harry" showed that the thyroid of children who drank fresh milk from cows in pasture at the time had
probably received a minimum dose of about 50 rad. Infants in St.
George, Utah, who consumed fresh milk may have received a dose
of 100 to 700 rad. For Hurricane, Utah, the calculations indicate
the possibility of doses in the range of 150 to 950 rad.

These values are of course far in excess of the Radiation Protection Guides yearly 0.5 rad to the thyroid gland for the general
population. Moreover, although high doses from individual shots
have been estimated, no systematic attempt has been made to total
the possible dose of iodine-131 to children from all Nevada tests.

The hazard of thyroid exposure to iodine-131 is a result not only
of nuclear tests in the atmosphere and at the earth's surface, but
also of certain underground nuclear tests that have vented. It has
been suggested (39) that, in many recent instances, underground
tests in Nevada were the principal source of iodine-131 fallout; this
view is supported by subsequent specific associations of domestic
underground tests with iodine-131 fallout. The Des Moines shot
of June 13, 1962, for example, caused iodine-131 levels in processed
milk to reach 1240 picocuries per liter in Spokane, Washington, a
week later (38). Calculations have also shown that fallout from the
New Mexico "Gnome" shot of December 10, 1961 may have caused
thyroid doses in the range of 7 to 55 rad in the vicinity of Carlsbad
(38).

It has been very difficult to effectively monitor fallout at points
distant from the Nevada Test Site since, carried swiftly by unusual
conditions of wind and weather, it has been deposited suddenly by
precipitation and has resulted in relatively high contamination
levels. Measurements taken at one hot spot—Troy, New York—were
detailed enough to estimate that, based on the Windscale experience,
6- to 18-month-old children might have received a total thyroid
dose of up to 30 rad of radioiodine if the cows had been in pasture

at the time *(40)*. Calculations have shown *(38)* that other local deposits of fallout scattered across the continent might have produced thyroid exposures to children of 5 to 35 rad (based on Windscale and Garner, respectively) *(41)* in Roswell, New Mexico, and 7 to 43 rad in Albany, New York, on April 25, 1953; 2 to 14 rad in Boston on April 6, 1953; 3 to 18 rad in Salt Lake City on May 7, 1952; and 2 to 12 rad in the same city on March 24, 1953. There is no way of knowing the number of hot-spot fallout contaminations that might have taken place throughout the United States since testing began.

Inadequate monitoring has been noted, particularly in Alaska, where the Eskimos have received high doses of cesium-137 and strontium-90 through the Arctic food chain *(42)*. Lichens, which secure their nourishment from the air, retain virtually 100 percent of the radioactive particles that fall into them. They are consumed, particularly in the winter, by the caribou, the animal that is the basic food in the Arctic.

There was a 50-percent increase in the average adult whole-body burden among the Eskimos of inland Alaska between 1962 and 1963 *(43)*. Also, by November 1963, strontium-90 levels across the United States had more than doubled since 1961 when samples were last taken of the Alaskan Eskimos. It is probable that strontium-90 levels had more than doubled in the Arctic as well. Although levels of cesium-137 and strontium-90 had, at last count, only reached two-thirds and one-quarter, respectively, of the levels set forth by the Federal Radiation Council, it is evident that concentrations have been increasing rapidly *(43)*. It has also been pointed out that the testing of Eskimos for cesium-137 in 1962 and 1963 was carried out during the summer months, when, according to a recent Finnish study of Laplanders who have the same problem as the Alaskan Eskimos, the cesium-137 body burden would have been at its lowest point *(43)*. The year-round average level is almost twice that of the summer months.

Tests for strontium-90 that were made on a few Alaskans showed that the new bone being formed had about four times the average United States concentration *(44)*. Swedish Lapps measured for cesium-137 had concentrations 30 to 40 times as high as the average of the control group from southern Sweden *(44)*.

Countermeasures

If atmospheric testing should be resumed, it would be possible to prevent or control the radioactive contamination of the atmosphere at the source, but only in the case of testing by the United States. Some control of our testing is feasible by providing for high fusion to fission ratios, high-altitude shots, subsurface and nonventing shots, the proper jacketing of bombs, and careful meteorological planning. (Prevention is also possible, of course, by the curtailment of testing.) The only protection that the United States has from fallout contamination from testing by Russia, France, Great Britain, and possibly by other countries, is in the form of countermeasures. These might include putting cows on stored winter feed so that milk will not be contaminated; holding polluted milk until the iodine-131 has decayed; placing all very young children, lactating mothers, and pregnant women on evaporated milk or powdered dry skim milk for the duration of the high levels; adding stable iodine to the diet; and removing strontium-90 from milk. However, such actions might require some form of compensation to farmers and might have highly political overtones. The Federal Radiation Council concluded in September 1962 that "iodine-131 exposures at the levels existing then involve health risks so slight that countermeasures applied to the food industries might have an adverse, rather than a favorable effect on public well-being" *(21)*.

The Federal Radiation Council has recommended three ranges of action to be taken for transient daily rates of radioactivity intake by "suitable samples of exposed population groups" (Table 11) *(28)*.

Table 11. Graded scales of action.

Ranges of transient rates of daily intake	Graded scale of action
Range 1	Periodic confirmatory surveillance as necessary
Range 2	Quantitative surveillance and routine control
Range 3	Evaluation and application of additional control measures as necessary

Table 12. Ranges of transient rates of intake (picocuries per day) for use in graded scales of action as in Table 11.

Radionuclides	Range 1	Range 2	Range 3
Radium-226	0–2	2–20	20–200
Iodine-131*	0–10	10–100	100–1,000
Strontium-90	0–20	20–200	200–2,000
Strontium-89	0–200	200–2,000	2,000–20,000

* In the case of iodine-131, the suitable sample would include only small children. For adults, the RPG for the thyroid would not be exceeded by rates of intake higher by a factor of 10 than those applicable to small chlidren.

The Federal Radiation Council has also identified as guides the amounts to be allowed in each of these ranges for various important radionuclides and states that all values should be averaged over a 1-year period (Table 12) (28).

The upper figures in range 2, based on the Radiation Protection Guides' annual limit (or lower, in the case of radioactive strontium), is the point at which the Council suggests that authorities begin to examine the possibility of taking countermeasures. The Council states that "appropriate, positive control measures" should be instituted only if intakes within range 3 continue for "a sufficient period of time," indicating that the *annual* average intake would exceed the upper limit of range 2.

The initial countermeasures taken in the United States were the first two mentioned above, used in Salt Lake City in August 1963 by the City Health Department in cooperation with the State Department of Health. Following increased nuclear testing in mid-July—both atmospheric and underground tests in Nevada—the radioactive iodine content of processed milk in Salt Lake City climbed to 2050 picocuries per quart on July 25 (7). A concentration of 9000 picocuries per quart was measured in the milk from one herd in Snyderville, Utah, on July 20 (7).

Since very few measurements had been made on milk after the Nevada nuclear weapons tests through mid-July, it was necessary to estimate the maximum level of iodine-131 in milk at a given location after the arrival of fallout. This was done by indirect methods; for example, by exponential time extrapolation of a milk measurement made 3 weeks after the arrival of the fallout back to 4 days after deposition, or by calculations based on the measurement of external gamma levels following arrival of the fallout (7). The assumption that fallout occurred 4 days after deposition is consistent with the limited number of iodine-131 measurements made at Alamo and Caliente, Nevada, following the July 14 "Small Boy" test. Thus, H. A. Knapp (formerly of the Fallout Studies Branch, Division of Biology and Medicine, U.S. Atomic Energy Commission) estimated fallout from the measurements of milk that were made by R. C. Pendleton (University of Utah) and G. S. Winn (chief, Industrial Hygiene Section, Utah Department of Health) at a few localities in the fallout pattern of the "Small Boy" shot in northeastern Utah (7). By three different methods of reasoning, Knapp concluded that iodine-131 levels in milk from limited areas in the vicinity of Altonah in northeastern Utah reached 100,000 picocuries per liter for a day or so on or about July 19, 1962. With less assurance, the evidence suggests that milk levels in the vicinity of Altonah reached 200,000 picocuries per liter, and it is not inconsistent with the highest estimates made from the data that the levels could have been as high as 380,000 picocuries per liter in a limited area near Fruitland, Utah (7, 45).

In evaluating the 1962 summer fallout in the Altonah area, Pendleton and his colleagues showed that at one station near Altonah the total intake of infants drinking 1 liter of milk per day was 800,000 picocuries (46). Although derived by a different method, this result is consistent with the estimate made by Knapp that the initial level of iodine-131 in milk was 100,000 picocuries per liter.

Since the countermeasures taken in six Utah counties in August 1962 were the first attempted anywhere, there was no precedent to follow and many difficulties slowed progress. Data indicate that the peak of radioactivity had passed when the controls were first applied, although the total radiation dose to the population from iodine-131 was undoubtedly lower than it would have been without the controls (47). Before the preventive actions went into effect, the children of Salt Lake City had been exposed to more than one-half of the levels set by the Radiation Protection Guides. Adding to this their exposure from the U.S.S.R. tests during the previous fall, they had received about 37,040 picocuries of iodine-131 per liter of milk from September 1961 to August 1962, or slightly more than the levels of the Radiation Protection Guides (48). Children in the outlying areas, such as in the vicinity of Altonah, had, however, received many times the Guides' level for the year.

The position of the Federal Radiation Council, which is the advisory body to the President on radiation matters, has been expressed in a number of ways. In its Report No. 4 of May 1963 (21), the Council stated:

Based on the advice of a special panel convened by the Council in the summer of 1962, it was concluded that radiation doses to the thyroid many times higher than those provided in FRC Report No. 2 would not result in a detectable increase in diseases such as thyroid cancer. . . . It is similarly concluded in this report that iodine-131 doses from weapons testing conducted through 1962 have not caused an undue risk to health. . . . The health risks from radioactivity in foods, now and over the next several years, are too small to justify countermeasures to limit intake of radionuclides by diet modifications or altering the normal distribution and use of food, particularly milk and dairy products.

However, at hearings on radiation hazards held in June 1963, Anthony J. Celebrezze, former Secretary of the Department of Health, Education, and Welfare, and, as such, chairman of the Federation Radiation Council (49), said that:

The council fully recognizes that fallout from nuclear tests or reactor accidents may result in local situations where protective actions would be desirable. . . . The Council has recognized also the need for providing guidance applicable to determining when such localized fallout levels might require intervention by appropriate authorities. . . . In developing such guidance for Federal and State officials, the following factors must be considered:

(1) Actions requiring interference with normal production, processing, and distribution of foods should be considered at higher dose levels than those established for use in limiting the release of radioactive material to the environment by nuclear industry. Thus, the radiation protection guides developed for normal peace-time operations cannot be used as the sole criterion for this purpose.

(2) Actions should be based on anticipated cumulative radiation doses over a period of time, such as a year, after examination of all important factors. The possible adverse health effects of the protective action must be examined very carefully.

(3) The function of the proposed guides and the way they should be used in making public health decisions must be very clear and not subject to multiple interpretations.

Global Implications

One of the most significant aspects of radioactive pollution is the global nature of its hazards. The long-lived radioisotopes, such as carbon-14, strontium-90, and cesium-137, which remain in the stratosphere and encircle the earth for many years, gradually deposit on all the countries over which they pass, affecting the populations of whole continents both externally and internally through the food chain. One nation's action of injecting radioactive pollutants into the atmosphere may affect another.

It is impossible to determine the total world production of radioactive pollutants. However, certain figures are available that help give some perspective on the problem.

Table 13 estimates the yearly radiation dose to specific organs and tissues in the rainfall areas of the United States from all nuclear weapons tests that are known to have been conducted by all countries from the start of testing through 1962. These doses, calculated for 70 years, are compared with the dose of natural background radiation that can be anticipated over a 70-year period. Based on these figures, radiation from testing seems, so far, to be negligible.

However, there are scientists who protest the use of national averages and who believe that, by spreading the data over a 70-year period, demographic dose data are neglected (50). They maintain, for example, that, while it was believed in 1958 that fallout from all previous tests amounted to only a few percent of background radiation, the fallout around Chicago and New York at the same time ran 70 percent of background for many months. Moreover, they affirm that doses to organs on top of total-body irradiation add to the significance of these demographic data.

Table 14 compares the dose commitment of radiation from natural sources, from medical and occupational sources, and from fallout to specific tissues and organs for the period 1954–1961. Dose commitments are also projected for future testing.

Table 13. Estimated radiation doses in the "wet" areas of the United States from all nuclear weapons testing conducted through 1962 (doses expressed in millirem) (21).

Tissue or organ	From tests conducted through 1961*	From tests conducted in 1962	From all tests conducted through 1962	From natural background
Whole body and reproductive cells				
1 year	10–25	24		
30 years	60–130	47	110†	3000
70 years	70–150	56	130†	7000
Bone				
1 year	30–80	83		
70 years	400–900	275	465‡§	9100
Bone marrow				
1 year	20–40	44		
70 years	150–350	130	215‡§	7000

* Taken from Table 1, Federal Radiation Council Report No. 3. Based on surveillance measurements made in 1962, the actual exposures are expected to correspond to the low end of the reported range. Actual exposures to bone and bone marrow are now expected to be even lower than the reported range. † The whole body dose is based on the average person receiving the highest exposure assuming that the person was born prior to the beginning of testing. Current estimates indicate that from tests conducted through 1961, the whole-body and reproductive cell doses for 30 and 70 years will be 63 and 74 millirem, respectively.   ‡ The bone and bone marrow doses are calculated for the average person born in 1963 since it is believed that this person might receive the highest bone dose of any age group.   § Doses in previous columns are not additive.

Table 14 indicates that the contribution of fallout to the dose rate, in relation to that from natural sources, for the period 1954–1961, is estimated to be only 11 percent for the gonads, 23 percent for bone, and 15 percent for bone marrow. Estimates for future tests per year of testing are 23 percent, 43 percent, and 28 percent, respectively. Although the percentages are small, it must nonetheless be recognized that large numbers of people throughout the world have been involved in the hazards of radioactive pollution

Table 14. Comparison of risk (dose commitment to all generations) (3). Figures in parentheses indicate contribution relative to natural sources.

Tests 1954–1961, dose commitment (mrem)			Future tests, dose commitment per year of testing (mrem)		
Gonads	Cells lining bone surfaces	Bone marrow	Gonads	Cells lining bone surfaces	Bone marrow
Natural sources					
1000 (1.00)	1040 (1.00)	1000 (1.00)	125 (1.00)	130 (1.00)	125 (1.00)
Medical and occupational					
300 (0.30)	?	400–800 (0.4–0.8)	37 (0.30)	?	50–100 (0.4–0.8)
Fallout from all but carbon-14					
41 (0.04)	128 (0.12)	84 (0.08)	7 (0.06)	20 (0.15)	13 (0.10)
Fallout from carbon-14					
70 (0.07)	116 (0.11)	70 (0.07)	22 (0.18)	37 (0.28)	22 (0.18)
Total fallout					
111 (0.11)	244 (0.23)	154 (0.15)	29 (0.23)	57 (0.43)	35 (0.28)

of the atmosphere and that many have received doses that ran far higher than the averages.

Man's knowledge of radiation and its effects is recent and incomplete. The struggle to learn more about its technical aspects—its involvement in the food chain and its effect on basic life processes—is complicated by extraordinary military, political, and economic considerations. Although the technical analysis of the extent of the risk is a highly involved and demanding scientific task, the judgment as to the acceptability of the risk involved in any particular course of action is properly the concern of those who must take that risk: in this instance, all of mankind.

References

1. Jammet, H. P., "Radioactive pollution of the atmosphere," in *Air Pollution*, WHO Monograph No. 46, pp. 381–432 (World Health Organization, Geneva, 1961).
2. Eisenbud, M., "Sources of radioactive pollution," in *Air Pollution*, A. C. Stern, Ed., vol. 2, pp. 153–174 (Academic Press, New York, 1962).

3. United Nations, General Assembly, *Report of the United Nations Scientific Committee on the Effects of Atomic Radiation,* Seventeenth Session, Supplement No. 16 (A/5216) (United Nations, New York, 1962).

4. Smets, H. B., "A review of nuclear reactor incidents," in *Reactor Safety and Hazards Evaluation Techniques,* vol. 1, Proceedings of a Symposium, pp. 89–110 (Vienna, 1962).

5. Lewis, W. B., *The Accident to the NRX Reactor on December 12, 1952,* AECL 232 (Atomic Energy of Canada Limited, Chalk River, Ontario, 1953); Neal, J., "Summary of air cleaning activities at Chalk River," in *Sixth AEC Air Cleaning Conference,* July 7–9, 1959, TID 7593, pp. 236–237 (1960).

6. Horan, J. R., and W. P. Gammill, "The health physics aspects of the SL-1 accident," *Health Phys.,* **9,** 177–186 (1963).

7. Knapp, H. A., *Iodine 131 in Fresh Milk and Human Thyroids Following a Single Deposition of Nuclear Test Fallout,* TID 19266 (U.S. Atomic Energy Commission, Washington, D.C., 1963).

8. Western, F., in *Fallout, Radiation Standards, and Countermeasures,* hearings before the Subcommittee on Research, Development, and Radiation of the Joint Committee on Atomic Energy, Congress of the United States, June 3, 4, and 6, part 1, pp. 228–238 (Government Printing Office, Washington, D.C., 1963).

9. United Kingdom Medical Research Council, *The Hazards to Man of Nuclear and Allied Radiation. A Second Report to the Medical Research Council, 1960,* Command Paper CMND 1225, Parliamentary Session 1960–61 (Her Majesty's Stationery Office, London, 1961).

10. Morse, J. G., "Energy for remote areas," *Science,* **139,** 1175–1180 (1963).

11. Davis, H. L., "Radionuclide power for space," part 1, *Nucleonics,* **21,** 61–65 (1963).

12. Daly, R., "Lost: somewhere in space, two pounds of plutonium 238," *Nuclear Inform.,* pp. 12–13 (May 1964).

13. Harvey, D. G., "Radionuclide power for space," part 2, *Nucleonics,* **21,** 56–59 (1963).

14. U.S. Atomic Energy Commission, *Nuclear Reactors Built, Being Built and Planned in the United States as of June 30, 1963,* TID 8200 (Office of Technical Services, Washington, D.C., 1963).

15. U.S. Atomic Energy Commission, *Major Activities in the Atomic Energy Programs, January–December, 1962* (Goverment Printing Office, Washington, D.C., 1963).

16. Dunham, C. L., Division of Biology and Medicine, U.S. Atomic Energy Commission, personal communication, 1963.

17. Martell, E., "Atmospheric aspects of strontium-90 fallout," *Science,* **129,** 1197–1206 (1959).

18. Machta, L., "Worldwide fallout since 1959—meteorological aspects," in *Radiation Standards, Including Fallout,* hearings before the Subcommittee on Research, Development, and Radiation of the Joint Committee on Atomic Energy, Congress of the United States, June 4, 5, 6, and 7, part 1, pp. 54–71 (Government Printing Office, Washington, D. C., 1962).

19. Staley, D. O., "Atmospheric circulation from fission-product radioactivity in surface air," *Science,* **140,** 667–670 (1963).

20. U.S. Weather Bureau, Atmospheric Radioactivity Research Project, "An-

nounced nuclear detonations 1945–1962," in *U.S. Atomic Energy Commission Health and Safety Laboratory Fallout Program Quarterly Summary Report, September 1, 1963–December 1, 1963,* HASL-142, pp. 218–242 (New York, 1964).

21. Federal Radiation Council, *Estimates and Evaluation of Fallout in the United States from Nuclear Weapons Testing Conducted Through 1962,* Report No. 4 (Government Printing Office, Washington, D.C., 1963).

22. Machta, L., and R. J. List, "Analysis of stratospheric strontium 90 measurements," in *Fallout from Nuclear Weapons Tests,* hearings before the Special Subcommittee on Radiation of the Joint Committee on Atomic Energy, Congress of the United States, May 5, 6, 7, and 8, vol. 1, pp. 741–762 (Government Printing Office, Washington, D.C., 1959).

23. U.S. Atomic Energy Commission, *Major Activities in the Atomic Energy Programs, January–December, 1962* (Government Printing Office, Washington, D.C., 1963).

24. Luning, K. G., H. Frolen, A. Nelson, and C. Ronnback, "Genetic effects of strontium 90 injected into male mice," *Nature,* **197,** 304–305 (1963).

25. Fergusson, G. J., "Upper tropospheric carbon 14 levels during spring 1962," *J. Geophys. Res.,* **68,** 3933–3941 (1963).

26. Fergusson, G. J., Institute of Geophysics, University of California, Los Angeles, personal communication, 1964.

27. Langham, W. H., and E. C. Anderson, "Radiation exposure to people from nuclear weapon tests through 1961," in *Radiation Standards, Including Fallout,* hearings before the Subcommittee on Research, Development, and Radiation of the Joint Committee on Atomic Energy, Congress of the United States, June 4, 5, 6, and 7, part 1, pp. 160–165 (Government Printing Office, Washington, D.C., 1962).

28. Federal Radiation Council, *Background Material for the Development of Radiation Protection Standards,* Report No. 2 (Government Printing Office, Washington, D.C., 1961).

29. Newell, R. R., U.S. Naval Radiological Defense Laboratory, Hunter's Point, San Francisco, personal communication, 1963.

30. Federal Radiation Council, *Background Material for the Development of Radiation Protection Standards,* Report Nos. 1 and 2 (Government Printing Office, Washington, D.C., 1960 and 1961).

31. Schubert, J., and R. E. Lapp, "Global radiation limits," *Bull. Atomic Scientists,* **14,** 23–26 (1958).

32. U.S. Atomic Energy Commission, *Atomic Tests in Nevada* (Government Printing Office, Washington, D.C., 1957).

33. U.S. Public Health Service, *Radiological Health Data,* **4,** 347–358 (1963).

34. ———, *ibid.,* pp. 285–290.

35. ———, *ibid.,* **5,** 231–239 (1964).

36. Greater St. Louis Citizens' Committee for Nuclear Information, "Strontium 90 fallout," *Nuclear Inform.,* pp. 1–2 (March–April 1963).

37. Stebbins, A. K., and R. P. Minx, "The high altitude sampling program," in *Radiation Standards, Including Fallout,* hearings before the Subcommittee on Research, Development, and Radiation of the Joint Committee on Atomic Energy, Congress of the United States, June 4, 5, 6, and 7, part 2, pp. 649–747 (Government Printing Office, Washington, D.C., 1962).

38. Greater St. Louis Citizens' Committee for Nuclear Information—Technical Division, "Local fallout: hazard from Nevada tests," *Nuclear Inform.*, pp. 1–12 (August 1963).

39. Martell, E. A., "Iodine-131 fallout from underground tests," *Science,* **143**, 126–129 (1964).

40. Lapp, R. E., "Nevada test fallout and radioiodine in milk," *ibid.*, **137**, 756–758 (1962).

41. The conclusions were consistent with those of H. A. Knapp (7), which were based on data from actual tests.

42. Bartlett, E. L., "Danger in the Arctic as radioactivity mounts," in *Fallout, Radiation, and Countermeasures,* hearings before the Subcommittee on Research, Development, and Radiation of the Joint Committee on Atomic Energy, Congress of the United States, June 3, 4, and 6, part 1, pp. 260–268 (Government Printing Office, Washington, D.C., 1963).

43. ———, "Senator Bartlett comments," *Nuclear Inform.*, p. 17 (November 1963).

44. Pruitt, W. O., Jr., "A new caribou problem," in *Fallout, Radiation, and Countermeasures,* hearings before the Subcommittee on Research, Development, and Radiation of the Joint Committee on Atomic Energy, Congress of the United States, June 3, 4, and 6, part 1, pp. 269–275 (Government Printing Office, Washington, D.C., 1963).

45. Knapp, H. A., "Iodine 131 in fresh milk and human thyroids following a single deposition of nuclear test fallout," *Nature,* **202**, 534–537 (1964).

46. Pendleton, R. C., R. D. Lloyd, and C. W. Mays, "Iodine-131 in Utah during July and August 1962," *Science,* **141**, 640–642 (1963).

47. Salt Lake City Department of Health and the Utah State Department of Health, *Utah's Experience with Radioactive Milk* (October 1, 1962).

48. U.S. Public Health Service, *Radiological Health Data,* **3**, 482–490 (1962).

49. Celebrezze, A. J., testimony, in *Fallout, Radiation, and Countermeasures,* hearings before the Subcommittee on Research, Development, and Radiation of the Joint Committee on Atomic Energy, Congress of the United States, June 3, 4, and 6, part 1, pp. 340–353 (Government Printing Office, Washington, D.C., 1963).

50. Lapp, R. E., Quadri-Science, Inc., Washington, D.C., personal communication, 1963.

CHAPTER 3

Metropolitan Organization for Air Conservation

Any program for air conservation in the United States, if it would be realistic, must take into consideration three factors of American life: (i) the growth of population and the rapid economic development in large metropolitan areas; (ii) the large number of independent government jurisdictions within these areas; and (iii) the flow of air across jurisdictional lines.

The first has been going on since 1790: Every census since then has shown a larger percentage of the nation's population living in metropolitan areas. The second is a reflection of the wide gap that exists between our inherited civic and political traditions and the realities of today. And the third is a physical reality.

If air flowed as water does, the task of air conservation in a metropolitan area would be greatly simplified. But air observes its own rules. Its flow is not channeled, and the origin of airborne waste is often difficult to trace. At times, when weather conditions are right, it may lie like a fetid blanket atop a city, holding within it the wastes of modern transportation and industry. But the most troublesome characteristic of an air mass over a city is its freedom to flow in any direction, with a cavalier disregard for the boundaries that separate governmental jurisdictions.

The Problem: Fractionation

Certain metropolitan areas are so structured that they have been able to unify their governments. Miami and Nashville, for ex-

195

ample, each consist of a metropolitan area contained within a single county. In each of these areas a substantial consolidation between the county government and the various municipal governments has created a single government capable of dealing in some unified way with the air pollution problems of the whole metropolis. Although neither Miami nor Nashville have had conspicuous success as yet in developing air pollution programs, they have a much more effective framework within which to develop them. The Bay Area in California is a metropolitan region that contains many counties and municipalities, each claiming autonomy in many matters; but they are all in one state. As a result, when sufficient consensus developed for an effective air pollution program, there was a center of power in Sacramento that could and did arrange for the establishment of a single air pollution control district for the entire area, with adequate coverage, power, and money to attract the necessary staff and to work out and impose the necessary program of controls.

But there are many large metropolitan centers where there is no consolidation, as in Miami and Nashville, or where the continuous urban area extends across the boundaries of two or even three states, precluding the exercise of any one sovereignty (short of the federal government) over the area's common problems. The metropolitan area centering on Chicago, for example, covers a large number of independent municipalities, mostly in one state but partly in another. The metropolis centering on Washington, D.C., includes areas governed by Maryland, Virginia, and the federal government. Because of the greater powers of county governments in southern states, however, the number of jurisdictions is not as great in the Washington area as it is in northern cities of comparable size. The continuous urban area centering on Philadelphia, for example, covers 11 counties in parts of three states and contains no less than 377 autonomous municipalities, exclusive of school districts and other special jurisdictions. The metropolitan area around New York City has been responsibly defined as including 551 municipalities in 22 counties in parts of three states.

However, it is not only the numbers of governments that impede the solution of metropolis-wide problems such as air pollution. In large, interstate metropolitan areas, at least four levels of government could engage in efforts to conserve air quality—the local municipalities, the counties, the states, and the federal government. In addition, even governments at the same level often have widely differing powers. In the Pennsylvania section of Philadelphia, for example, there are first- and third-class cities, boroughs, and first- and second-class townships, each with different powers. Similar differences exist among the boroughs, townships, and second- and third-class cities in the New Jersey section of this metropolis. And in the Delaware section, still further differences exist, inasmuch as, unlike the other two states, large parts of Delaware are unincorporated, and in these areas the county alone is responsible for providing government services below the state level (1).

The current trends in these complex metropolitan areas intensify the problems of air conservation. These areas are growing very rapidly in population, in industry and commerce, and in the number of motor vehicles. Their parts—the central city and the suburban communities—are becoming more and more specialized, as the younger, better educated families move outward, taking centers of retail trade and even industry with them, and leaving behind the main offices of banks, the major professions serving business, the larger cultural institutions, the bulk handling of raw materials, and ghetto-like concentrations of the underprivileged. This specialization has made the various parts of the metropolis more dependent on one another as each has become less and less self-sufficient economically. At the same time, by accentuating the differences in social status and income, this specialization has increased the difficulties of working out cooperative procedures among the hundreds of governments involved.

If all parts of the metropolis had the same kinds of people, resources, and aspirations, or even the same mixture of these characteristics, the many-segmented system of government might be able to collaborate more readily. But the fact is that some parts of the metropolis have the factories that pay large taxes; others have the houses that need revenue for schools and other services. Some parts have residents of high income and capacity for civic leadership; other parts have social degradation that cries out for citizen concern. Some parts have large lots, three cars in every garage, acres of greenery, and other amenities; other parts are in the grip of developers who crowd the maximum possible density of apartment houses on every square inch of available land. Some parts are the haves, some are the have-nots. The result is not only marked differences in bargaining power, but also in the competence of the bargainers. It is not surprising that many of these segmented sections refuse to come to the bargaining table, even when the issue is such a pervasive one as the conservation of the air that is common to all of them.

What are some of the practical consequences? As differences breed distrust and disagreement between city and suburbs, between towns in one state and those in another, the wind continues to blow an increasing burden of pollutants across the many governmental boundaries. For example, the air pollution control program of Philadelphia has made great headway, but its residents can nevertheless be seriously affected by pollution from nearby industrial communities beyond the city limits that have little or no air pollution control. Householders in lower Bucks County, Pennsylvania, find that after a rainy night the east wind from New Jersey has brought sulfur compounds from a plant across the Delaware River and that these compounds have reacted chemically with the paint on their homes and have caused widespread discoloration. The citizens do not have any political instrument available for eliminating the offending pollutants other than a roundabout appeal through federal officials who, until recently, had no enforcement powers. Similarly the smoke from New Jersey trash fires often enshrouds Manhattan skyscrapers. The Interstate Sanitation Commission, an agency created by New York and New Jersey some years ago to work primarily on sewage problems, has recently begun to take an interest in air pollution, but it will be some time before its powers, funds, and public support are equal to the problems presented by pollution crossing state lines in that crowded metropolitan area.

Would private litigation solve the problem? Why don't the Bucks County householders seek an injunction against the plant in New Jersey? First, the householders are confronted with the usual impediments to litigation in this field—the difficulty of proving that the damage to the plaintiff's property was caused by the defendant and not by someone else, and the expense and trouble involved, whether one householder sues by himself, or whether he tries to organize his neighbors to bring a class suit, or whether the municipality sues on behalf of its residents. Second, when the defendant is in another state there are special difficulties. Where did the right of action arise—in New Jersey, where the plaintiff claims the pollutants were emitted, or in Pennsylvania, where the damage occurred? Which laws apply—those of New Jersey or those of Pennsylvania? Which courts have jurisdiction? Probably not those of Pennsylvania, which can hardly impose their decision on a company located in New Jersey. A proceeding in the New Jersey courts is hardly calculated to suit the convenience or pocketbook of the plaintiff. And if he resorts to the federal courts, should he sue in the federal court in Pennsylvania or in the federal court in New Jersey?

It may be unfortunate, but it is nevertheless true, that the answers to some of these questions are by no means clear. In short, the path of the plaintiff in our hypothetical case is strewn with pitfalls, and escaping them would require competent counsel in both states and a correspondingly long purse. The difficulty of finding the proper defendants, of getting the initial papers in the suit properly served on them, and then of proving that they are indeed the ones who caused the damage would be complex indeed if litigation were to be undertaken, for example, by the Manhattan skyscrapers against the undoubtedly elusive participants in the burning of trash in New Jersey. Experience indicates that private litigation is subsequently less fruitful than political action, which can produce legislation to impose regulations that can be enforced administratively. Yet the victims of pollution in one state cannot participate directly in this political process against the emitters in another.

Even getting the facts about the metropolitan air cover is difficult. Philadelphia operates about a dozen monitoring stations, but these are almost all located within the city limits, which encompasses an area of about 125 square miles, whereas the 11-county metropolitan area covers about 4500 square miles. Using this system to analyze the air over the metropolis is like trying to understand a novel by reading 20 pages in the middle of the book. If Philadelphia were to establish a comprehensive system of monitoring stations throughout the metropolitan area, it could proceed in either of two ways: surreptitiously, or with the cooperation of the municipalities involved. However, the latter might or might not believe that this would be in accord with their self-interest. Some private businesses monitor outside city limits, but they are naturally not disposed to communicate their findings to anyone, least of all to any government agency. The monitoring being done under academic auspices and that being performed by the state government in the suburban area that lies within Pennsylvania, although available to the city government, are so far quite limited in scope.

For similar reasons, the establishment of regulations is extremely difficult in a large metropolitan region. To be effective, such regulations must be uniform throughout a wide area—not merely in the vicinity of a particular source. The many boundaries running through a large metropolitan area—city limits, county, and even state lines—require not merely parallel action, but uniform action, if such regulations are to be effective. Similarly, other techniques that have been proposed to foster air conservation must be uniformly applied. Zoning controls in one jurisdiction are meaningless if a nearby jurisdiction, perhaps with quite different economic development or income level, has other aims for its zoning policies. In such metropolitan areas as those centering on New York City or Philadelphia, the power to determine zoning policy is still firmly imbedded at the local level. In view of the present division of power among the levels of government and in view of present attitudes (or, perhaps it would be more accurate to say, lack of attitude) of the great majority of the residents of such areas, no county, state, interstate, or federal body has power to direct zoning changes. Some specialized agencies may have certain powers of veto; other agencies may have power of condemnation, and may have or can attract the public or private funds that are needed to carry out desired types of development. However, under present conditions, any control on the use of land is imposed on the vast majority of private developments at the local level.

Other techniques that are often mentioned as a means of controlling air pollution are based on the government's power to tax (see Chapter 6). It is suggested that deterrent taxes, graduated according to the quantities or characteristics of the undesirable material emitted, be imposed on those responsible for the pollution. Similarly it is proposed that tolls be imposed on motorists to encourage them to leave their cars at home and travel by public transportation, and thus relieve the atmosphere of the unconsumed hydrocarbons and the nitrogen oxides that would have resulted from their driving.

If such fiscal devices could be made to work at the federal level, they would not be impeded by the fractionation of metropolitan areas. Federal taxation in the form of the tariff has been used for years, not to raise federal revenues, but to help certain industries. The most powerful tool of all, the federal income tax, has been used to encourage private contributions to charity and education, to foster exploration for new oil reserves, and to promote employee pension plans.

In the field of air pollution, proposals have been made to permit accelerated amortization, for income tax purposes, of the cost of installing pollution control equipment. Highway tolls to encourage air conservation, on the other hand, would be quite unprecedented at the federal level. Undoubtedly state governments do have the power to impose highway tolls for such a purpose, or they could authorize the agencies now gathering such tolls for purely fiscal reasons to continue such collections for air conservation purposes after the fiscal obligations had been discharged. But would it help the situation appreciably in an interstate metropolitan area if one state had such a policy and the others did not? Does a sufficiently large percentage of the traffic in a metropolitan area move along roads that can be controlled for toll-collecting purposes? And would the tolls have the desired result, in view of the very large number, undoubtedly a considerable majority, of motorists who, because of the sprawl of metropolitan development, would want to travel between places that are not now and may never be economically served by public transportation?

In short, the complex metropolitan areas are attracting an ever-increasing number of those who will contribute to air pollution as well as those who will suffer from its effects. However, because of the geographical incongruence between government structure on one hand and the location of the airshed on the other, metropolitan areas are seriously hampered in imposing either the traditional or the newer types of measures to promote air conservation.

In other parts of the world the metropolitan phenomena—concentration of population in large urban areas, growing intensity of air pollution in those areas, and incongruence between inherited local

government structures and modern needs—are surprisingly similar
to those observed in the United States. Constitutional differences,
however, sometimes offer greater opportunities for reform. In England, for example, metropolitan London was organized under the
London County Council some 75 years ago, and recently, after
further growth had brought about the need for reform, a new
metropolitan government for the expanded urban area was established. As in this country, there were many differences of opinion
and many vested interests were affected. But Parliament is omnip-
otent, and when conflicting views had been brought into reasonable
compromise within the dominant political party, the reform was
enacted.

Some Solutions

In this country the constitutional position is more complex, especially in our interstate metropolitan areas. Congress does not have
the power to rearrange local government, and no state legislature
has the power to rearrange local government beyond the borders
of the state. Under these circumstances, a variety of methods have
been used to encourage metropolitan cooperation. The area without
many jurisdictional problems has an easier time of it, of course, but
some of the following methods have been used with some success
(2).

Informal Cooperation and Parallel Action

The oldest and easiest methods by which two or more governments can pursue a common policy are informal cooperation or
parallel action. These methods can involve a large number of
municipalities where the issue is free from controversy, where such
cooperation or joint action involves no extra cost, and where the
independence of the governments is in no way impaired.

For example, in the area centering on Philadelphia, some 150
municipalities in Pennsylvania and New Jersey have cooperated in-
formally on a network for the apprehension of fugitives from justice.
This same kind of cooperative agreement could be used for air
pollution control.

If a central city, for example, adopted suitable regulations, their effectiveness would be considerably strengthened if the suburban municipalities adopted the same regulations, even though there were no binding agreement to do so and even though no higher level of government or special governmental agency assumed this responsibility.

Contracts

Such informal arrangements quite naturally lead to other legally binding agreements—the service contract, where one government agrees to buy a service from another at an agreed price; the executive agreement, where two governments (for example, two states) enter into a contract binding each to a particular course of action; or the formal compact, which is usually an elaborate contract between two or more governments, arranging comprehensively for a fully worked out course of action to be followed by the parties. (In the case of a compact between two or more states, the U.S. Constitution requires congressional approval.) Under such contracts the obligations assumed and the costs incurred, often for considerable periods of time, limit the freedom of action of the parties. However, for simpler types of contracts, the issues are usually ones that involve little controversy and arise out of grim necessity. In the metropolitan area centering on Philadelphia, there are at least a thousand such contracts, with sewage the most common subject. In the Los Angeles area, the county has even contracted with some municipalities to render all services required. Under more formal compacts, for example, three suburban counties entered into a compact with Philadelphia to subsidize commuter railroads and to improve commuter service.

Such contracts could assist materially in the abatement of air pollution in metropolitan areas. A small municipality with limited resources could purchase inspection or monitoring services from a larger municipality under a service contract, and in the simpler metropolitan areas a compact among several municipalities might bind each of them to a common policy for air conservation. And if an interstate agency to deal with air pollution were to be created in a large metropolitan area, with comprehensive powers to establish standards and exercise controls, the framework for such an agency would in all probability be provided by an interstate compact.

Transfer of Functions

Parallel action for entering into contracts is comparatively easy; the autonomy of the participating governments remains unchanged, except for the obligations and costs voluntarily assumed. Other methods of metropolitan organization, however, are more drastic in that they affect the actual structure or jurisdiction of the governments involved. Of these methods, the simplest is the transfer of functions. In many cases a government is too small, either in geographic coverage or in economic resources, or both, to perform satisfactorily certain functions—for example, the disposal of sewage or the preparation of comprehensive plans for development. By legislative action, these functions may be transferred to a larger unit of government (for example, the county), which, because of its greater size and more varied economic resources, is better able to perform them. In some parts of the country, the transfer of functions may make the county look increasingly like a metropolitan government. Although this technique can be helpful in many situations, in a multicounty or interstate metropolitan area, transfer to a higher level would reduce the number of governments performing a function, but it would not produce the necessary uniformity since there would still be no one government covering the whole metropolis with power to deal with air pollution.

Extraterritorial Jurisdiction

Another such method is to grant extraterritorial jurisdiction. In some parts of the country this procedure permits a central city of a metropolitan area to exercise limited powers outside its boundaries. For example, a city may own parks or operate sewage disposal works beyond the city limits. It seems doubtful that such power would ever be given to control sources of pollution outside the city, but by an appropriate grant of extraterritorial jurisdiction a city might be given the valuable right of establishing air monitoring stations in areas outside its customary jurisdiction.

Annexation

A still more drastic procedure permits a city to annex, and thereby make some adjacent suburban area part of its own territory. Many cities have grown in this way, and have thereby extended their boundaries to coincide more nearly with the expanding area of urbanization around them. However, in recent years the suburban areas have been more and more successful in resisting such annexation. A notable exception was the action of the Tennessee Legislature in 1955, when it gave Nashville the power to annex adjoining territory without the consent of its residents. This annexation did much to bring about the consolidation between Nashville and Davidson County referred to earlier. Except for the fact that annexation might lead to consolidation, it is not of great current interest as a means of bringing governmental boundaries into greater congruence with airsheds.

Incorporation

Another similar process is incorporation. Under this procedure a hitherto rural area, usually governed only by a county, organizes itself into a formal municipality. While such a new municipality could be set up with important powers to cooperate with its neighbors, incorporation is more often used as a device to prevent a larger community, for example, a nearby city, from making the area a part of the city by annexation.

Consolidation

A much more fruitful method to extend boundaries is consolidation. As Dr. Martin points out (2), in the 19th century there were four major city-county consolidations—Boston, Philadelphia, New Orleans, and New York City. In the most recent example, Nashville and Davidson County have consolidated into what is, for all practical purposes, a new governmental unit. As with the transfer of functions from smaller to larger units of government, this method can have marked potential for more comprehensive air conservation programs in metropolitan areas that are within a single county; but it cannot have far-reaching consequences in the larger metropolitan areas, especially those that are interstate. No one seriously expects that the hundreds of governments involved in a metropolis such as Philadelphia or New York would consolidate into one government; while some consolidation might be helpful if it were politically feasible, this method will never bring together such a complex metropolitan area.

Voluntary Association of Officials

It is clear that the larger metropolitan areas, if they are to deal in any unified way with their problems, must devise additional governmental techniques. Yet the rapid growth, increasing specialization, and multiple segments of the larger areas make any effective collaboration extremely difficult. One novel metropolitan institution that has taken hold in eight or ten areas, including the largest in the country, is the voluntary association of officials. These associations bring together the principal personalities—usually the chief elected official of each county and municipality—so that they may become better acquainted, exchange information on metropolitan problems, and establish working committees, usually on problems that are relatively free from controversy, such as better library service or gathering data on a regional basis. These conferences have emerged in both small and large metropolitan areas. In the complex metropolitan areas centering on Washington, D.C., Philadelphia, and New York City, they give promise of providing a useful official focus for metropolitan consciousness. Such conferences cannot order anyone to do anything, but an air pollution committee set up by such a conference could undertake, with official sanction, a valuable campaign to publicize methods of control and to encourage member governments to adopt air conservation programs.

Special Districts

The voluntary association of officials can play an important advisory and hortatory role, and in a large metropolis it may be one of the few official voices in the metropolitan wilderness; but its lack of power makes it far less effective for air pollution abatement than the device that has been successfully used in several less-fractionated metropolitan areas—namely, the special district or authority. This is a unit of government that has been created to perform one or more limited functions within a defined geographical area. The Bay Area Air Pollution Control District, which is authorized to deal with air conservation problems throughout an entire metropolitan airshed, is an example of such a body. There are many other metropolitan areas where this device would also be appropriate. The fact remains, however, that it is easier for the residents of the Bay Area, who are all within one state, to go to Sacramento and secure legislation for an air pollution control district, than it would be for the residents of the three states that make up metropolitan Philadelphia, for example, to go to Harrisburg, Trenton, and Dover and obtain simultaneously and in the same form a similar agency. If this were to be done in a metropolis involving several states, it would no doubt have to be based on an interstate compact that would require congressional approval as well.

Regional Agency

This was, indeed, the basis of the Delaware River Basin Commission—an example of still another kind of intergovernmental cooperation, the regional agency. The commission was created by an interstate compact approved by the four states through which the Delaware River flows, and in this instance the federal government not only gave its concurrence but also became a party to the compact. The commission has extensive powers over the water resources of the Delaware, including power to study and control the pollution of the river. It is, however, a special-purpose agency, and has no power over such matters as air pollution, which are beyond its clearly defined charge. The commission is a heartening example of the possibilities of cooperation, even within such a highly complex area. However, it took some 30 years of extended public discussion, bickering and negotiation before the commission was established, and this fact does not give too much encouragement to the possibility of an air conservation agency, with similar powers and responsibility, being created in any less time.

Metropolitan Government

In theory, of course, the ultimate in metropolitan organization is a general-purpose government, superior in power to the counties of the metropolis, and joining under one general jurisdiction, under one "city-state," the parts of the various states that make up the larger metropolitan areas. In North America, the nearest approach to this theoretical form of government is found in Toronto, where the parliament of the Province of Ontario subjected 15 municipalities in the Toronto area to a metropolitan government with extensive powers over metropolitan affairs. The Davidson County–Nashville experience has been somewhat comparable, and Dade County, Florida, now exercises important metropolitan powers over the area centering on Miami. However, most observers would say that any such drastic rearrangement of powers and governmental structure in our interstate metropolitan areas is so unlikely that it is not even a subject for serious discussion.

State Action

Some of the difficulties that are involved in obtaining simultaneous and parallel action by several states and by Congress (as required by the Constitution) when an interstate compact is proposed have been discussed. Unilateral state action, however, can be effective when there are too many obstacles to a formal compact. The constitutional power to act is clear. And, indeed, in most metropolitan areas the outlook is more optimistic for getting something done through unilateral state action than through interstate action. But an important impediment to state action must be noted. Historically, at least, most states have been dominated by their nonmetropolitan areas. As a result, large cities have had difficulty in obtaining what they needed from their state capitals, few of which are located in large metropolitan centers. In 1960, for example, the Pennsylvania legislature enacted a statute to create air pollution boards in all parts of the state except the counties in which Philadelphia and Pittsburgh are located. Ostensibly, this was because these cities already had air pollution control programs, but the decision not to integrate them administratively into the new state system no doubt reflected the city-upstate relationship.

Federal Action

One method of dealing with metropolitan issues remains—turning the problem over to the federal government. There is little question that the federal government has the constitutional authority to concern itself with air pollution, especially in the case of interstate airsheds. Of more general application would be the federal police power, and especially its traditional concern for human health. The well-developed programs of the U.S. Public Health Service and the Food and Drug Administration attest to the traditional federal concern about toxic substances. Federal grants for the construction of sewage disposal plants have been a well-recognized method of encouraging the purification of our more important rivers. Although the federal government has, for some years, had a vigorous program of research and training in connection with the air pollution problem, pressures are mounting for further federal involvement in this field.

The Clean Air Act, approved by President Kennedy on December 17, 1963, continues major federal programs of research, especially on motor vehicle exhaust and fuels that contain sulfur. It also continues federal support of training programs; authorizes federal grants to state, regional, and municipal agencies in support of their air pollution control programs; and encourages interstate or regional agencies working on air pollution problems. But the principal innovation of the statute is its recognition of current deficiencies in controlling the pollution that is carried across state boundaries. After setting up extensive safeguards to give local officials opportunity to act, the statute authorized the U.S. Attorney General to bring suit to abate any sources of interstate pollution (see Chapter 4).

While the constitutional basis for this extension of federal power seems secure, questions may well be raised about its implications. Many citizens may believe that the control of manufacturing and similar activities should, if possible, be retained at the local level, and that federal intervention tends not only to increase costs but also to exclude local jurisdictions from determining policy. Congress has apparently been impressed, however, with the mounting evidence that, especially in interstate metropolitan areas, airborne pollution is an increasing menace to human health and that these areas have not been able to organize themselves to adequately cope with the problem.

If the residents of our larger metropolitan areas—and they are constantly increasing—prefer to obtain clean air through action by their state and local governments, they face formidable problems of organization. Many procedures have been devised for intergovernmental action, but few are readily applicable to the larger and more complex areas. Citizens who would object to the metropolis abdicating to the federal government will want to seek out like-minded citizens in all parts of the metropolitan area and join with them in studying the pollution problem and in setting up suitable machinery to control it. Ultimately the surest base for an effective program of air conservation will be a prolonged and intensive program of citizen education.

This is a familiar process to Americans. From the earliest days of our society, Americans have shown a capacity for voluntary citizen activity to tackle difficult public issues. The practice of citizen action on local issues has become so widespread that organizations such as the National Municipal League and the League of Women Voters have published how-to-do-it guides. The complex problems of an interstate metropolitan area, however, are of a different order of magnitude, and require new techniques especially suited to the region. The Regional Plan Association of the three-state region centering on New York City has shown the way by assembling a professional staff to do a planning job for a region that lacks an official regional planning agency. In the three-state region centering on Philadelphia, the citizen organization known as Penjerdel (3) has sponsored research on metropolitan problems and has carried on a varied program to arouse public interest. This program has included systematic staff contacts with more than a hundred citizen organizations in all parts of the 11-county area; popular publications and public conferences on regional issues, including air pollution; promotion of new county-wide citizen organizations; and encouragement of the Regional Conference of Elected Officials, a voluntary association of county and local officials from throughout the metropolitan area.

In this task of mobilizing citizen concern, the scientist can have an important role. He can bring his expert knowledge of the causes of pollution, the means of its dissemination, and its effects on health and property. But much more significantly, he can play his part as a concerned citizen by joining with other citizens throughout the area in which he lives to increase public understanding of the problem and to support those public officials working toward better metropolitan organization for air conservation.

References

1. It is worth noting in passing that these divisions prevail not merely in the public sector, but in the private sector as well. In the 11-county region centering on Philadelphia there are 25 autonomous community chests. One suburban county alone has 12 visiting nurse societies. A survey of the region a few years ago disclosed 4000 citizen organizations that might reasonably be expected to include in their programs some concern for regional development. In the days when reform was merely a matter of changing the government of one city, the leaders of civic life could gather periodically at lunch, exchange views about what was needed, organize city-wide movements, and make their influence felt. But if it is a question of innovation in a metropolitan setting, it is far more difficult for like-minded citizens from different parts of the metropolis to get to know one another, to come together with any frequency, and to combine their efforts, quite apart from the much greater complexity of the problems they face and the numerous and fluctuating audience of city and suburban officeholders to whom they may wish to apply their pressure. Citizen effort toward metropolitan reform is no sport for the short-winded.

2. The summary of these methods is based on a recent monograph, *Metropolis in Transition*, prepared by Dr. Roscoe C. Martin of Syracuse University for the U.S. Housing and Home Finance Agency.

3. For further material on the Penjerdel program see "The indispensable one-hundredth of one per cent," *Planning 1963*, pp. 198–212, published by the American Society of Planning Officials; "Cleaner air through community action," *Proceedings* of the 1962 National Conference on Air Pollution.

CHAPTER 4

Air Conservation and the Law

More than 600 years ago, English law began to reflect concern about the pollution of the air that men breathed. In 1306, the use of "sea coal" was forbidden on penalty of death. Queen Elizabeth is said to have forbidden the burning of coal in London during sessions of Parliament. In 1661, John Evelyn wrote a book on air pollution that offered a novel plan to solve London's problem: He wanted to move all industry to the leeward side of the city.

The first legal cases in England to abate air pollution were brought under the common law doctrine of nuisance. Smoke was not deemed a nuisance *per se.* Thus, a plaintiff would have to prove that smoke actually caused injury to persons or property. This is often difficult to prove today, in spite of the advances made in science and technology; it was nearly impossible to prove centuries ago. Although recent legislation in the United States has frequently made emission of smoke a nuisance in and of itself, the courts have not been unanimous in their acceptance of such broadening of the common law doctrine.

Despite the evolution of the legal attitude toward emission of smokes and fumes, and in spite of the adoption of air conservation legislation in many states and communities, the common law and its doctrine of nuisance are still being used by aggrieved parties in air pollution disputes. Indeed, in an opinion delivered at the end of 1963, the United States District Court in Oregon directed an aluminum company to install equipment for more efficient removal of fluoride gases. The court gave its opinion in a case filed by a number of orchard owners, who asked the court for an injunction in order to abate the nuisance. The court held that Oregon statutes did not, as the defendant alleged, preempt the field of air pollution, making a common law action impermissible.

According to the court, not only did the orchard owners still have all of their rights under common law, but emissions of gases that cross property lines constitute a trespass, and a continuing trespass might well be considered a nuisance as defined under common law (1).

Although the orchard owners were successful in this case, litigation by private individuals in air pollution cases is often costly, complicated, and ineffective.

Legal Considerations

Attempts to cope with the problem of air pollution on a community-wide basis through legislation will probably be more effective than litigation. But such legislation must be carefully drawn so that it does not run afoul of American constitutional guarantees and limitations. Thus, state law must not usurp federal power, and no law may infringe on the due process and equal protection requirements of state and federal constitutions.

Many devices employed in interstate commerce are sources of air pollution. A jet aircraft on takeoff produces more air contaminants than 1000 automobiles. Ships and railroads are also sources of air pollution. Since the Constitution confers the power to regulate interstate commerce on the federal government, the question arises as to the power of a state and its subdivisions to regulate the sources of air pollution that result from interstate commerce. In construing the applicable provisions of the Constitution, the courts have developed the doctrine that the states may regulate interstate commerce under two conditions: (i) The matter to be regulated is of a type that normally comes within the regulatory power of the states—for example, the "police power" of the states to safeguard the health of their people. (ii) Congress has done nothing to regulate the activities in question; or such action as it has taken can be construed as indicating an intent not to "preempt" the field, but to leave it to regulation by the states.

In the field of air pollution, there is considerable evidence that both of these conditions prevail: Since pollution affects the public health, a state regulation would be within the general police power of the state. And Congress does not appear to have preempted the field:

The Committee recognizes that it is the primary responsibility of state and local governments to prevent air pollution. (2).

In recognition of the dangers to the public health and welfare, injury to agricultural crops and livestock, damage to and deterioration of property, hazards to air and transportation, from air pollution, it is hereby declared to be the policy of Congress to preserve and protect the primary responsibility and rights of the state and local governments in controlling air pollution, to support and aid technical research to devise and develop methods of abating such pollution and to provide Federal technical service and financial aid to state and local government air pollution control agencies . . . and institutions in formulation and execution of their air pollution abatement research programs (3).

In the face of an express congressional intention not to preempt the field, it would appear that local agencies could control vehicles in interstate commerce if their regulations did not violate other provisions of the Constitution.

Both federal and state constitutions contain prohibitions against a governmental agency taking private property without due process of law. If a government agency enacted a statute that would result in an unreasonable curtailment of or the complete dissolution of an otherwise lawful business, such a statute would constitute the taking of property without due process of law. In order to comply with due process and equal protection requirements of state and federal constitutions, any air pollution regulatory statute must observe certain requirements of law, which are:

1) The statute must be reasonable (that is, the means chosen by the legislature to abate air pollution must be reasonably calculated to achieve that objective).

2) The statute must not arbitrarily discriminate among areas or among industries.

3) The statute must be clear. If a law is vague to the extent that its meaning cannot be ascertained, it is invalid.

Regulatory Devices

A number of devices may be, or have been, employed in different parts of the United States to make air conservation regulations effective. In some instances, legislatures have adopted specific regulations; in others, legislatures have created control boards empowered to take administrative action to eliminate pollution. Enforcement may be effected by injunction or by imposing criminal penalties. In Los Angeles County and Detroit, a permit is required to operate any facility that might be a source of air pollution. Failure to obtain such a permit is a misdemeanor, quite apart from the question of whether or not the facility actually is violating substantive provisions of the air pollution statute or regulations.

Injunction proceedings would ordinarily pose serious problems for the plaintiff. Traditionally, in order to obtain an injunction, it is incumbent upon the petitioning party to show that irreparable injury would result if the offending party were allowed to continue a particular activity. In most cases it is difficult to prove this, because (i) in our present state of knowledge, it is often difficult to determine the type of emitter that caused the injury, and (ii) even if the type of emitter were known, there are often so many of the same type in a particular airshed that it is difficult to identify the one causing the damage.

However, many of our newer statutes provide that any violation of any provision of the applicable air pollution control statute, rule, or regulation may be enjoined. That is, in order for A to get an injunction against B, it is not necessary to prove that B injured A, but merely that B carried on his activities in a manner that violated the air pollution regulation. It should also be noted that a person may be enjoined before he begins operation. Thus, without waiting for the discharge of the air pollutant, the aggrieved party could be granted protection from future damages.

Criminal penalties also act as a deterrent, and, in some cases, are perhaps the most effective. It should be noted, however, that a criminal penalty can be exacted only after there has been a violation.

By requiring permits to operate, the air pollution control boards have a continuing opportunity to inspect and correct deficiencies before the contaminant is discharged into the atmosphere. Plans for constructing and operating equipment are carefully scrutinized before the permit is issued.

Efforts to Control Air Pollution

The per capita cost of air pollution in the United States each year probably amounts to $50 or more. In comparison, in 1963 all public agencies—local, state, and federal—spent less than $25 million to conserve our air, or only about 14 cents per capita.

Although air pollution is a nationwide phenomenon, it has not yet become a community problem everywhere. Being primarily a by-product of our industrial civilization, it is most commonly found around population centers. Virtually all urban areas with populations of 50,000 or more have air conservation problems. Of the 64.5 million people who were living in such areas in 1960, 35.6 million faced a major problem, 18.7 million a moderate problem, and only 10.2 million a minor problem. In more general terms, in 1960 more than 100 million people, or 90 percent of the total urban population of the United States, faced air conservation problems of varying degrees of seriousness (4) (Fig. 1).

The current situation is just part of the problem. Each day significant planning decisions are made concerning the location of new subdivisions and factories and the handling of intra-area transportation that will affect the air conservation problems of 10, 25, or even 50 years from now. In a rapidly expanding society such as ours, the proper coordination of these developments with an overall air conservation plan is at least as important as the necessarily piecemeal, *post hoc* problem of controlling and eliminating existing pollution.

Local efforts. Most of the effort in the control aspect of air conservation has been, and will undoubtedly continue to be, expended at the local level. While expensive research facilities may be beyond the means of most localities, enforcement at this level has the advantage of flexibility and adaptability to a particular situation, and it seems just insofar as the brunt of the financial responsibility falls on those who are creating and suffering from the problem. Despite the fact that more than $8.5 million was spent by local (including mu-

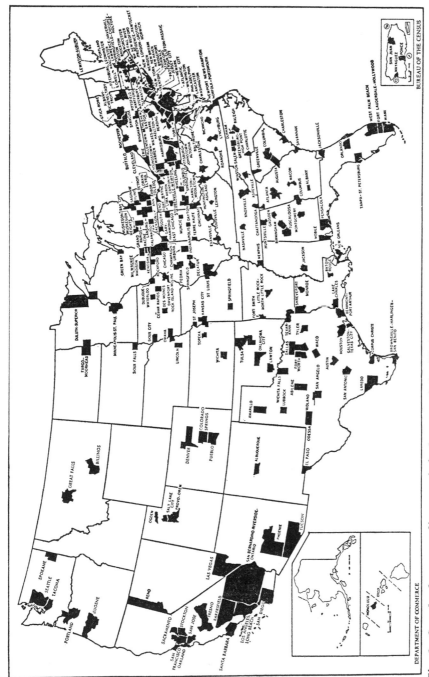

Fig. 1. Standard metropolitan statistical areas of the United States and Puerto Rico in 1960. Area definitions are by the Federal Committee on Standard Metropolitan Statistical areas under the direction of the U.S. Bureau of the Budget.

nicipal, county, and metropolitan areas) agencies during 1963, only about half the population of affected areas is presently covered by a local control program (Table 1). Only 106 local programs have full-time staffs, and of these, only 28 have 5 or more employees. In 1961 only 85 local agencies spent $5000 or more. Obviously, in many areas not even a token effort is being made (Table 2).

How much does it cost to finance an adequate control program? The report of the Surgeon General's Committee on Environmental Health Problems suggested 40 cents per person per year as a possible cost for a "reasonably comprehensive program" (5). By this standard, only four local agencies in the entire country had adequate programs in 1961 (Table 3). In 1963, Ballman and Fitzmorris (6) presented a more comprehensive picture of the cost of an adequate local program. They proposed three degrees of effort: (i) action in response to complaints only, (ii) a nominal program involving inspections and permits as well as answering complaints, (iii) an intensive program with sampling and monitoring, and evaluation activities in addition to those provided for in (i) and (ii). The three types of program cost an estimated annual minimum of $11,000, $32,000, and $100,000, respectively. The authors judged that, in general, only communities of more than 250,000 would need intensive programs. Such a program would involve annual per capita expenditures in the range of 20 to 40 cents; the higher figure would apply to the smallest (250,000) unit. More or less nominal programs were judged as necessary for most localities in the 50,000 to 250,000 range, at a per capita cost of 15 cents, depending on the size of the community and the problem. A "complaints only" program would cost 40 cents per capita for cities of 25,000, the smallest size considered in the report, and relatively less for larger cities.

How does a particular locality's performance stand up against these recommended levels of expenditure? Tables 4 and 5 show per capita expenditures for 73 selected cities in 1961 (see Fig. 2 for their geographic distribution); appropriation levels, except in isolated cases, have not changed significantly since then. If a city is not listed in Tables 4 and 5, it probably does not have a program. The average per capita expenditure in 1961 for the 85 agencies mentioned earlier was only 10.8 cents. Obviously, America's local air pollution control agencies do not make up in intensity of effort for

Table 1. Frequency of local programs (4).

Population class	Number of places in class (1960)	Number served by local air pollution control agency spending $5000 or more per year (1963)	Percentage
1,000,000 +	5	5	100
500,000–1,000,000	16	13	81
250,000–500,000	30	20	67
100,000–250,000	81	32	40
50,000–100,000	201	49	24
Total (50,000+)	333	119	36

Table 2. Expenditures of local agencies spending $5000 or more (1961) (4).

Amount	Number of agencies	Amount	Number of agencies
$ 1,000,000	1	$25,000–50,000	10
500,000–1,000,000	2	15,000–25,000	12
250,000–500,000	2	10,000–15,000	18
100,000–250,000	8	5,000–10,000	21
50,000–100,000	11		

Table 3. Per capita expenditures of local agencies spending $5000 or more (1961) (4).

Amount (in cents)	Number of agencies	Amount (in cents)	Number of agencies
50–60	2	15–20	12
40–50	2	10–15	16
30–40	3	5–10	20
25–30	5	0–5	16
20–25	9		

Table 4. Local agencies with budgets of $5000 or more and spending 10 cents or more per capita (1961) (4).

Name	Per capita (in cents)	Population (1960) (in 1000's)	Name	Per capita (in cents)	Population (1960) (in 1000's)
Los Angeles County	57.0	5970	Milwaukee County, Wis.	17.5	733
San Bernardino County	52.0	500	San Francisco Bay Area	16.7	3364
Ilion, N.Y.	49.0	10	Orange County, Calif.	16.7	698
Cleveland Heights, Ohio	45.3	62	Syracuse, N.Y.	16.7	215
Perth Amboy, N.J.	34.2	38	St. Louis, Mo.	15.8	747
Wheeling, W.Va.	32.1	53	Salt Lake City, Utah	15.8	189
Cincinnati (area), Ohio	30.4	542	Newark, N.J.	15.6	403
Niagara Falls, N.Y.	27.4	102	Providence, R.I.	15.0	206
Asheville, N.C.	27.2	59	Allegheny County, Pa.	13.3	1629
Cleveland, Ohio	27.1	870	Zanesville, Ohio	12.8	39
Kingsport, Tenn.	26.6	26	Chattanooga, Tenn.	12.5	128
Monroe, Mich.	26.1	23	Richmond, Va.	11.4	218
Hillside Township, N.J.	23.8	21	Roanoke, Va.	11.4	97
Knoxville, Tenn.	22.7	110	Green Bay, Wis.	11.2	63
Riverside County, Calif.	22.2	302	Madison, Wis.	11.1	126
Sandusky, Ohio	21.9	32	Buffalo, N.Y.	11.1	530
Fond du Lac, Wis.	21.4	33	Detroit, Mich.	10.9	1654
Dayton, Ohio	21.3	258	Winston-Salem, N.C.	10.8	111
Watertown, N.Y.	21.2	33	Erie, Pa.	10.8	138
McCracken County, Ky.	20.9	57	Columbus, Ohio	10.7	469
Eugene, Ore.	20.0	50	Chicago, Ill.	10.4	3512
East Chicago, Ind.	19.3	58	Jefferson County, Ky.	10.4	606
East Providence, R.I.	19.1	42	Youngstown, Ohio	10.3	166
East Cleveland, Ohio	18.4	38	Sacramento County, Calif.	10.0	500
Tonawanda, N.Y.	17.9	84			

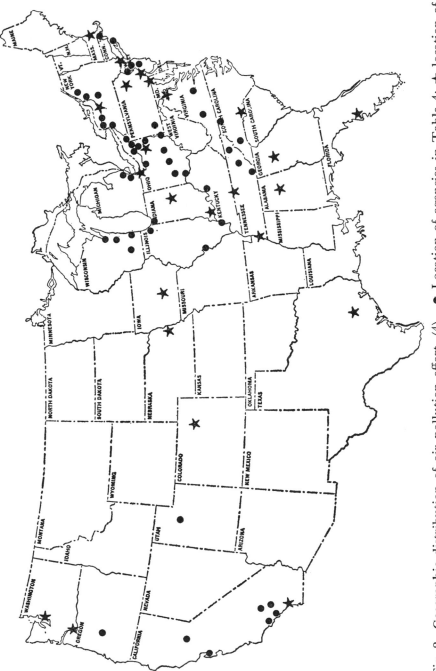

Fig. 2. Geographic distribution of air pollution effort (4). ● Location of agencies in Table 4; ★ location of agencies in Table 5.

what they lack in population covered. An across-the-board broadening and deepening of the local coverage seems in order. For example, if the 64.5 million people living in cities of 50,000 or more, all of which have an air pollution problem, were covered by programs with an average cost of 20 cents per capita, certainly a reasonable figure in light of the foregoing estimates, the total cost would be $13 million. This sum is half again as much as the expenditure for all local air pollution control programs in 1961.

However, the local picture is not uniformly dismal. Pittsburgh has made considerable progress in cleaning itself up, and so have

Table 5. Local agencies with budgets of $10,000 or more and spending less than 10 cents per capita (1961) (4).

Name	Per capita (in cents)	Population (1960) (in 1000's)
New York City, N.Y.	9.5	7710
Charlotte, N.C.	9.5	210
Polk-Hillsborough Counties, Fla.	8.5	592
Philadelphia, Pa.	8.4	1971
Indianapolis, Ind.	8.1	469
San Diego County, Calif.	7.9	1000
Nashville, Tenn.	7.9	167
Baltimore, Md.	7.6	922
Evansville, Ind.	7.2	140
Omaha, Neb.	6.7	300
District of Columbia	5.6	746
Akron, Ohio	5.6	288
Des Moines, Iowa	5.3	208
Lehigh Valley Area, Pa.	5.0	278
Portland, Ore.	4.6	371
Toledo, Ohio	3.8	316
Birmingham, Ala.	3.5	341
Harris County (Houston), Texas	3.4	1243
Rochester, N.Y.	3.2	316
Denver, Colo.	3.1	494
Atlanta, Ga.	2.7	485
Boston metropolitan area, Mass.	2.6	1998
Memphis, Tenn.	2.6	492
Seattle, Wash.	2.2	552

Detroit and Cincinnati; the Los Angeles County program has set a national and international example in air pollution control since its inception in 1947. Although the County's 1948 population of 3.9 million and 9800 industries had grown to 6.5 million and 16,000 by 1960, the volume of contaminants entering the air from stationary devices in 1960 was less than half that of 1948 (7). In 1961 Los Angeles spent 57 cents per capita on air pollution control (it has a particularly knotty problem), and its $3.4 million total was 40 percent of the total local effort in the country.

State efforts. California was the first state to enter the air conservation field.* In 1947 it enacted a statute to authorize the establishment of air pollution control districts on a county or regional basis. Since then eight such districts have been set up, giving California the most comprehensive local air conservation program of any state. Twelve other states have also enacted similar statutes, either blanket or specific authorizations for the establishment of local districts (Table 6). In 1948, Oregon took a first step toward the establishment of a state control authority. By 1955, the year of the first federal air pollution statute, only three other states had followed suit. However, in the 8 years since then, 22 more states have entered the field, and California, Oregon, and the other pioneers have broadened and deepened their air conservation activities (Table 7 and Fig. 3).

State statutory authority falls into three broad categories: the local option and home rule arrangements noted earlier, control programs staffed by state officials, and programs of research and technical assistance to local units (Table 6). Not all aspects of state programs are subsumed under these categories, however. California, New Hampshire, Ohio, and Wisconsin all provide for some kind of tax relief to encourage the construction of pollution control devices. Both California and New York have provisions that require cars to be equipped with crankcase ventilation systems. Under requirement of California law, the State Department of

---

* Although air pollution control activities occupy the major part of the efforts of local programs, we have described these programs, generally, as air conservation programs because many states, following California, are engaged in research, monitoring, and establishment of emission and air quality standards. The state programs may not yet recognize air conservation as an explicit goal, but such activities form the basis for air conservation.

Table 6. Extent of state statutory authority *(8)*.

State	Control by state officials authorized	Local option specifically authorized by state	Research and technical assistance program authorized	Any other authority
Alabama				
Alaska	☆		☆	☆
Arizona		☆	☆	
Arkansas				
California	☆ (P) †	☆	☆	☆
Colorado			☆	
Connecticut			☆	
Delaware	☆		☆	
District of Columbia	☆ (L) ‡			
Florida	☆	☆ (L)	☆	
Georgia				
Hawaii	☆			
Idaho	☆		☆	
Illinois	☆		☆	
Indiana	☆			
Iowa		☆ (L)		
Kansas				
Kentucky		☆		
Louisiana				
Maine				
Maryland	☆		☆	
Massachusetts	☆ (L)	☆ (L)		
Michigan				
Minnesota				
Mississippi				
Missouri		☆ (P)		☆
Montana				
Nebraska		☆ (P)		
Nevada		☆		
New Hampshire				☆
New Jersey	☆		☆	☆
New Mexico				
New York	☆		☆	☆
North Carolina			☆	
North Dakota				☆
Ohio			☆	
Oklahoma			☆	
Oregon	☆	☆	☆	
Pennsylvania	☆		☆	
Rhode Island		☆ (P and L)		
South Carolina		☆ (P and L)		
South Dakota				
Tennessee			☆	
Texas				
Utah				
Vermont				
Virginia				
Washington		☆	☆	
West Virginia	☆		☆	
Wisconsin		☆		☆
Wyoming				
Totals	13 and 3 partial and/or limited	6 and 7 partial and/or limited	19	8

† P, partial; not all aspects of air pollution covered. ‡ L, limited; not all jurisdictions in state are affected.

Health drew up what is, to date, the most complete set of air quality and emission standards, and several other states have authorized a similar set of standards.

Although the states are becoming increasingly involved in air conservation and are branching out into new areas of activity, the total effort is still far from reaching desirable levels; very few states, with California as the leader, are adequately meeting the problem.

Table 7. Record of all significant legislation at the state level—control, research, local option, and other (8).

Year	Before federal entry into field States passing major air conservation laws
1947	California
1948	Oregon
1949	None
1950	None
1951	None
1952	Kentucky
1953	None
1954	Massachusetts, New Jersey
1955	California

Year	Since federal entry into field* Number of states passing major laws	States passing first major law
1956	None	
1957	7	Delaware, Florida, Hawaii, Nevada, New York, Ohio, Washington
1958	2	Alaska
1959	3	Idaho, Tennessee
1960	3	Pennsylvania
1961	8	Illinois, Indiana, Oklahoma, West Virginia, Wisconsin
1962	2	Arizona
1963	11	Colorado, Connecticut, Maryland, North Carolina, Utah

Total number of states having significant air conservation legislation (cumulative)

Year:	47	48	49	50	51	52	53	54	55	56	57	58	59	60	61	62	63
No.:	1	2	2	2	2	3	3	5	5	5	12	13	15	16	21	22	27

* State legislatures meet in legislative session usually only in odd-numbered years.

Only 16 states have some form of control authority, 13 some sort of local option authorization, 19 the power to conduct research and technical assistance activities, and 8 other authorities. Implementation of the authority granted presents an even less favorable pic-

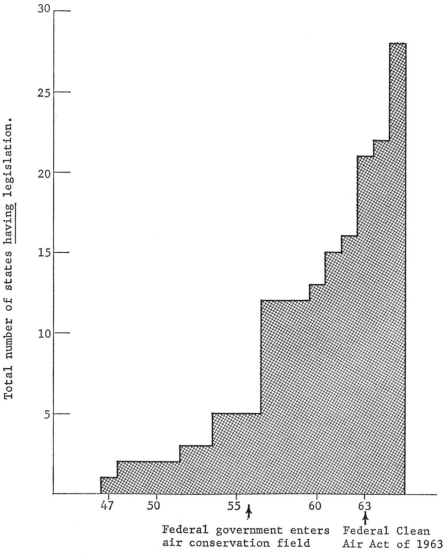

Fig. 3. Number of states having significant air conservation legislation, 1947–1963 (cumulative) (8).

ture. In 1961 only 17 states spent $5000 or more per year for air conservation (Fig. 4), and at present only a handful more (Colorado, Connecticut, Illinois, Indiana, Ohio, and West Virginia) have reached this level. Although the total state expenditure of $2 mil-

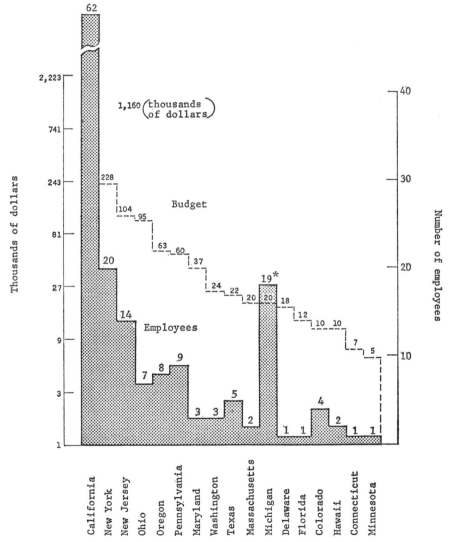

Fig. 4. Budgets and number of employees of state air conservation programs (all states spending more than $5000 per year) (4). * Some or all employees are part time.

lion in 1961 has increased more than 50 percent since then, still only a dozen or so states have more than token programs. The legislative performance in 1963 struck an encouraging note, however. Five states (Colorado, Connecticut, Maryland, North Carolina, and Utah) passed major air conservation laws for the first time, and six other states enacted major relevant legislation. Future budget sessions will tell whether this activity is part of a trend or merely an isolated flurry.

Federal action. One of the major keys to the expansion of local and state air conservation activity will undoubtedly be the intervention of the federal government.

Public Law 84-159 (1956), "an act to provide research and technical assistance relating to air pollution control," marked the first major involvement of the federal government in air conservation. This law directed the Secretary of Health, Education, and Welfare to prepare research plans, conduct research, and support other research work; encourage cooperative activities by state and local governments; disseminate information; study, on request, specific local problems; make grants and enter into contracts for surveys, research, training, and so forth. Under this act, extended by PL 86-365 (1959) and PL 87-761 (1962), the Division of Air Pollution was established in the Public Health Service; it has remained the center of federal air conservation activity. Public Law 86–493, passed in 1960, directed the Surgeon General to study the problem of pollution caused by motor vehicles; the resulting report, "Motor Vehicles, Air Pollution, and Health," was published in 1962. Federal expenditures in the field have grown from $1.7 million in 1956 to $13 million in 1964 (Fig. 5).

During this 9-year period the main impetus of the federal program has been in research, both at the Robert A. Taft Sanitary Engineering Center in Cincinnati and through grants and contracts. Direct impact on local and state programs has extended no further than limited training programs for personnel and technical assistance, mainly in the form of pollution surveys. A little more than $8 million, less than 15 percent of the total appropriated, went to support these activities during the period 1955–1965 (Fig. 6).

In 1961, the report of the Committee on Environmental Health Problems (5) urged greater federal assistance to states and local

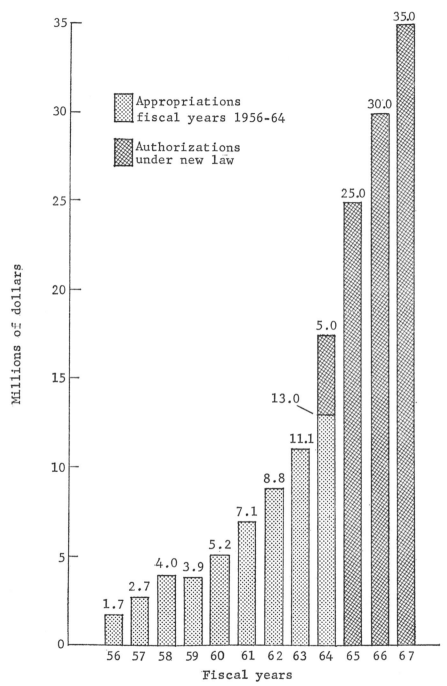

Fig. 5. Federal expenditures in air conservation.

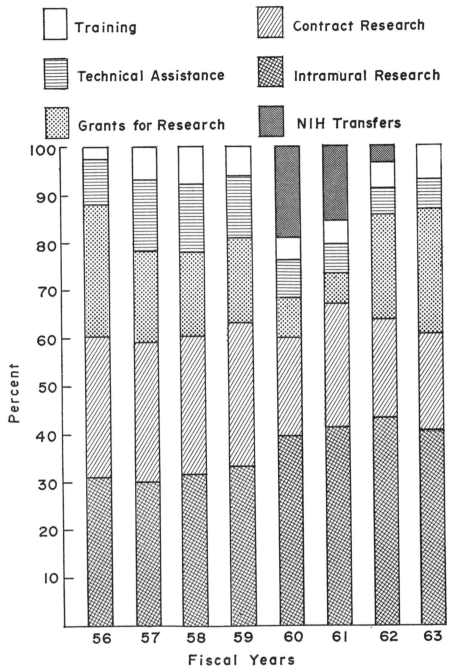

Fig. 6. Distribution of total federal appropriations, 1956–1963 (9).

governments in evaluating air pollution problems and in developing effective air pollution control programs. Congress responded to this and similar recommendations in HR 5618, the Clean Air Act of 1963, which became law in December 1963. Section 4 of that act provides that up to 20 percent of each year's appropriation (maximums: 1964, $3.6 million; 1965, $5 million; 1966, $6 million; and 1967, $7 million) may be used to make grants to air pollution control agencies to aid in "developing, establishing, and improving programs for the prevention and control of air pollution." These grants may not exceed two-thirds of the cost, except in the case of intermunicipal or interstate (regional) agencies, for which they may not exceed three-fourths. It is further provided that no agency may receive a grant if it reduces its nonfederal funds during the year in which it receives the grant; the objective of the grants is to "provide impetus to the establishment and improvement of regulatory air pollution programs in the states and local communities" [to quote former Congressman Kenneth A. Roberts (D–Alabama), the bill's author], and in no sense is it to supplant existing state and local efforts. Grants under Section 4 are to be made with "due consideration to (1) the population, (2) the extent of the actual or potential air pollution problem, and (3) the financial need of the respective agencies" applying for grants. Since the sums involved in these grants are about one-fourth to one-half of the total current local and state expenditure, most existing local programs will undoubtedly grow rapidly, and the incentive of federal monies may encourage many now inactive areas to initiate programs.

More than 38 million people lived in 24 interstate Standard Metropolitan Statistical Areas in 1960, and tens of millions more live in such areas adjacent to neighboring states (Fig. 1); all of these areas are believed to have air pollution problems. The special incentive to interstate programs in the grant regulations reflects a general concern with the problem of interstate air pollution control in the Clean Air Act. Section 2 encourages interstate agreements and compacts, and gives the explicit consent of Congress to the making of such compacts and the formation of interstate agencies. (At present, only one such compact exists, that of 1961 between New Jersey and New York in which the authority of the Interstate Sanitation Commission was extended to include air pollution control.) Section 5 provides an elaborate mechanism for the intervention of the United States in interstate air pollution disputes. Under it, the Secretary of Health, Education, and Welfare can call a conference to discuss such a problem if requested by an aggrieved state, or by an aggrieved locality with the consent of the state, or if he has reason to believe that a dangerous interstate situation exists. If, after such a conference, effective remedial action is not taken, the Secretary can recommend necessary action to the appropriate agency or agencies. If, after 6 months, such recommendations have not been followed, the Secretary can convene a public hearing. The recommendations of the hearing board would be binding on the parties involved; if the abatement required had not been achieved after a 6-month period, the Secretary can direct the Attorney General to bring suit on behalf of the United States to secure abatement. Section 5 gives the federal government considerable discretionary authority to engage directly in the control of interstate pollution, even without the consent of the state being injured. Thus, in its first foray into the area of enforcement, Congress has taken what may prove to be a far-reaching step.

Section 5 also provides that the same adjudication machinery may, at the discretion of the Secretary, be used to settle purely intrastate situations if request is made by a state or by a municipality with the consent of the state. In such a case, a written request from the governor of the state involved is required before the Secretary can request the Attorney General to bring suit. This provision may be of great benefit to states with no statewide, super-local control agency. A final provision that will undoubtedly prove directly helpful to the states is Section 3 (c) (2) , which directs the Secretary to conduct research and establish criterions for harmful air pollution agents in relation to their effects on human health and welfare, and to make these criterions available to state, local, and interstate agencies. The overall expansion of the federal research effort, implied by the great increases in authorization levels (270 percent during the 4 years covered by the law) , will also redound to the benefit of other agencies, but in an indirect way, as will the provision for accelerating the attack on motor vehicle and fuel pollution. Section 3 (c) (2) requires that periodic reports be made to Congress on the state of research on these problems and to include any recommendations for further legislation.

The Future

It has been shown that the scope of the air conservation problem is vast, while that of the attempts to cope with it is limited. However, there are definitely some encouraging signs. First, in 1963 there was an unprecedented volume of state legislation in the field and a growth in appropriations. Second, the Clean Air Act of 1963 provided for, among other things, not only an extensive program of grants to encourage increased state and local action, but also federal control machinery that may be invoked by states to help solve their own internal problems as well as their problems with neighboring states. But progress in air conservation still depends upon determined local effort, for it is primarily at this level that the control and prevention of pollution must be carried out. To date, air conservation at the local level seems much weaker that at higher levels of government; the vital task is to see that this situation is remedied.

References

1. R. L. Renken *et al.* vs. Harvey Aluminum (Incorporated), Civil Case No. 61–207. The opinion, dated December 23, 1963, was by Judge John F. Kilkenny, U.S. District Court, District of Oregon.
2. Report No. 389, 84th Congress, 1st Sess. 3.
3. 69 Stat. 322; 42 U.S.C. Sec. 1857.
4. Schueneman, J. J., *Air Pollution Problems and Control Programs in the United States*, Paper No. 62–84 (U.S. Department of Health, Education, and Welfare, Public Health Service, Robert A. Taft Sanitary Engineering Center, Cincinnati, 1962).
5. Department of Health, Education, and Welfare, U.S. Public Health Service, *Report of the Committee on Environmental Health Problems to the Surgeon General* (Government Printing Office, Washington, D.C., 1962).
6. Ballman, H. C., and Fitzmorris, T. J., "Local air pollution control programs—a survey and analysis," *J. Air Pollution Control Assoc.*, **13**, 486–495 (1963).
7. Congressman Everett G. Burkhalter, speaking in the *Congressional Record*, July 24, 1963, during the debate on HR 6518.
8. Department of Health, Education, and Welfare, U.S. Public Health Service, Division of Air Pollution, *A Digest of State Air Pollution Laws*, Publication No. 711 (Government Printing Office, Washington, D.C., 1963).
9. *A Study of Pollution—Air*, a report to the Committee on Public Works, U.S. Senate, 1963.

CHAPTER 5

Air Pollution Control

The effective control of air pollution depends upon the combined application of technology and law under a sound administrative program. The first section of this chapter will deal with "control technology," which here refers to the techniques that may be used by owners of pollution sources to minimize the undesirable effects of emissions. The second section will describe the development of ambient air quality standards: California is used as an example because of its exceptional efforts to solve air pollution problems.

At the end of the chapter are a number of figures and tables that provide cost data for a variety of air pollution control methods.

Control Technology

Air pollution control technology is more than a hundred years old, if the British Alkali Act is considered the starting point in its history. Private and public owners of processes have been engaged in air pollution control for many years. The problems have ranged from the old ones of smoke, dust, and corrosive gases to the modern ones of radioactive pollution, biological agents such as nerve poisons, viruses, and miscellaneous chemicals that are used in agriculture.

During the past century, control techniques have been developed and applied to an increasing number of problems. An important factor in the growth of present-day controls has been a more critical evaluation of the annoyances and health hazards that are caused by air pollutants when compared with the costs of control measures. There is a great deal of information in the literature with regard to the control methods that are being used here and abroad. Of special value are reports on engineering accomplishments and the specific cost data of industries that have installed control equipment. These reports indicate that many industries are making serious attempts to preserve the quality of the air and that some of them are willing to encourage the use of similar equipment by releasing engineering and cost data. This attitude should be encouraged as much as possible since it contributes materially to the application of new processes and improvements without years of delay.*

As disclosure becomes more common, reports undoubtedly will include the additional evaluations that are necessary in order to accurately determine the cost of corrective air pollution measures. Some of these evaluations relate to improvement in product quality, reduction in the cost of maintenance and insurance, taxation factors, and improved employee morale and community relations. (Some of the additional cost factors, which vary with each situation, will be explored in a discussion of the economics of costs and benefits.)

In establishing a control program, it is necessary to consider carefully the reasons for control as well as the type and degree of control that are required for the particular circumstance. The conclusions will vary with the size of the operation, its location, community attitudes, the cost of control, and the various engineering possibilities. In any case, a meaningful evaluation of the effectiveness of a proposed control program requires a knowledge of the physical and

---

* Typical reports on cost estimates and efficiencies for various unit operations used in dust collection are shown in Fig. 1 and Tables 2 and 3. Included are economic comparisons of cyclones, filters, and scrubbers. These show that the cost of control per unit volume of treated air decreases with the volume of the gases to be processed. At high capacities this cost levels off to a point where it is not much affected by a further increase in throughput. For control purposes it is important to know, not only the overall efficiency, but the kind of materials collected. Figure 2 shows the degree of collection of particles of various sizes in three collectors of different efficiency. It is clear that the low-efficiency equipment collects mainly the coarse particles while the fine ones escape. As a rule, cost increases rapidly with greater efficiency and also with the attempts to collect more and smaller particles. Tables 4 through 8 and Fig. 3 show examples of calculations for various types of controls, their probable cost and their anticipated or demonstrated collection efficiency for specific industrial operations. These operations include a grey iron foundry (Table 4), steel plant (Table 5), chemical drying operations (Table 6), fluid catalytic cracker (Table 7), and dust collector for coal-fired heating and power plants (Table 8 and Fig. 3). Table 9 lists typical costs of both basic and control equipment installed in 77 different types of industrial operations in Los Angeles.

chemical nature and biological effects of the emitted dust, droplets, and gases, both before and after control.

For example, a 1959 technical report of the San Francisco Bay Area Air Pollution Control District reviewed a number of control possibilities for a foundry (Table 4); in the control of grey iron cupola dust and droplets, the possibility of using a collector with 90-percent efficiency (by weight) was evaluated. The collected material would consist mostly of coarse particles that otherwise would fall out near the foundry. On the other hand, most of the light-scattering, smaller particles would escape in a dense plume. In this case, the location of the plant and the economy of operation were not considered adequate reasons for such an unsatisfactory solution, which would permit lung-penetrating particles to spread over vast areas while the relatively nontoxic large particles would be collected.

The control agency, however, knew of two alternative methods: (i) Different melting equipment and clean scrap metal, which, together, would eliminate the need for afterburners and dust collectors, or (ii) cloth filter collectors and afterburners with heat exchangers. Thus, instead of using the "90 percent" collector, the Control District enacted a regulation that required the application of alternative methods that would achieve a higher degree of control.

The moral is that the control of air pollution has become a highly specialized field of engineering and that the assistance of professional pollution control engineers is necessary in order to obtain maximum benefit.

One of the greatest difficulties, and the main reason for differences of opinion, is the determination of degree of control. Eventually, perhaps, a better knowledge of community health and annoyance criterions will alleviate some of these difficulties. The establishment of well-defined standards would help industries and other segments of the community in proper long-range planning, and would help control officials avoid controversies since their actions would be based on officially recognized health and annoyance values.

Applying Control Technology

In order to control any one of the pollutants from a single source, the entire chain of events leading to the undesired effects must be examined to determine which link should be changed. The chain starts with fuel and raw materials and continues through processing equipment and methods, exhaust speed and location, transport through the atmosphere, and finally transformation by sunlight or moisture in the atmosphere.

When the limitation of air pollution emissions is being considered, the management of an activity can examine its operations from the following standpoints:

1) *Should the process or equipment be modified or replaced?* If replacement results in the removal of obsolete equipment, such a change may be profitable. For example, when they were firmly pressed by air pollution control, many brass foundries learned how to increase their profits by replacing ordinary crucibles and cupolas with induction electric or reverberatory melting furnaces. Substituting public sanitary landfill at less than $1 per ton of rubbish plus hauling costs, in place of incineration at $5 to $10 per ton, is another example.

2) *Should the material being used, including fuel, be changed?* Such changes, especially when combined with minor or major equipment changes, are occasionally profitable or provide less costly control of air pollutants than do tail-end control installations. An example is the installation of specially designed stokers for Scotch Marine boilers, coupled with changes in coal specifications. These served to control smoke from large freighters on the Great Lakes at a decided profit, and also improved the working conditions of the firemen who had previously shoveled more than a ton of coal an hour into the furnaces.

3) *Should the procedure used in operation and maintenance of process equipment be modified?* Any changes in equipment and materials require some retraining of personnel. Sometimes changes in operating procedures alone will provide adequate air pollution control. One example is the change to a more nearly continuous feeding, as against large batch processing. With equipment such as incinerators, this can often reduce overloads and excessive air pollution, and can reduce deterioration of equipment. Improved maintenance practices—for example, on diesel truck engine pumps, injectors, and filters—can control smoke while saving fuel and reducing engine wear.

4) *Should a tail-end convertor of pollutants be added?* The addition of a flame-type or catalytic afterburner, for example, can change evaporated paint solvents to nonpolluting carbon dioxide and water (plus a small amount of unwanted oxides of nitrogen). With a well-designed heat-exchanger, such an afterburner on a paint-drying oven can sometimes provide preheated air and reduce the net operating costs or develop a profit.

5) *Should a tail-end collector of pollutants be added?* Collectors, which separate, capture, and concentrate dusts, droplets, or selected gases from the exhaust gas stream, must have facilities for handling, treating, and disposing of the concentrated materials. Opportunities for producing useful materials in this manner occasionally offset the cost of collection in part, in full, or at a profit. For example, lead dust from the melting of metal scrap and hydrogen sulfide from gas and oil processing are now usually recovered at a profit. Fly ash from pulverized coal-burning power-generating stations is increasingly marketable at prices that reduce but, reportedly, do not fully cover the cost of collecting, handling, and burying the unsold portion.

6) *Can there be improvements in the dispersion of pollutants into the atmosphere?* The purpose of dispersion is to reduce the undesirable effects from contact and from interfering with visibility, including the frequency and duration of pollution-induced fogs and hazes. Horizontal and vertical separation from sensitive operations are useful for some emissions.

Tall stacks and chimneys allow exhaust gas streams to become better dispersed than do shorter stacks, resulting in lower concentrations at nearby ground level. Although this is helpful, large dust particles and drops that would otherwise have fallen near the source may travel a greater distance. Although not yet appreciated by many architects, even when ordinary operations would not indicate the need, tall chimneys serve as safety measures in the event of an accidental malfunction that would involve gases, microscopic dusts, or droplets. The height of stacks is limited by aviation safety requirements as well as by construction costs.

Acquiring land and establishing private restrictions on the use of neighboring land is another method of achieving improved dispersion of pollutants by, in effect, increasing the distance between source and neighbor.

Dust and gas detecting instruments, together with wind instruments located near the neighbors who might be affected, can sometimes be used to guide production processes that can be modified to match the weather, and also to signal the operator when a malfunction begins. This "shipmaster" approach is sometimes used for operations over large areas that modify their operations to match weather conditions and observed field concentrations. Emission rates that are governed by weather predictions have been used, for example, to permit more sulfur dioxide to be released, under some conditions, at nonferrous ore smelters.

Economics in Control Technology

Reports on the costs of applying air pollution control techniques are usually expressed in terms of (i) capital cost of the major equipment, excluding the costs of installation and utilities; (ii) capital cost of the completed installation, excluding the value of the occupied land, the value of any occupied building space, and some of the disposal equipment, such as trucks or tank cars; (iii) increases in yearly operating and maintenance costs, directly associated with manpower assigned to the control equipment, replacement parts, changes in raw material, and use of utilities; and (iv) ratio of control installation capital cost to basic process equipment capital cost.

Less frequently, such cost reports are expressed in terms of (i) total capital cost of the completed installation, including the shared value of occupied land and buildings and disposal-removal equipment; (ii) ratio of the total cost of control installation to total operating plant capital cost; (iii) net yearly operating and maintenance costs or savings from all changes associated with the application of air pollution controls, including reduced maintenance of other equipment and buildings, improved product quality and reduced product rejections, recovery of previously wasted heat and useful materials, direct savings from modernizing equipment for production and handling of material, property tax and income tax factors, and improved employee morale and community good will; and (iv) net costs or savings per unit of product or services in terms that are familiar and recognizable by the customer who buys the product or uses the service. For example, when sanitary landfill replaced open dump burning on the West Coast, the use of franchised private rubbish collectors and disposers added a monthly charge of 25 cents per family. Estimates of net cost in terms of fractional cents per mile driven have been publicly displayed for motor vehicle crankcase blow-by controls, taking into account the fuel savings that partly offset the costs of installing and maintaining the device for the remaining useful life of the car. Similar figures are being used to determine the public's attitudes with regard to motor vehicle tail-pipe exhaust control devices. Net figures are especially significant because some of the devices are likely to replace present noise mufflers, which have a limited life. Unfortunately net savings are rarely reported publicly in customer terms.

When management must take some action with regard to a major air pollution problem, it examines the plant, the equipment, and the manufacturing processes in order to determine the necessary corrective measures. This usually results in the discovery of several opportunities for modernizing, only some of which are directly involved with the air pollution problem itself. The economic benefits of these steps to the management as well as to the economy of the country are obvious, especially when they also conserve limited natural resources.

As one of many types of examples, several oil refineries found that, when they applied all of the best available air pollution control techniques to their refinery operations, at a capital expenditure of between 3 and 5 percent of total refinery investment, one-half of the expenditures provided prudent profits by their customary standards (3-year payout for productive equipment, 7-year payout for utility equipment), one-quarter of the expenditures returned a profit at a slower rate of 2 to 5 percent annually which was not considered prudent, and the other quarter was a loss. On the whole, they seem to have found that the total expenditures balanced out at a slight profit. In addition, the resulting conservation of hydrocarbons and sulfur was a definite gain to the nation.

Increases or reductions in the cost of producing any specific product or service because air pollution control technology was applied are spread in much the same way as any other externally induced cost increase or saving, with one exception. Special tax reductions have been made in some political jurisdictions because of the benefits to the community when air pollution is controlled.

Rapid tax write-off for capital costs of air pollution control equipment is being provided in more state income tax laws. Ad valorem property tax relief is also being provided in more state and local jurisdictions by statute or by policy. According to one recent report, the local tax assessor was instructed by the city administration to be moderate in evaluating all air pollution control equipment.

Increases in cost that cannot be fully overcome by better operating methods and changes in raw material specifications could be passed on to the customer or to the supplier where competitive pricing factors permit, or the owner could absorb the costs in the form of reduced profits. Examples of each type could be cited, with the caution that each situation requires separate evaluation.

One common experience in passing additional labor costs on to the supplier is found in the case of automobile scrap yards when the open burning of car bodies is prohibited. When all the scrap yards in an area are under the same limitation, the steel mills, scrap-metal brokers, and wholesale scrap-metal yards with balers establish prices for stripped car bodies in competition with similar quality scrap from other sources. The cost of hand-stripping the car body is therefore reflected in the reduced price that retail scrap dealers will pay for a junked car. In the San Francisco Bay Area the additional $1 to $2 for the cost of labor per car was accompanied by a drop in the advertised prices offered to private car owners for "junkers."

Questions are frequently raised about the effect of imposing air pollution controls on operations that are marginal because of undercapitalization, obsolescence, or other reasons. Over a period of many years, there have been only a very few instances of an operation failing to survive at the same location, and in only a handful of instances has an operation relocated to another community when air pollution control costs were a significant factor. Insofar as it is known, these shifts were not a significant detriment to the economy of the community. In most instances, the marginal operations were strengthened by modernizing when faced with the need for air pollution controls.

Specialized Control Equipment and Techniques

Most of the technology for air pollution control makes use of ordinary devices, practices, and knowledge of mechanical, chemical, electrical, civil, industrial, and agricultural engineering (1). However, a number of special adaptations have been developed and applications of better control technology at relatively lower costs are continuing at a rapid pace.

Some tail-end control techniques are as follows:

1) Settling chambers are large boxes into which exhaust gases are led so that dusts and drops can fall out into quiet areas for removal in concentrated form while the exhaust gases move along and out. These chambers are less suitable for smaller, lighter dusts and droplets since their slower settling rates would require a chamber too large to be practical. They are also useful in allowing time for hot gases and incandescent particles to be cooled, especially by the injection of water. They are frequently used for first-stage collection.

2) Target boxes and baffled chambers are also large boxes for removing larger and more dense dusts and drops. They usually contain one or more baffles that produce some radial acceleration to throw the particles downward.

3) Cyclones use radial acceleration in a double vortex that throws particles toward the outside wall and downward. They are more effective on smaller particles than chambers and smaller boxes, but greater energy is required to move the gas stream through the unit.

4) Filters block and restrain particles, thus removing them from the moving gas stream. The materials being filtered soon form a bridge over each opening to restrain smaller particles after the "cake" is built up. The filters must be vibrated, shaken, collapsed, washed, or otherwise cleaned or removed periodically lest they introduce a resistance too great for the gases to overcome with the available fans or blowers. Other than for soot, filters seem to have

no limit to their effectiveness in handling the smallest particles, even down to the size of large molecules.

5) Electrostatic precipitators operate by establishing a gradient between a charging wire or plate and a grounding plate so that charged particles are collected and removed in concentrated form.

6) Scrubbers and gas washers, using water or some other liquid, combine a number of techniques, ranging from cyclones and target boxes through filters and bubble towers to high-liquid-pressure jet collectors and high-gas-pressure venturi scrubbers. They are all effective in cooling hot gases but they frequently introduce serious problems with regard to treating waste water, and sometimes they are not able to handle nonsoluble dusts. They are especially useful in handling soluble dusts, droplets, and gases, but cool, humid plumes of exhaust gas may not be adequately dispersed. The cool, drooping chimney plume has been a serious cause of dissatisfaction with British sulfur dioxide scrubbers that handle boiler gases from large power generating stations. Scrubbers are generally less effective than filters or electrostatic precipitators in disposing of extremely small dust particles.

7) Open-flame afterburners in refractory chambers are used to burn low concentrations of combustible gases and droplets, such as in the last passages of incinerators or in primary sections of foundry cupola collection systems.

8) Solid adsorbers and catalytic afterburners are used to capture or burn up low concentrations of combustible gases and droplets that are relatively free of dusts and mineral ash that might coat them. Similar to the open-flame afterburner but requiring less fuel, they are useful in controlling odorous gases in dilutions of parts per million and parts per billion.

9) Vapor retention and the recovery systems of floating roof tanks and similar devices limit the loss by evaporation of such volatile liquids as gasoline, especially when the tanks are being filled and when the vapor pressure increases because of the warming effects of the sun on aboveground tank sides with stationary roofs.

Some of the control techniques that involve changes in equipment or methods are as follows:

1) Metal salvage incinerators with relatively cool primary chambers have been developed so that the metal will not oxidize or

volatilize as readily while the insulation or other combustibles burn off. These units also have hot secondary chambers with afterburners and supplemental air supplies to complete the burning of the gases, dusts, and droplets from the primary chamber. These incinerators, with various devices for handling scrap cable, drums and barrels, and so forth, provide the best controlled substitutes for open burning of scrap metal. They can be equipped with tail-end collectors for maximum control in sensitive neighborhoods or larger areas.

2) Coal stokers and over-fire jet systems are available for small- and medium-sized coal-burning furnaces to replace batch firing by hand, to introduce the fresh fuel and air at predetermined rates and locations, and to move the fuel along as it burns until the ash is moved for convenient removal. They are a great improvement but are not as clean as natural gas and oil burning.

3) Composting of ordinary rubbish usually provides better air pollution control than open burning or good incineration, but the price that can be obtained for the compost in competition with other fertilizers and soil builders apparently requires some type of subsidy if the method is to compete with sanitary landfill. This subsidy sometimes takes the form of salvage rights for metal, bottles, rags, waste paper, and cardboard.

4) Plowing in and discing under agricultural field wastes is often used as a substitute for open-field burning. It is sometimes limited by the possibility of propagating pests and disease. For other commodities and locations, the limitation is economic because the time required for decomposition delays planting the next crop or the decomposition increases the demand for water or fertilizer per acre.

5) In order to control smoke and soot emissions, outdoor heaters of the return stack type have been especially developed for use in orchards and with field crops that require protection against frost. They are also used on construction projects in cold weather.

6) Incinerators for burning rubbish at rates of a hundred to a few thousand pounds per hour were extensively redesigned and tested in the Los Angeles County Air Pollution Control District and resulted in greatly improved air pollution control. The costs are about the same as for good incinerators that emit considerably more pollution, but the Los Angeles types are not as subject to overloading because of the special configurations of grates, baffles, air inlet ports, and afterburners.

7) Several types of instruments to measure process gas are used to signal operators and feed back to control adjustments. These include photoelectric smoke detectors, continuous oxygen analyzers on cement kilns to prevent the formation of hydrogen sulfide, temperature indicators to control afterburners, and sulfur dioxide analyzers.

8) Sulfur recovery plants that remove hydrogen sulfide from fuel gases in order to reduce sulfur dioxide pollution are in general use even for relatively small operations (5 tons per day).

9) Self-sealing doors on coke ovens, used in place of manual sealing with special clay, are air pollution control devices because, when well maintained, less gas is lost during the coking process.

10) Paved receiving yards and enclosed truck-receiving rooms at animal rendering plants are control techniques that prevent the accumulation of putrescible materials that cannot be housed or hosed down the drain.

11) The substitution of dry rendering for wet rendering at such plants reduces the amount of contaminated, odorous water vapor that is emitted into the air or is condensed and released to sewers, from which it vents to the air as each batch is completed and the pressure in the container is relieved.

12) The substitution of wet steam cleaning and wet sandblasting for dry sandblasting of walls of dirty buildings effectively controls this localized type of air pollution.

13) Hard surfaced parking lots and other storage areas reduce dust emissions on dry, windy days.

14) Portable brush chippers that permit the use of the chips as a mulch, or that reduce the cost of hauling brush and limbs to centralized disposal areas, serve as control techniques by reducing the incentive to burn this type of waste on the site.

15) Vacuum leaf sweepers operated by local governments serve as a control technique similar to brush chippers.

There is little doubt that engineering science now has the techniques for applying control measures to each of the following pollutants and sources, but costs have discouraged the development of the necessary devices: (i) dilute oxides of sulfur from burning sulfurous fuels and minerals; (ii) dilute oxides of nitrogen from all sources of combustion, large and small, stationary and moving; (iii) microscopic dusts from general rubbish incinerators; (iv) microscopic dusts, incompletely burned gases, and other odorous and corrosive gases from coke oven pushing and quenching operations as well as from beehive coke ovens; (v) reactive hydrocarbons, odorous gases, and microscopic dusts from gasoline engines, diesel engines, and engines of jet aircraft; (vi) reactive hydrocarbon evaporation losses from gasoline distribution and marketing equipment; (vii) odorous gases from paper pulp mills, especially chemical recovery furnaces; (viii) reactive hydrocarbons from paint spraying and air drying; (ix) reactive hydrocarbons and microscopic dusts and droplets from the burning of agricultural field wastes; (x) odorous gases from open-field decomposition of some agricultural field wastes and poultry wastes; (xi) microscopic dusts from coal dryers; and (xii) dusts from specialized agricultural practices, such as peat dust that is used in growing bleached asparagus.

Included in this list are pollutants for which there is a solution, but, because it would require major changes in local economics or because it would appear to require such changes without compensating benefits to the localities involved, the solution is not acceptable.

Sanitary landfill is available as a nonpolluting substitute for incineration of rubbish. However, in some localities the hauling distances approach the 30- to 50-mile range that is generally considered to be the distance at which modern municipal incinerators are less expensive. Microscopic dusts, although not oxides of nitrogen or oxides of sulfur, can be controlled with very high efficiency collectors, but these are not yet used on incinerators in the United States. Smaller rubbish incinerators can be replaced by more frequent collection service and centralized disposal, even in the most crowded city areas.

Sulfur-free natural gas or low sulfur, low ash, light fuel oil can be substituted for coal and heavy fuel oil at a higher but still moderate cost, even in large power plants, in order to eliminate dust and oxides of sulfur and to reduce oxides of nitrogen. Very high efficiency dust collectors can be used with large coal and heavy oil burning furnaces. Water-based production paints can be substituted for more hydrocarbon-based paints. High efficiency dust collectors can be applied to coal dryers. Gasoline distribution and marketing equipment can be modified to prevent evaporation of hydrocarbons. Odorous gases from chemical recovery furnaces at paper mills can be converted or collected.

Motor Vehicles as Special Control Problems

The increased use of motor vehicles has aggravated the 30- to 50-year-old problem of localized smoke and odorous gases from poorly maintained or poorly fueled vehicles. Ordinary tune-ups and occasional major maintenance correct these emissions; suitable fuel for diesels controls some of their smell and helps to control their smoke.

The increasing use of motor vehicles during the past 25 years has added to the atmosphere enough carbon monoxide and photoreactive nitrogen oxides and hydrocarbons, including ethylene, so that the total of stationary source pollutants plus motor vehicle pollutants has caused a new kind of air pollution mixture on sunny days in more and more areas—the Los Angeles–type of smog.

Several significant time factors have an important bearing on control technology for pollution from motor vehicles:

1) Even with an all-out crash program, several years are usually required to field-test a new type of engine. This is in part due to the wide range of driving environments and driver habits that must be anticipated. An even longer period of time is usually needed to field-test a new type of pollution control accessory because of the large number of new car engines and types of cars as well as the even larger number of variations in older models already on the road.

2) The average life of an automobile is about 11 years. This means that if control improvements are made only on new cars, they cannot produce a rapid reduction in motor vehicle emissions.

The engine wastes 5 to 7 percent of the gasoline supplied to it, and, of this amount, about one-third blows by the pistons into the crankcase. The crankcase blow-by devices return almost all of it to the engine to be burned. These devices are being installed on all new cars sold in the United States.

Several prototype tail-end exhaust control devices are being field-tested now, and four were certified in June 1964 by the California Motor Vehicle Pollution Control Board. They are designed to reduce hydrocarbons by 80 percent averaged over 12,000 miles. At present no reduction of the oxides of nitrogen is planned even though convincing evidence points to the need for this control. Further controls will be needed as the use of automobiles increases.

These will almost certainly consist of changes in engine design and fuel.

Some of the fuel additives, including antiknock compounds, apparently add microscopic dusts to the atmosphere (see Chapter 2, section 7). To what extent these dusts will be controlled by present prototype tail-end control devices is not fully known, but it is expected that some portion of them will be trapped. There is a definite interest in the possibly harmful effects of the increased lead concentrations in metropolitan areas from the antiknock compounds. The control of lead may become more urgent if studies show that the present concentrations are more detrimental to health than earlier investigations indicated. There is also a need for health studies on the effects of other fuel additives.

Diesel-engined vehicles, especially buses with frequent curb-stops, characteristically emit photoreactive hydrocarbons and oxides of nitrogen that have not yet been controlled. These emissions, in the form of odorous gases, occur even when the vehicles are so well maintained and fueled that they are practically smokeless. No control devices or precise standards of accepted emission have been developed for these gases, even in California, which is the world's leader in motor vehicle pollution control. There are some indications that odorous emissions from even two-cycle diesel engines (which are generally considered to be more offensive than emissions from four-cycle diesels) can be greatly reduced by derating each engine size so that its peak power and torque output are deliberately reduced. London has a highly effective program for controlling diesel smoke which is applied to buses run by the London Transport Executive.

This universally recognized nuisance pollution will probably be controlled in the future, but when is not quite certain.

Prospects for the general use of fuel-cell powered automobiles are distant and remote and are somewhat shadowed by the fact that some types of these continuously fed electrochemical battery systems emit undesirable air polluting gases, especially when they are not well maintained. Storage batteries and the use of induced electric power from overhead or street-level cables are also considered only remote possibilities. However, the huge electric generating plants that would be needed to supply the latter would require considerably better air pollution controls than now exist. There would, however, be distinct advantages in using electric motors in enclosed areas, such as a college campus.

A frequent written comment that seems reasonable to many people stresses the notion that a significant amount of the black dust in each community is caused by the wearing down of rubber tires and of asphalt surfaces. However, the adequacy of supporting data, including particle size, is questionable. There is also speculation that, since these materials are primarily organic, the wearing down may be in the form of some type of flameless oxidation, resulting in combustion products. If it should be determined that significant amounts of dust are emitted from these sources, this would present an additional problem for developing suitable control technology. Calculations show that the amounts are relatively small.

Development of California Ambient Air Quality Standards

There are two well-developed systems of ambient air quality standards, each of which derived its original impetus from important questions of public policy. The standards in the Soviet Union were largely the outgrowth of efforts to determine the distance from factories and power plants at which to build housing. That is, the Russians were concerned with point source effects. The standards in California derived much of their impetus from the community-wide air pollution produced by motor vehicle exhaust and the need for control.

This report is concerned with the concepts behind the development of ambient air quality standards in California.

Background for Standards

By 1958 it had become apparent that a major effort would be needed to control motor vehicle emissions if the photochemical air pollution in Los Angeles, San Francisco, and other urban areas was to be abated. Previous efforts had involved the control of emissions from industrial plants or the banning of backyard incinerators. Authorities recognized that the effort and expense that would probably be required to control motor vehicle exhaust would be of an entirely different order of magnitude. Dealing as it would with the vital and sensitive area of personal use of motor vehicles—the very symbol of American mobility—there was agreement that local control programs should yield responsibility to the State of California.

Governor Edmund G. ("Pat") Brown, in a special message to the Legislature on February 10, 1959, said:

> . . . The time has now come for California to take the lead and establish standards for the purity of the air.
>
> Standards for safe air will give local control officials and health officers a measuring stick for smog. It is essential that we know what level of pollution threatens death or illness, or impairs the health of our people. Unless we establish these guideposts, we risk our happiness, our health, and indeed our lives.

In response to this request the 1959 Legislature enacted the following addition to the Health and Safety Code Section 426.1:

> The State Department of Public Health shall, before February 1, 1960, develop and publish standards for the quality of the air of this State. The standards shall be so developed as to reflect the relationship between the intensity and composition of air pollution and the health, illness, including irritation to the senses, and death of human beings, as well as damage to vegetation and interference with visibility.
>
> The standards shall be developed after the Department has held public hearings and afforded an opportunity for all interested persons to appear and file statements or be heard. The Department shall publish such notice of the hearings as it determines to be reasonably necessary.
>
> The Department, after notice and hearing, may revise the standards and shall publish the revised standards, from time to time.

Scientific Basis for Standards

By 1959, a substantial amount of information had been accumulated, mostly from industrial toxicology, about the health effects of single substances. These were usually expressed in threshold limit values for 8-hour exposures of healthy workmen. The levels chosen were based on a number of different criteria: (i) a level that produces only minor, acute health effects or injures a very small proportion of workmen, (ii) a level that is believed to cause no illness or toxic effect during a lifetime, (iii) a level that need not be exceeded because of technologic reasons, or (iv) a level that is not uncomfortable to high proportions, say 90 percent, of previously unexposed workmen.

A small amount of information was available on the effects of atmospheric pollution to the general community. Most of this had been obtained from naturally occurring events, such as the Donora, Meuse Valley, and London air pollution disasters. It was recognized that community air pollution almost always involved many substances and that the individuals running the greatest risk of illness or possible death were those with preexisting illness or whose age or other medical conditions rendered them particularly sensitive. It was also recognized that community air pollution might occur over a larger portion of the day than 8-hour occupational exposures.

Associated with this body of information was a change in emphasis from concern about producing unique or specific diseases to concern about aggravating preexisting disease or contributing to the development of diseases that might be caused by a variety of different exposures and conditions. In a sense, this was a shift of concern from the effect of community air pollution as a specific toxicant to its effect as an agent that might impair health. Detriment to public health was interpreted to include, for example, irritation of the senses, damage to vegetation, and interference with visibility.

Development of Policy for Ambient Air Quality Standards

In response to the Legislature's directive to adopt air quality standards, Department of Public Health staff meetings developed a series of propositions, and these were then submitted to a panel of departmental advisers, the Subcommittee on Ambient Air Quality Standards and Research. Among these propositions, either in explicit or implicit form, were the following:

1) The Department's concern should not be confined exclusively to the photochemical pollutants, but the Department should concern itself with any type of air pollution that could produce the effects stipulated in the Legislative directive.

2) The complete abolition of air pollution was a logical impossibility. The standards should define levels for some pollutants at which specified effects could be predicted, but should not be viewed as desirable degrees of air cleanliness.

3) Any standards set must be based on sound data and concurred in by scientists in air pollution and related fields.

4) The standards relating to human health and well-being should be based on the groups of persons in a population who are most sensitive to air pollution effects, provided such groups be definable in terms of age and medical status.

5) Since air pollution could produce a multiplicity of effects, it was inevitable that the standards be set at several different levels.

6) The technical and policy statements upon which decisions were to be based would be published in full.

Choice of Three Levels and Their Definitions

It was possible to assemble a list of possible and measurable air pollution effects:

1) Acute sickness or death

2) Insidious or chronic disease

3) Alteration of important physiological function, such as ventilation of the lung, transport of oxygen by hemoglobin, or dark retention (the ability to adjust eye mechanisms for vision in partial darkness)

4) Untoward symptoms, that is, symptoms that, in the absence of an obvious cause, such as air pollution, might lead a person to seek medical attention and relief

5) Sufficient discomfort from air pollution to cause individuals to change residence or place of employment

6) Damage to vegetation

7) Impaired visibility

The seriousness of the effect was considered a useful guide in determining the urgency for control. Thus, multiple levels could indicate gradations in the urgency for which control programs should seek results.

These considerations led to the definition of three levels; the need for names of the levels is still being debated. They are used, however, to indicate the relative sense of urgency.

I. *"Adverse"* level. The first effects of air pollutants are those that will probably cause untoward symptoms or discomfort. Although they are not known to be associated with the development of disease, even in sensitive groups, such effects can disturb the population stability of residential or work communities. The "adverse" level is one at which eye irritation occurs. Also in this category are levels of pollutants that lead to costly and undesirable effects other than those on human beings. These include damage to vegetation, reduction in visibility, or property damage of sufficient magnitude to constitute a significant economic or social burden.

II. *"Serious" level.* Concentrations of pollutants, or possible combinations of pollutants, that are likely to cause insidious or chronic disease or significant alteration of physiological functions in a sensitive group define the "serious" level. Such an impairment of function implies a health risk for persons in such a sensitive group, but not necessarily for those in good health.

III. *"Emergency" level.* Levels of pollutants, or combination of pollutants, and meteorological factors likely to lead to acute sickness or death for a sensitive group of people define the "emergency" level.

Choice of Substances for Table of Standards

In developing air quality standards, first priority, of course, has been given to some of the motor vehicle exhaust constituents, particularly those associated with photochemical air pollution; but additional substances have been included and will be included in the future work of the California State Department of Public Health. A number of substances have already been discussed with the department's subcommittee. However, a substance, or a group of substances, was included in the list only after the investigative work had been carried far enough along so that all the information needed to set standards had been reviewed.

Suggestions for additional substances may originate in health departments, air pollution control districts, or with members of the departmental staff. They are then reviewed by the staff and the possibilities, if promising, are explored by collecting information on the sources, concentrations, and possible effects that may be relevant to setting air quality standards. It is in this manner that the substances listed in Table 1 have been chosen.

Table 1. California Table of Standards of Ambient Air Quality (2).

Pollutant	"Adverse" level	"Serious" level	"Emergency" level

Photochemical pollutants
  Hydrocarbons
  Nitrogen dioxide
  Oxidant
  Ozone
  Photochemical
    aerosols
	"Oxidant index"
	0.15 ppm for 1 hour by the potassium iodide method (eye irritation, damage to vegetation and reduced visibility)
		Footnote 1
		Footnote 2
		Not applicable
		Footnote 3
		Not applicable
			Footnote 1
			Footnote 2
			Not applicable
			Footnote 4
			Not applicable

Carbon monoxide	Not applicable	30 ppm for 8 hours or 120 ppm for 1 hour (interference with oxygen transport by blood)	Footnote 5
Ethylene	0.5 ppm for 1 hour or 0.1 ppm for 8 hours (damage to vegetation)	Not applicable	Not applicable
Hydrogen sulfide	0.1 ppm for 1 hour (sensory irritation)	Footnote 6	Footnote 7
Particular matter	Sufficient to reduce visibility to less than 3 miles when relative humidity is less than 70 percent	Not applicable	Not applicable
Sulfur dioxide	1 ppm for 1 hour or 0.3 ppm for 8 hours (damage to vegetation)	5 ppm for 1 hour (bronchoconstriction in human subjects)	10 ppm for 1 hour (severe distress in human subjects)
Sulfuric acid	Footnote 8	Footnote 8	Footnote 9
Carcinogens	Not applicable	Footnote 10	Not applicable
Hydrogen fluoride	Footnote 11	Footnote 12	Not applicable
Lead	Not applicable	Footnote 13	Footnote 13

(1) Hydrocarbons are a group of substances most of which, normally, are toxic only at concentrations in the order of several hundred parts per million. However, a number of hydrocarbons can react photochemically at very low concentrations to produce irritating and toxic substances. Because of the large number of hydrocarbons involved, the complexity of the photochemical reactions and the reactivity of other compounds such as nitrogen dioxide and ozone, it is not yet possible to establish "serious" and "emergency" levels for hydrocarbons. From the public standpoint, the concentration of those hydrocarbons which react photochemically should be maintained at or below the level associated with the oxidant index defined in the "adverse" standard.

(2) Five parts per million of nitrogen dioxide for 8 hours will produce temporarily decreased respiratory function in animals. High levels (150–220 ppm) in short exposures produce fibrotic changes in the lungs of man that may end fatally. More data on human exposures will be needed prior to setting a standard.

Organization of Relevant Data

When a substance or a group of substances has been selected for consideration, the staff of the Air Pollution Medical Studies Unit either compiles the relevant information from the literature and from authoritative sources by consultation and prepares a report, or it arranges to have a consultant prepare such a report. The report consists of data on concentrations of substances, the source

---

(3) Ozone, at 1 ppm for 8 hours daily for about a year, has produced bronchiolitis and fibrositis in rodents. Extrapolation of these data to man is difficult. Functional impairment data have been reported; at 1.25 ppm some effect is observed on residual volume and diffusing capacity. The variability of the tests was not reported. Additional data would be needed before a standard is set.

(4) A value of 2.0 ppm of ozone for 1 hour may produce serious interference with function in healthy persons, and the assumption is made that this might cause acute illness in sensitive persons.

(5) Given certain assumptions concerning ventilatory rates, acute sickness might result from a carbon monoxide level of 240 ppm for 1 hour in sensitive groups because of inactivation of 10 percent of the body's hemoglobin. In any event, it is clear that when a population exposure limit has been set for carbon monoxide, because of exposures from other sources, community air pollution standards should be based on some fraction of this limit.

(6) Hydrogen sulfide is not known to produce chronic disease in humans but there may be durable sequelae from acute exposures. The disagreeable odor may interfere with appetite in sensitive groups of persons at about 5 ppm. At high concentrations loss of the sense of smell occurs. This has been reported at 100 ppm for exposures lasting 2 to 15 minutes. Conjunctivitis and mild respiratory tract irritation have been reported at levels of 50–100 ppm for 1 hour.

(7) Acute sickness and death with neurotoxicity may occur at concentrations of several hundred parts per million. It is very unlikely that these levels will occur in community air pollution.

(8) A sulfuric acid mist level of 1 mg/m³ with an average particle size of 1 micron will produce a respiratory response in man. It is not possible to generalize from this for all air pollution conditions, because under natural conditions, particulate size will vary. Only with large droplets would sensory irritation be produced without other physiological effects.

(9) A level of 5 mg/m³ of sulfuric acid mist for a few minutes produces coughing and irritation in normal individuals. Presumably, it could cause acute illness in sensitive groups of persons in a period of 1 hour.

(10) Carcinogens include a few organic compounds such as some polycyclic hydrocarbons and some metals such as arsenic and chromium. Studies on effects of such substances are currently under way, but there are not sufficient data, at present, to set standards. In the meantime, it is recommended that concentrations of carcinogens in air should be kept as low as possible.

(11) Hydrogen fluoride and other airborne fluorides settle upon and some are absorbed into vegetation. When forage crops containing 30–50 ppm of fluoride measured on a dry weight basis are regularly consumed over a long period the teeth and bones of cattle may show changes, depending upon age, nutritional factors, and the form of fluoride ingested. Such changes may or may not have any economic effect. Fluorides at these levels do not necessarily cause injury to the forage plants themselves. However, injury may be produced in certain species of vegetation upon long-term exposure to low levels of atmospheric fluorides.

(12) The irritating properties of hydrogen fluoride in experimental human exposure have been manifested by desquamation of the skin at concentrations of 2–5 ppm. Mucous membrane irritation also occurs from hydrogen fluorides but quantitative data are not adequate to support a standard.

(13) It is clear that lead levels should be set on the basis of average values for long periods. While data are abundant concerning human response to 8-hours-a-day, 5-days-a-week exposures, data are insufficient for the effects of the continuous exposure inherent in community air pollution. While laboratory studies will be pursued with vigor, it becomes very important that local agencies collect data on existing lead levels. Since lead exposures are from multiple sources, community air pollution standards should be based on a portion of the total limit for population exposure.

of the pollutant, the time course of the pollutant, and the characteristics of unusually sensitive groups of people or categories of plants
and the likelihood of their being affected. The crucial statements,
however, are the relationship between time and concentration and
specific effects. When such information has been adequately confirmed, it is customary to prepare a proposed basis for standards.
The entire report, including the proposed basis and the numerical
values derived from them, is then reviewed with the Department
of Public Health's Subcommittee on Ambient Air Quality Standards and Research. In most cases, outside consultants with special
knowledge of each pollutant are also invited to review the report.
The subcommittee must then decide whether the information is
adequate to support an air quality standard. If the decision is in
the affirmative, the report and the suggested standard are then referred for review to the department's Advisory Committee on Air
Sanitation. If it also approves, the proposed standard is then submitted to the State Board of Health, which, after public hearings,
may incorporate it in the State Administrative Code.

However, in some cases the proposed basis for standards cannot
be developed because of the lack of a key piece of information. The
missing information then becomes an important part of the department's periodic statement on "Research Needed for Standard Setting." When there is insufficient information, the department
usually prepares a footnote to the Table of Standards, indicating
the extent to which information is available and some of the principles on which additional studies might be based.

In some cases a specified substance will not be expected to have a
relevant effect at each of the three levels. In this case, the entry in
the Table of Standards is "not applicable." For example, carbon
monoxide is not known to reduce visibility, damage vegetation, or
produce sensory irritation; hence an "adverse" standard is not
applicable.

Where an entry is made in the Table of Standards, the basis on
which the standard is set is also included.

Compared with occupational health standards and with some
standards from other areas for air quality criteria, these standards
are explicitly related to the state of information with regard to
specified pollutants and specified effects. It does not include any

safety factors since it was thought more desirable for the control agency to include such factors of safety as may seem indicated. For example, for effects at the "serious" or "emergency" level, a larger factor of safety would be indicated. A major reason for this firm tie between research and established fact and the standards was the necessity of using standards as a guide for the very substantial and expensive alterations in the technology of motor vehicles and for other purposes in connection with the control of stationary sources.

What the Standards Are Not

The standards that are set for single pollutants are not necessarily applicable to combinations of pollutants, to physiological effects under unusual weather conditions, or to pollutants occurring in aerosol form or in combination with aerosols. For these reasons, a standard that is given for a pollutant ordinarily without effect at that level should not be interpreted as a guarantee that levels below that point are safe or free from effect.

The history of public health research contains many examples of substances that were once considered innocuous, but which were later shown to be hazardous or harmful. There is no reason to expect that our knowledge of air pollutants will be different. For these reasons, the standards of air quality are not intended to provide a sharp dividing line between air of satisfactory quality and air of unsatisfactory quality, but only to approximate levels at which certain definite undesirable effects, on the basis of present information, can be anticipated. Furthermore, as methods of analysis change, it is quite possible that the standards will be altered; therefore, standards should be considered as dependent upon methods for measuring pollutants, the criteria for selecting the most susceptible group in the community, and the duration of exposure to the pollutant.

For the sake of convenience, standards were expressed for only a limited number of time periods. For example, the data may apply to a 1-hour period or an 8-hour period. In some cases, local conditions that are particularly relevant for photochemical pollutants may or may not be present. Since the oxidant index may be influenced by other contaminants, such as sulfur dioxide, it should not be applied directly to areas that have different climatic conditions. The same consideration does not apply for the carbon monoxide standard, which seems to be a reasonable standard for application in any community. As indicated in "Technical Report on California Standards for Ambient Air Quality and Motor Vehicle Exhaust," the effects of sulfur dioxide are probably different in the presence of other oxidizing atmospheres than they are in the reducing atmosphere of London. Possibly this is because of the association of sulfur dioxide with fog droplets or with other particles.

Extension and Evaluation of Standards

The Department of Public Health periodically reevaluates existing standards in the light of new evidence and considers additional substances from time to time when the need for standards is justified by the available facts. Particular attention, of course, is given to those substances for which blanks exist in the tables and for which additional information is being accumulated.

Consequences of the Standards

The most immediate consequence of the air quality standard was the development of Motor Vehicle Emission Standards, which were initially prepared concurrently by the California State Department of Public Health. These standards were for hydrocarbon emission levels that were designed to reduce the "oxidant" and for carbon monoxide. The motor vehicle exhaust standards have since been incorporated in the program of the California Motor Vehicle Pollution Control Board and efforts to control motor vehicle exhaust and hydrocarbon emissions from the crankcase are based on these standards.

The California effort has led the Air Pollution Control Association to consider ambient air quality standards in several recent annual meetings and it has stimulated various groups to hold seminars and symposiums. In addition, other state and national governments and the World Health Organization (3) have been studying them.

Possible Future Trends in Air Quality Standards

It is recognized that once formulated, standards tend to be copied and retained without the necessary critical evaluation. For this reason, the most important commitment is to a continual reevaluation and modification, when necessary, of air quality standards.

The use of air quality standards in urban planning or zoning has been pointed out by Holland *et al.* (*4*) , who have presented a fundamental equation that signifies one importance of standards. The equation is

$$
\begin{array}{ccc}
\text{Contaminant} & \text{Dilution} & \text{Community standard} \\
\text{emissions to} \quad = & \text{capacity of} \quad \times & \text{for desirable} \\
\text{be permitted} & \text{air resource} & \text{air quality}
\end{array}
$$

This equation implies that once desirable air quality standards are formulated, and an estimate of the dilution volume of an air mass is obtained, then the atmospheric resources can be allocated among a group of possible polluters. Because it omits a term for self-cleansing, as well as for other reasons, this equation should be considered a simplification. Nevertheless, this relationship may well be considered the fundamental equation of community-wide air conservation. The technical difficulties in obtaining accurate estimates of dilution capacity should not be underestimated nor should the metamorphosis of pollutants that might occur in the atmosphere.

Two additional criteria need to be considered for inclusion in the basic scheme of air quality standards. The first is a level below which no biologically significant effect or effect on esthetic values can be detected. Such "no effect" levels are the basis for air quality criteria in the Soviet Union, and the "Technical Report" suggests that such levels could now be developed for sulfur dioxide. Such a criterion has not been used so far because it would require more engineering and control resources than is reasonable; in addition, it tends to suggest that public health, in the sense of avoidance of disease, requires such a standard. In reality, a range of standards that represents a series of predictions with regard to consequences, not necessarily associated with morbidity and mortality in the classical sense, is a relatively new idea in public health. Nevertheless, it was just such an extension of these standards that was recommended by the World Health Organization's Inter-Regional Symposium on Air Quality Criteria in August 1963 (3).

In considering a possible atmospheric air quality standard for lead, the consensus of the experts was that the atmospheric concentration of lead should be kept below a level that would cause an increased burden on the health of the community. In other words, the body burden of a potentially hazardous substance should not be permitted to increase. This second criterion does not now fit into the existing ones but it should probably be considered.

Some recent studies with sulfur dioxide have suggested that this substance may be associated with shortening life in experimental animals. It is quite reasonable to include this criterion, together with the production of chronic disease, in the "serious" level.

It is to be expected that over a period of years air quality criteria will be extended to a number of different substances as well as to combinations of substances. The difficulties in accomplishing the latter will certainly be greater than establishing criteria for a single substance. However, the photochemical pollutants already have an index, the "oxidant index." It is not inconceivable that an index, based on some bioassay, might be established for carcinogenic substances, nor is it inconceivable that an index might also be developed for sulfur dioxide in combination with soots or other particles.

It is hoped that some of the concepts upon which ambient air quality standards have been developed will also be applied in other areas of environmental hazard. This would perhaps be the case for radiation exposure standards for the community and for exposure to agricultural chemicals. In a sense, the recent changes in the values for industrial threshold limits represent the incorporation of some of the ideas contained in the air quality standards; for example, substances are now segregated according to whether a single, acute exposure or a prolonged exposure is more relevant. There is also some special indication for substances that can be absorbed through the skin.

The very intimate relationship between the use of research information and air quality standards deserves to be stressed. The need for air quality standards should provide a goal and program for air pollution research for a long time.

References

1. It is evident that the number of control techniques for different types of a wide variety of operations with air pollution potentials is tremendous and would require an enormous, ever-changing encyclopedia for listing and moderate discussion. There is as yet no complete collection of written information on this subject. The most comprehensive collection of such information available to the general public is in the Robert A. Taft Sanitary Engineering Center and the Technical Assistances Branch of the Division of Air Pollution, Public Health Service, U.S. Department of Health, Education, and Welfare, Cincinnati, Ohio. Excellent collections of control technology information are also available in the larger state and local air pollution agencies, and in those universities doing either extensive air pollution graduate training or research. There are many excellent collections in industrial and association libraries, including the Air Pollution Control Association, which are available in varying degrees to nonmembers. Cases of practical control of various operations in industry appear regularly in the *Journal of the Air Pollution Control Association,* 4400 Fifth Avenue, Pittsburgh 13, Pa., and frequently in the more general engineering journals. The Air Pollution Control Association, in cooperation with U.S. Public Health Service and the Library of Congress, publishes the *APCA Abstracts,* which contain information about control methods on an international scale. Similar information, although not as detailed, is available in the *Chemical Absracts* of the American Chemical Society and in other engineering indexes.
2. As amended by the State Board of Public Health, March 16, 1962, and incorporated into the California Administrative Code, Title 17, Chapter 5, Subchapter 3, article 1.
3. "International agreement on air quality criteria," editorial by J. R. Goldsmith, *Arch. Environ. Health,* **9,** 5 (1964).
4. Holland, W. D., A. Hasegawa, J. R. Taylor, and E. K. Kauper, "Industrial zoning as a means of controlling area source air pollution," *J. Air Pollution Control Assoc.,* **10,** 147 (1960).
5. *Industrial Ventilation* (American Conference of Governmental Industrial Hygienists, ed. 7, Cincinnati, Ohio, 1962).
6. "Modern dust collection," NCA Fuel Engineering Data, Section F-2 (National Coal Assoc., Washington, D.C., 1962).
7. Orr, C., and J. M. DallaValle, "Source control by filtration," in *Air Pollution,* A. C. Stern, Ed. (Academic Press, New York, 1962), vol. 2, pp. 292–312.
8. Adapted from C. J. Stairmand, "The design and performance of modern gas-cleaning equipment," in *Training Course Manual* (Robert A. Taft Sanitary Engineering Center, Cincinnati, Ohio, 1962). Read before the Institute of Chemical Engineers, London, November 1959.
9. *Air Pollution in the Bay Area, Technical Report and Appraisals* (Bay Area Air Pollution Control District, San Francisco, rev. ed. 2, 1962).
10. NCA Fuel Engineering Data (National Coal Assoc., Washington, D.C., 1961).
11. Chass, R. L., "The status of engineering knowledge for the control of air pollution," in *Proceedings of National Conference on Air Pollution* (Department of Health, Education, and Welfare, U.S. Public Health Service, Washington, D.C., 1962), pp. 272–280.

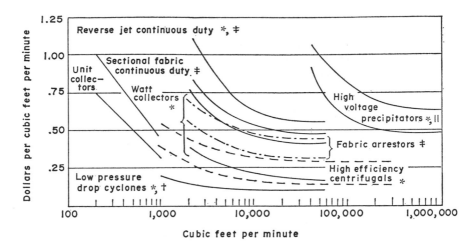

Fig. 1. Cost of wind operations in centrifugal collections (5). * Collectors are normally furnished without exhausters, 7 cents per cubic foot per minute has been added for exhausters.   † Where collectors are normally furnished without dust storage hoppers, 3 cents per cubic foot per minute has been added for dust storage hoppers.   ‡ Price of collectors in the group could be more accurately estimated on the basis of number of square feet of media for fabric arrestors, as there are wide variations for a given exhaust volume, dependent on the application. Estimates assume flow rates of 3 feet per minute through fabric arresters and 15 feet per minute through reverse jet designs. || Price of electrostatic precipitators will vary with the contact time and electrical equipment required. Prices shown are for fly ash installations when high velocities of 300 to 600 feet per minute are usual. Precipitators for metallurgical fumes, and so forth, will be considerably higher in cost per cubic foot per minute. *Accessories included*: Careful analysis of components of equipment included is very important. Some collector designs include exhaust fan, motor, drive, and starter. In other designs, these items and their supporting structure must be secured from other sources by the purchaser. Likewise, while dust storage hoppers are integral parts of some dust collector designs, they are not provided in other types. Duct connections between elements may be included or omitted. Recirculating water pumps and/or settling tanks may be required and may not be included in the equipment price. *Installation cost:* Installation cost can equal or exceed the cost of the collector, depending on the method of shipment (completely assembled, sub-assemblies, or completely knocked down).

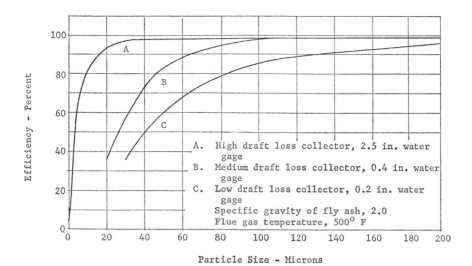

Fig. 2. Fractional efficiency curves for three types of inertial collection (*6*).

Table 2. Cost of unit operations filters (7). Present-day F.O.B. median costs of various filter types in terms of gas-handling capacity are given. The data include only the filters and their frames or enclosures. Installation, fan, and motor costs are not included, even though it often happens with fabric filters, for example, that the cost of fan, motor, structural steel, and installation, taken together, may exceed the cost of the filter unit. It is important not to interpret the cost of a filter as indicative of quality. Each filter type has a specific application to which it is better suited than others.

Type of filter	Median costs in dollars per 1000 cfm* for				
	1000 cfm	5000 cfm	10,000 cfm	20,000 cfm	30,000 cfm
Woven fabric or felt†					
Tubular	400	300	250	220	220
Panel		720	510	460	460
Reverse jet (felt)		950	720	650	
Fiber (throwaway)	7	7	7	7	7
Knitted metal (viscous)	15	15	15	15	15

* Cubic feet per minute, cfm.   † Costs based on air-cloth ratio 2 cfm/ft².

Table 3. Cost of unit operations showing an economic comparison of various collection systems (60,000 cfm; 68° F; 5 grains/ft³) (8).

Equipment	Effi-ciency	Capital cost Total*	Capital cost Per cfm	Pres-sure drop (inches of water, gage)	Power ($/yr)	Gallons of water per 1000 ft³	Water cost ($/yr)	Main-tenance ($/yr)	Total operat-ing cost ($/yr) †	Capital charges ($/yr) ‡	Total cost ($/yr)	¢/1000 ft³
Simple cyclone	65.3	9,240	.14	3.7	4,732			168	4,900	924	5,824	0.02
High-efficiency cyclone	84.2	17,640	.28	4.9	6,328			168	6,496	1,764	8,260	0.029
Irrigated cyclone	91.0	21,840	.36	3.9	5,634	4.0	1,848	420	7,952	2,184	10,136	0.034
Multicyclone	93.8	19,320	.31	4.3	5,544			168	5,712	1,932	7,644	0.027
Electrostatic precipitator	94.1	85,960	1.43	0.6	1,736			700	2,436	8,596	11,032	0.038
Irrigated electrostatic	99.0	147,840	2.46	0.6	3,136	2.5	1,232	1,120	5,488	14,784	20,272	0.070
Conventional fabric filter	99.9	49,280	.81	4.0	5,264			8,940§	14,168	4,928	19,096	0.066
Reverse-jet fabric filter	99.9	47,600	.78	5.0	11,172			7,560‖	18,732	4,700	23,492	0.082
Gravitational spray tower	96.3	51,240	.84	1.4	6,650	18.0	9,240	840	16,730	5,124	21,854	0.075
Wet impingement scrubber	97.9	28,840	.48	6.1	8,120	3.0	1,540	840	10,500	2,884	13,384	0.047
Self-induced spray type	93.5	24,360	.42	6.1	7,896	0.6	308	560	8,764	2,436	11,200	0.028
Venturi scrubber	99.7	42,000	.70	22.0	29,596	7.0	3,388	840	33,824	4,200	38,024	0.128
Disintegrator scrubber	98.5	66,640	1.12	5.0	63,560	5.0	2,380	560	66,500	6,664	75,104	0.257

* Includes accessories and erection.　† Assuming 8000 hr/yr operation.　‡ Ten percent of capital cost.　§ Includes complete change of bags once a year.　‖ Includes complete change of bags twice a year.

Table 4. Cost and efficiency of control equipment or method in grey iron foundry (9). Data on the size of the operation: 48" I.D. melting rate, 8 tons per hour; 4000 scfm tuyere air; 4000 tons of net castings per year; estimated plant investment, $500,000; castings are worth $350 per ton.

| Air pollution emission (lb/hr) | | | | Collection efficiency or recovery (%) | | | Cost of air pollution abatement facilities | | | | | |
| Particles and droplets | | Gases | | | | | Capital investment ($) | | | Operating cost ($/yr) | Plant investment (%) | Cost increase in production (%) |
0–5 microns	>5 microns	Organic	Others	Particles, 0–5 microns	Gases		Major equipment	Auxiliary equipment	Total			
						No control						
40	160	30	1,325	0	0		0	0	0	0	0	
						Afterburner						
35	140	3	30	0	97		1,000	1,000	2,000†	200	0.4	0.05
						*Wet cap**						
35	90	2	25	0	98		10,000	10,000	20,000†‡	2,200	4	0.5
						*Scrubber**						
25	15	2	25	30	98		17,500	12,500	30,000	4,500	6	0.6
						Scrubber§						
10	0.4	1.8	25	65	98		10,000	20,000	30,000†‡	4,500	6	0.6
						Baghouse (*)						
3	0	3	30	92	97		30,000	20,000	50,000†‡	5,000	10	1.0
						Electrical (*) precipiator						
3	0	3	30	92	97		45,000	30,000	75,000	6,500	15	1.2

* Includes afterburners. † Estimated installation costs published by American Foundrymen's Society. ‡ Estimates from similar installations on West Coast. § Estimate prepared by Bay Area Foundry Industry, January 16, 1959.

Table 5. Cost and efficiency of control equipment or method for a steel plant (9). Data on the size of the operation: 5- to 60-ton open hearths, four-furnace operation; melt department value, $2,500,000; total plant value, $25,000,000.

| Air pollution emissions (lb/hr) | | | | Collection efficiency of recovery (%) | | Estimated cost of air pollution abatement facilities | | | | | |
| Particles and droplets | | Gases | | | | Capital investment ($) | | | Operating cost per year | Plant investment (%) | |
0–5 microns	> 5 microns	Organic	Others	Particles, 0–5 microns	Organics and gases	Major equipment	Minor equipment	Total		*	†
						Present					
95	10	5	5	0	0	0	0	0	0	0	0
						Scrubber					
60	5	5	3	40	20	65,000	135,000	200,000	30,000	8.0	0.8
						Baghouse					
9	0	5	5	92	0	200,000	225,000	425,000	40,000	17.0	1.7
						Electrical precipitator					
9	0	5	5	92	0	500,000	300,000	800,000	50,000	32.0	3.2

* For melt department only.   † On total plant value.

Table 6. Cost and efficiency of control equipment or method in a chemical drying operation (9). Data on the size of the operation: 50,000 tons per year of sodium phosphate (137 tons per day); estimated plant investment, $2,000,000.00.

Air pollution emissions (lb/hr)				Collection efficiency of recovery (%)		Cost of air pollution abatement facilities				
Particles and droplets		Gases		Particles, 0–5 microns	Organics and gases	Capital investment ($)			Operating cost ($/yr)	Plant investment (%)
0–5 microns	> 5 microns	Organic	Others			Major equipment	Auxiliary equipment	Total		
No control										
400	13,000									
Primary cyclone										
160	390			60		15,000	5,000	20,000	2,000	1
Secondary multitube cyclones										
100	39			75		35,000	5,000	40,000	4,000	2
Secondary wet scrubber										
8	4			95		40,000	30,000	70,000	8,000	3.5
Baghouse										
4	0			99		50,000	40,000	90,000	9,500	4.5

Table 7. Cost and efficiency of control equipment or method for third catalytic cracker at a petroleum refinery (9). Data on the size of the operation: more than 42,000 barrels per day (catalyst circulation, 3,000 tons per hour). Estimated fluid catalytic cracker investment, $15,000,000.

| Air pollution emissions (lb/hr) | | | | Collection efficiency or recovery (%) | | Cost of air pollution abatement facilities | | | | | |
| Particles and droplets | | Gases | | | | Capital investment ($) | | | Operating cost ($) | Percentage of refinery investment* | Percentage of plant investment† |
0-5 microns	> 5 microns	Organic	Others	0-5 microns	Organics and gases	Major equipment	Auxiliary equipment	Total			
						No control					
						(This condition never exists at catalytic cracker; catalyst cost, $200 to $400 per ton)					
						Cyclones					
100	850	50	500	70	0	220,000	20,000	240,000	15,000	0.19	1.6
						Electrical precipitator‡					
15	25	50	500	85	0	540,000	560,000	1,100,000	20,000	0.85	7.3
						Replacement electrical precipitator‡					
15	25	50	500	85	0	540,000	960,000	1,500,000	20,000	1.15	10.0

* Percentage of refinery investment is based upon an estimated $130,000,000 for a refinery with a daily output of 100,000 barrels. † Percentage of plant investment is based upon an estimated $15,000,000 for a 42,000 bbl/day fluid catalytic cracker.   ‡ Collection efficiency of 0- to 5-micron particles is estimated at 85 percent; actual overall efficiency is 98 percent.

Table 5. Cost and efficiency of coal-fired heating and power plants (10).

Type	Collecting action	Recommended application	Efficiency relative to particle size	Draft loss (inches of water)	Space required (ft²/1000 cpm)	Typical costs ($/1000 cfm)	Other considerations
Cinder trap	Gravity	Smaller plants with under feed, vibrating, chain and traveling grate stokers	30 to 40% for 45 microns and smaller; 75% or more for particles over 45 microns	0.1 to 0.5 (natural draft usually sufficient)	3 to 5	100 to 200	Used mainly to eliminate cinder nuisance in immediate plant area
Medium draft loss	Inertia	Smaller plants with very critical on-grate firing	To 65%; all over 25-micron size	0.4 to 1.5	1 to 3	100 to 200	Abrasions may occur; made in a variety of designs to fit job
Single cyclone (large diameter)	Centrifugal force and inertia	On-grate firing at high rates and some spreader stokers	50 to 90% for particles over 20 microns	0.5 to 2.0	3 to 5	125 to 250	Made in a variety of designs. Care required to fit design to job
Multicyclone (small diameter tubes)	Centrifugal force and inertia	Spreader stoker	75 to 90% for particles over 10 microns	2.0 to 6.0	1 to 1.5	150 to 300	Abrasion may be a problem
Wet scrubber	Gravity	Spreader stoker and pulverized coal firing	70 to 90% depending on particle size; 75% over 2 microns	13 to 20	2 to 16	200 to 1000	Caking and corrosion may be a problem, also water recovery
Electrostatic precipitator	Electrical attraction	Pulverized coal firing	85 to 99%, submicron to 10 microns (high efficiencies call for series installation with multi-clone collector)	0.1 to 0.5	Large	300 to 1000	Continuous cleaning necessary
Siliconized glass filter	Filtering	Pulverized coal firing	98 to 99% for submicron to 44 microns	1 to 6	3 to 15	600 to 1000	Exit temperature limited to 600°F maximum

Table 9. Typical costs of basic and control equipment installed in Los Angeles County (11). The types of control devices installed vary widely in cost and collection efficiency. Among them are electric precipitators, baghouses, afterburners, separators, scrubbers, absorbers, and various types of vapor collection equipment. Each type of device possesses advantages and limitations that must be considered carefully. Each source poses different problems in terms of volume, temperature, and characteristics of the waste emitted. The degree of control which a community requires will dictate, in the main, which type of control device will be utilized and, hence, the cost of the control system. This table gives a list of typical basic and control equipment installed in Los Angeles County during the last 14 years. In some cases, the cost of the control equipment is only a small fraction of the cost of the production equipment. In other cases, the cost of control equipment is greater than the cost of the basic equipment.

Source	Size of equipment	Cost of basic equipment	Type of control equipment	Cost of control equipment
Airblown asphalt system	500 bbl/batch	$ 10,500	Afterburner	$ 3,000
Asphalt concrete batching plant	200,000 lb/hr	150,000	Scrubber	10,000
Asphalt saturator	6 by 65 by 8 ft	40,000	Scrubber and electric precipitator	50,000
Asphalt tile production	5,000 lb/hr	150,000	Baghouse	5,000
Borax drying and classifying	10,000 lb/hr	1,000,000	Baghouse and scrubber	10,000
Bulk gasoline loading rack	667,000 gal/day	88,000	Vapor control system	50,000
Carbon black plant	2,000 gal/day	5,000	Baghouse	5,000
Catalytic reforming unit	2,400 bbl/day	265,000	Flare and sour water oxidizer	6,000
Ceramic tile production	8,000 lb/hr	200,000	Scrubber	10,000
Chip dryer, aluminum	2,500 lb/hr	3,000	Afterburner	3,000
Chrome plating	4 by 5 by 5 ft	2,000	Scrubber	800
Coffee roaster	3 ton/hr	35,000	Cyclone and afterburner	8,000
Concrete batching plant	900,000 lb/hr	125,000	Baghouse	10,000
Core oven	8 by 8 by 12 ft	4,000	Afterburner	1,500
Crucible furnace, yellow brass	4 furnaces @ 850 lb each/heat	2,500*	Baghouse	17,000
Crude oil distillation unit	37,000 bbl/hr	3,060,000	Vapor control system	10,000
Cupola, gray iron	48" ID	40,000	Baghouse and quench tank	67,000
	27" ID	25,000	Baghouse and quench tank	32,000
Debonder	500 brake shoes/hr	1,800	Afterburner	300
Deep fat fryer, food	1,000 lb/hr	4,000,000	Afterburner	1,500
Delayed coker unit	9,300 bbl/day		Scrubber (serving 3 cokers)	385,000
Drum reclamation incinerator	60 bbl/hr	10,000	Afterburner	2,000
	200 bbl/hr	25,000	Afterburner	5,000
Electric arc furnace, steel	18 ton/heat	75,000	Baghouse	45,000
Electric induction furnace, brass	2,000 lb/hr	75,000	Baghouse	2,700
Enamel frit drying	1,500 lb/hr	25,000	Baghouse	3,000
Fiberboard production	32,000 lb/hr	10,000	Electric precipitator	15,000
Fire-retardant manufacturing	1,000 lb/hr	25,000	Baghouse	2,000
Fixed roof storage tank for gasoline	80,000 bbl	50,000	New floating roof tank	132,000
Flue-fed incinerator	Most sizes	4,000-7,000	Afterburner	2,500
Fluid catalytic cracking unit	40,000 bbl/day	7,460,000	Electric precipitator	1,040,000
			CO boiler	1,770,000
			Cyclones	165,000
			Blowdown systems, vapor manifold, and flare	363,000
	7,400 bbl/day	1,747,500	Electric precipitator, vapor manifold, and flare	131,000
Galvanizing kettle	4 by 30 by 4 ft	25,000	Baghouse	3,000
Gritblasting machine	6 ft³	9,300	Baghouse	1,700
Insecticide manufacturing	1,000 lb/hr	10,000	Baghouse	3,000
Insulation production, including cupola, blow chamber, and curing oven	5,000 lb/hr	13,000	Baghouse, scrubber, and afterburner	30,000
Liquid hydrogen manufacturing	32 ton/yr	8,392,000	Flare	17,700
Lithographing oven	240 ft/min	78,000	Afterburner	15,000
Multiple-chamber incinerator, industrial and commercial	50 lb/hr	800		
	500 lb/hr	6,500		
	6,000 lb/hr	75,000		
Multiple-chamber incinerator, pathological	50 lb/hr	1,000		
	200 lb/hr	4,500		
Multiple-chamber incinerator, wire reclamation	100 lb/hr	1,200		
	1,000 lb/hr	15,000		

* Each

Table 9 (continued)

Source	Size of equipment	Cost of basic equipment	Type of control equipment	Cost of control equipment
Multiple-chamber incinerator, with continuous feed bin	250 lb/hr 3.000 lb/hr	$ 5,000 45,000		
Natural gas plant	20,000,000 ft³/day	220,000	Vapor manifold and flare	$ 5,000
Oil-water separator	300,000 bbl/day	170,000	Floating roof	80,000
	350 bbl/day	17,000	Cover	700
	3,500 bbl/day	32,000	Floating roof	8,000
Open hearth furnace, steel	60 ton/heat	200,000	Electric precipitator	150,000
Phosphate fertilizer production	2,000 lb/hr	10,000	Baghouse	5,000
Phthalic anhydride manufacturing plant	25,000,000 lb/yr	1,200,000	Afterburner and baghouse	195,000
Pipe coating, including spinning, wrapping, and dipping	4–10 lengths/hr	23,500	Scrubbers	32,000
Pneumatic conveyors (minerals)	200 to 5,000 lb/hr	2,000	Cyclone and baghouse	2,000
Pot furnace, type metal	16,000 lb	9,000	Afterburner	3,000
Rendered grease processing	6 ton/day	10,000	Contact condenser and afterburner	2,500
Rendering cooker and drier (batch)	4 ton/batch	10,000	Surface condenser and afterburner	15,000
Rendering cooker system (continuous)	15 ton/hr	100,000	Surface condenser and afterburner	25,000
Rock crushing and sizing	300,000 lb/hr	75,000	Scrubber	2,000
Rotogravure press	5-color, 44-in. web	340,000	Activated carbon filter	40,000
Rubber Banbury mixer	1,000 lb/hr	25,000	Baghouse	3,000
Sandblast room	8 by 12 by 8 ft	1,600	Baghouse	3,000
Sewage treatment digestion	900,000 gal/day	800,000	Water seals and flares	7,000
Sewage treatment headworks	250,000,000 gal/day	550,000	Covers	20,000
Sewage water reclamation	17,000,000 gal/day	1,500,000	Covers and aeration tanks	25,000
Sewer pipe manufacturing	20,000 lb/hr	1,000,000	Baghouse	10,000
Ship bulk loading	2,500 ton/hr	500,000	Baghouse	168,000
Smoke generator and smokehouse	11 by 14 by 11 ft	18,000	Precipitator, scrubber, and afterburner	42,000
Sulfuric acid plant	250 ton/day	1,900,000	Electrostatic precipitator	150,000
Sulfur recovery plant	2 parallel units, 65 ton/day each	1,400,000	Incinerator	30,000
	10 ton/day	265,000	Incinerator	5,000
	2,840 lb/day	30,000	Incinerator	1,000
	8,000 lb/day	60,000	Incinerator	1,000
Sweat furnace, aluminum	3,000 lb/hr	3,500	Afterburner and baghouse	3,500
Synthetic rubber manufacturing	30,000 ton/yr	1,600,000	Vapor manifold and flare	250,000
Synthetic solvent dry cleaner	60 lb/batch	14,000	Activated carbon filter	3,000
Varnish cookers (2)	250 gal/each	4,000	Afterburner	5,500
Wallboard production	60,000 lb/hr	1,500,000	Baghouse	100,000

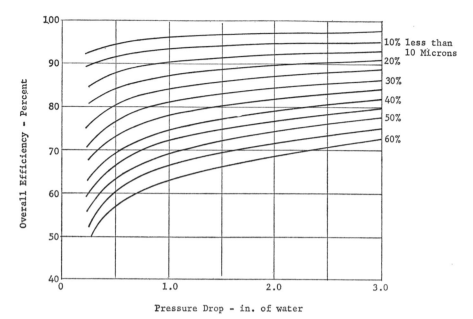

Fig. 3. Performance of typical mechanical cyclone dust collector (6).

CHAPTER 6

Socio-Economic Factors

Air pollution is a social and economic problem. Its cause and its solution may be found in man's relationship to man, and in his relationship to his tools and his economic life.

The first section of this chapter will deal with air conservation as a social problem, and the second will consider the application of economic analysis to air conservation.

Air Conservation as a Social Problem

Although little has been written in the field of sociology on the subject of air conservation, we may learn a great deal from the work of those sociologists who have studied social change and social problems, and how the public accepts and uses new knowledge.

Human reaction to environmental change depends not only on the precise nature of the change, but also, to a large extent, on factors of space and time. L. J. Carr (*1*) suggests four categories to describe environmental conditions in flux:

1) *Focalized-instantaneous change.* In the context of air pollution, such disturbances as the collision of river barges (one of them carrying chlorine) or a fire at an oil refinery could fall within this category. Evacuation is the most common response until the danger is past.

2) *Diffuse-instantaneous change.* Iodine-131 fallout from the explosion of a nuclear test weapon may affect many people over a broad area in a short span of time. The response to this kind of environmental change most often involves alerting residents in affected areas to take the steps necessary to avoid exposure until the danger is past.

3) *Focalized-progressive change.* Some environmental disturbances affect small geographic areas in a gradual and cumulative fashion, such as the progressive decay of a residential area that results in a slum. A viewer of this phenomenon would be hard pressed to detect any change through daily observation, but periodic surveys would reveal the cumulative changes. The periodic expansion of an industry may result in air pollutants being released into a section of the community to an increasing degree. The response of residents to this kind of change is akin to their response to focalized instantaneous change—evacuation. But the departure of residents is also progressive and the homes they vacate are filled by others who may be attracted by cheaper rents. Those who cannot afford to move to unaffected areas, together with their new neighbors, learn to tolerate or adapt to the changes as an inescapable fact of life.

4) *Diffuse-progressive change.* Many vast metropolitan areas and their environs are affected by slow but steadily increasing volumes of wastes that are introduced into the atmosphere as a consequence of urbanization. The steady movement of people to metropolitan areas to work in manufacturing plants or in service industries increases the available labor market and the need for more goods and services. More residents need more homes, each contributing its wastes to the air. More workers travel greater distances in their automobiles to more plants and businesses. Each adds to the burden.

When a city grows up in a place where nature cannot dispose of its wastes with sufficient speed, the need for air conservation programs becomes progressively evident.

A change that falls into the fourth category represents a distinctly social problem. It is of concern not only to individuals or industries but also to society as a whole. For such a change is a "phenomenon, for the appearance of which no one individual or few individuals are responsible, which threatens injurious results for many persons, and the removal or control of which is completely beyond the ability of one person or a few individuals" (2).

It is far easier to solve a problem if a single cause can be isolated for attack. But the data presented in this study clearly show that there is seldom a single source of pollutants. No one industry is solely responsible. No one individual with his automobile creates the situation. Air pollution is a consequence of a multitude of normal and permissible acts of individuals operating in a technologically advanced society.

James Bossard (3) has described the steps or stages through which society normally solves its problems:

1) Gradual recognition that a problem exists, accompanied by growing community discontent

2) Discussions of the problem by individuals and groups

3) "Reforms," usually intuitively arrived at, ill-advised, often attempted by individuals and groups in a disorganized fashion

4) Failure of the first efforts, followed by requests for careful studies and more information

5) Identification of the basic factors that created the problem and development of policies

6) Application and interpretation of the policies by administrators

Resistance to Change

Each stage of the natural historical development of a social problem and its solution is met with different kinds and varying degrees of resistance (4). Thus, "one of the major psychological obstacles to any kind of change is the prevailing habit systems of people, the tendency to repeat old adjustment patterns as long as the environment permits" (1, p. 129). Through the use of normal defense mechanisms, people can close their eyes to all kinds of facts, even though, from a rational point of view, such facts may be essential to their physical or social existence (5, 6). Moreover, it is normal for intelligent men to behave inconsistently. They may hold to a set of principles and, without being conscious of the inconsistency, they may behave in a way that contradicts those principles.

In addition to psychological factors, economics may play a major role in resisting the solution of social problems (see page 281).

In any society a constellation of values will arise that supports acceptable and expected economic behavior in the various social units that compose the whole (7). Making a living according to the accepted rules is basic to man's participation in society. Economic values are therefore apt to preempt and dominate other values that are cherished at the same time. Should conflict arise between them, as Carr notes (1, p. 130), people may turn to economic values to protect their vested interests, power, and privileges by developing elaborate rationalizations, or through other psychological mechanisms. However, economic resistance is not wholly nor even predominantly psychological in origin. In resisting social change, man may actually fulfill his responsibility to a large group interest and, in so doing, perform acts opposed to his own personal views.

The resistance of a manufacturing executive to the installation of equipment to reduce the air pollutants produced by his firm does not necessarily indicate that he is indifferent to community welfare. He is faced with the problem of balancing his responsibility to the community against his responsibility to the stockholders who have invested their money and expect a profit. Norton E. Long (8) points out that, in attempting to meet these conflicting responsibilities, the executive faces a problem that may force him to choose between two different loyalties. This may result in severing his relationship with the community as an important leader, or in losing his job.

Social systems, like the individuals and groups making them up, also develop identifiable patterns of adaptation to environmental conditions and resistance to change that are essential to their integration and survival. Functional resistances are those that are a consequence of the system in operation and its interrelationships with other systems. Three major causes of functional resistance to social change are (i) interdependence of social units, (ii) indirectness of impact, and (iii) systemic inertia (1, p. 129).

Any system is composed of two or more interacting parts or units (9). The relationship between these units is such that a change in any one of them tends to affect the others. The larger and more complex the system, the more difficult it becomes to predict the effect of a specific change in one unit; effects may produce still other effects in a chain reaction. Thus, the manager of a manufacturing plant can reason, "If I introduce expensive equipment to control wastes, I shall have to increase the unit cost of my product. My competitor located in City X will then be able to undersell me, my company will lose money and become bankrupt, and I and my employees shall lose our jobs." Faced with the possibility of losing a livelihood, not only the manager, but his 700 employees, will, quite naturally, resist the change.

"Indirectness of impact" also causes resistance—a consequence of the inability to see a relationship between the units of the system. The effects of environmental change may be slow to appear and may not be obviously related to their causes. The person who can see no connection between his chronic respiratory condition and the contaminated air he breathes is not easily moved to support a program designed to rectify the condition. The barrier created by indirectness of impact is public apathy and indifference.

"Systemic inertia" refers to the resistance of a social system to the elements that do not fit or are inconsistent with the system's pattern of operation. For example, the presence of skilled mechanics in England delayed mass production in that country. Systemic inertia cannot resist all innovation or change. Systems, and particularly social systems, have adaptive mechanisms that permit a great deal of modification. Only those attempts at modification that cannot be integrated with the operation of the on-going system must fail.

All three of these functional resistances to the solution of the problem of air conservation require some analysis.

With reference to the interdependence of the units in the system, the objective in seeking a solution should be to find "coincidences of interests." For example, units in the social system can be expected to support air conservation objectives for quite separate reasons. The replacement of heavy automobile traffic by electric public transportation in urban areas may be supported in order to reduce commuter fatigue and to reduce traffic accidents. The elimination of individual disposal of trash may be supported for sanitary reasons. The elimination of low-grade household heating units may result from slum clearance.

The problem of air conservation is especially hampered by "indirectness of impact." Air pollution is generally a "diffuse-progressive change," and the deterioration of the environment is so gradual that the public rarely can define it as a social problem.

While "systemic inertia" is generally viewed as a basic resistance to social change, it may be used to achieve a desired result. This principle was illustrated dramatically by the success of Saul Alinsky

(10). After others had failed in dealing with the social problems in a Chicago community referred to as "back of the yards," Alinsky analyzed the existing social system (power structure, language, values, loyalties, and dominant interaction patterns) and successfully introduced social reforms into the going system.

Informing the Public

David Riesman *(11)* has written that many scientists who have had a disappointing experience in attempting to communicate with the public have concluded that one "must choose between moral preachment divorced from factuality on the one side, and technical discourse divorced from morality on the other . . . ." Fortunately, as Riesman notes, the choice of content and style of presentation is far more complex than this.

How the scientist passes on the information, however, is but one part of the communication problem. Many social scientists have tried to determine how the public receives information.

Much of the research on communication has been based on a straight-line model for the communication process that was originally stated by Harold Lasswell in the form, "Who says what in which channel to whom with what effect" *(12)*. As early as 1948, the assumptions of this model were questioned in studies conducted at Columbia University. Lazarsfeld, Berelson, and Gaudet, in their study of voting behavior, *The People's Choice (13)*, suggested that information from the mass media was received by "opinion leaders" in each community "who in turn pass on what they read and hear to those of their every-day associates, for whom they are influential" *(14)*. Elihu Katz reports that the concept of a "two-step flow of communication" has been tested in a number of different research efforts and "the original hypothesis is largely corroborated" *(14)*. Studies after *The People's Choice* have sought to perfect methods for identifying opinion leaders *(15)*, defining their characteristics, and establishing the ways in which they wield their influence.

Most studies show that individuals in the community turn to different persons for opinion leadership, depending on the particular issue in question. Thus, there are marketing leaders, fashion leaders, public affairs leaders, and movie leaders, and although some persons appear as leaders in more than one area, there is no evidence to indicate that a leader in one area will also be a leader in another (16, p. 334). Moreover, "the power of the opinion leader in marketing, fashions and movie-going, which finds expressions in informal persuasion and friendly influence, probably does not derive from wealth, or high position but from casual, everyday contact with peers" (16, p. 325).

There is evidence that opinion leaders expose themselves more to the mass media and are less resistant to change than nonopinion leaders in the community. And it is also clear that different kinds of opinion leaders expose themselves to different kinds of mass media. For example, Robert K. Merton differentiates between the "local influential" and the "cosmopolitan influential." The "local influential" is interested in knowing as many people in the community as possible, in reading the local newspaper, and in belonging to local organizations. The "cosmopolitan influential," on the other hand, prefers to get to know fewer people, but to know them in depth. He reads magazines and journals that deal with events outside the community, and he belongs to national organizations and societies in which his special skills and knowledge can be used (17). Merton says that information from the mass media seldom has a direct effect, but that it is responded to selectively, and its content is filtered and evaluated according to the values of the primary group to which the receiver belongs (18).

Closely related to the concepts of opinion leadership and the influential people in the community is the concept of the community power figure. It is often asserted that most communities are "run" by a small group of highly influential people and that the clique has complete control over the significant events that occur. While this is a popular view that has been supported by some studies of community power structure (19), the prevailing view is that power in a community is not monolithic (20). On the contrary, research findings show that power exerted in action programs for social change is generally shared by a plurality of community groups. These groups form coalitions to deal with specific action programs and then dissolve to re-form in new combinations as new needs arise (21). Functionaries in the various community systems can apparently exert considerable influence over their own systems and over the community when the issue relates to the functions served by the system.

In summarizing a review of *Studies on Community Studies,* Sanders states, "The more we learn about the comparative study of communities, the more we find that their power structures vary widely from rigid hierarchical to the nearly amorphous, fleeting coalitions of people with some measure of power" (*22,* p. 44).

Overcoming Resistance

In efforts to solve air pollution problems, communities must be studied in order to identify the different loci of power, and the functionaries who occupy dominant positions in the system must become involved so that the systemic inertia of these systems can be used advantageously. Particular attention should be given to two major systems—health and education.

The health system in most communities is already imbued with an ideology that automatically receives air conservation as a natural complement, and it also has the structures and material resources to help conduct such a program. For instance, city and county health departments already have procedures for enforcing health standards. Their staffs usually include specialists trained in epidemiological research. Both research and sanctions are important elements to an air conservation program. Unfortunately, the ties between community health systems and other community systems are limited (*22,* p. 380). On the other hand, its ties with larger systems beyond the community may compensate for this deficiency. The diffuse nature of the air pollution problem means that systems extending beyond the political boundaries of a municipality must become involved. The literature on metropolitan planning increasingly notes the necessity for consolidating smaller urban units. This calls attention to the fact that "urban sprawl" or "megapolis" constitutes a social problem in its own right (*23*) (see Chapter 3).

The educational system offers another opportunity for imaginative programming as soon as simple and inexpensive devices for measuring atmospheric pollution can be developed and made available. In many schools, natural science concepts, such as temperature, humidity, air pressure, and so forth, are introduced as early as the second grade. High school students seeking information for a ninth-grade science project on the part each industry plays in the pollution problem might have a profound effect on local industrial leaders.

Studies should be carried out now to help us understand not only what technology can best be applied to reduce the pouring of wastes into our atmosphere, but also what systems have to be activated in order to encourage the application of this technology in a given community. By combining our knowledge, through physical science, of what can be done, with our knowledge, through social science, of how it can be done, and given the structure of the community and the opinions held by its residents, it will be possible to overcome the pessimistic view that now presents a barrier to social change.

Economic Analysis and Air Conservation

Air conservation clearly belongs to that class of economic functions that calls for public action. Air is not protected by tenure, and is therefore subject to overuse in the absence of explicit public policies to prevent it. In this respect it is analogous to the open range with unrestricted grazing, fishing on the high seas, public parks without control of access, and the city streets. Furthermore, air pollution is generally difficult to trace from one source to one receptor. Diffusion of responsibility and damage makes contractual or legal procedures inapplicable. In addition, the unprotected air resource moves continually across property lines so that the cost of pollution is to inflict damage on all other resources. Overuse of the open range, fisheries, or parks primarily damages competitive exploiters of the same resource. Overuse of the air may damage everyone whom it envelops.

General Principles

Can economic analysis be of service in framing public policy for air conservation, especially since air is a resource traditionally considered "noneconomic" and since it means applying natural science to public policy?

The difference among disciplines is not in the material things with which they are concerned, but in the aspects of the same things that they measure. Thus, a physicist's yardstick may be mass or temperature, while that of the economist is value. Each discipline, in its own terms, comprehends most of the universe. "Value" is not something apart from people, but springs from human desires and aversions. It is a misleading use of words to distinguish "human damage" (from air pollution) from "economic damage." Economic analysis begins with the postulate that man is the measure of all things. Direct damage to human health and happiness is more directly "economic" than intermediate damage to artifacts, which are simply means to health and happiness.

Economic analysis can be applied to more than just the goods that are traded in the market place. To evaluate public policy is also a function of economic analysis. For example, taxes and subsidies may be imposed in such a way that they motivate and constrain activity in much the same way that prices would. Activities may be limited by requiring licensing and controlling the number of licenses. The economic value of the activity may then be measured by observing the prices at which the licenses sell or rent.

"Benefit-cost analysis" and "welfare economics" are subdisciplines that deal with evaluating nonsalable benefits. For example, there is much in the economics literature on the justification and size of flood-control projects, the benefits of which are almost entirely non-salable. Ground-water control has been the subject of considerable economic analysis and it offers a close analogy to air conservation.

One of the primary contributions and purposes of economic analysis is to facilitate judgments among alternatives by reducing them to a common measure. The economist's measure, exchange value, is designed to serve as a means of communication and reconciliation between otherwise disparate disciplines and interest groups. Once the economist's measuring stick is accepted, it is possible to not only judge between simple alternatives, but also to render detailed quantitative judgments on how much the enhancement of air quality is worth in terms of cost, time, and place. It is possible to decide which of many options is best, securing maximum net benefits over costs. It is possible to decide that some things must be sacrificed entirely, or that others need not be restricted at all.

And, having made such decisions, it is possible in the interests of distributive equity, to devise means to compensate the losers from the gains of the winners.

Thus, economic analysis serves an essential function in social decision-making, arbitrating among the rival claims of different interest groups and disciplines. There is little room in it for absolutism; it is an art of communication and compromise.

The air conservationist would agree with the fact that we should not clean the air at the expense of polluting the water. That kind of expense is very obvious within his frame of reference. However, the economist would generalize further. He would object to carrying air conservation to such a point, for example, that men would be deprived of their livelihood, or education had to be neglected, or homes had to go cold in winter. And he would go still further, and not sacrifice anything to air conservation that had a social value greater than the social value of the air improvement. And he would seek means to measure social value objectively, without reference to his own scale of values, by checking values fixed in free markets that reflect the likes and dislikes of all people.

The economist generally expects that any problem will have several solutions, some alternative and some complementary. He is schooled to put them together in an optimal package, computing the trade-offs at the margins between them, or the point at which one should be entirely scrapped and replaced by another. However, all his techniques postulate a common measuring rod—exchange value.

Economists have made progress in devising methods to measure the social benefits from such nonsalable services as flood control and recreation facilities. Much remains to be done, and much that has been done remains to be widely understood. Thus, we would be sanguine to claim that most economists could measure benefits from air conservation within, say, 30-percent accuracy. Nevertheless, there are workable methods. The appraisal of impaired earning capacity due to sickness or injury, for example, is a recognized art. Appraisal of land values is another. The two arts together should go far toward helping us measure the net benefits of air conservation.

Increased land values as a result of improved air quality are an excellent first approximation for measuring net benefits since land values tend to capture the net social benefits of a location—that is, gross benefits less the auxiliary costs of exploiting them. Of course, one cannot simply compare two areas, or the same area at different times, and impute the difference in land values to air quality, for there are many other factors involved. But social scientists have long since passed the stage of throwing up their hands in despair when they cannot establish simple functional relationships. They have developed the art of multiple correlation analysis, and it should be possible, with adequate study of many sets of data, to establish the relationship of air quality to land values with a higher degree of certainty than, for example, to relate cigarette smoking to lung cancer.

Another approach is to observe how much families and industries privately spend to enhance air quality inside buildings. The value of a public water supply, for an analogy, can be estimated quite accurately by observing private spending for individual pumped wells. Industrial air quality control is a thriving business, and experienced engineers can supply data on the cost of achieving various levels of air quality and on whether it is worth the expenditure. It is also instructive to study the advertising for home humidifiers, electrostatic precipitators, air conditioners, and the like, noting the relative emphasis on different benefits to health and property.

The economist's approach cannot displace the medical approach of public health officers, but only supplement it. Public health officials are presumably aware of the long-term effects of air pollution on organic function, a factor that might escape the attention of the average citizen. The economist's measures have the weakness of being based only on average sentiments, perceptions, and opinions. Thus, in smogbound Los Angeles, the price of land for residential building is second only to New York, reflecting a consumer preference that says "Damn the smog, full speed ahead!" Public health officers, armed with superior technical information, might be aware of health effects from this smog immersion which, if they were widely known, would reverse the migration into Los Angeles. No economist would argue that market values deserve great respect when they are based on imperfect knowledge, and he would support public health officials in exercising some power based on their superior knowledge. He would prefer that the knowledge be shared universally, but he recognizes the high cost and the inherent difficulties involved.

The economist would insist, however, that public health officials act contrary to market judgments only on the basis of superior knowledge, not on the basis of differing personal values. He would further insist that they make every effort to widely disseminate the knowledge on which their judgments are based, and he would deplore any tendencies toward cabalism and mandarinism. And, knowing the universal human weakness for cabalism, he would urge that all claims to power that are based on inside information be viewed and periodically reviewed with piercing and skeptical eyes.

Interrelationship of Policies

The web of human institutions and market and fiscal relations are complex enough so that "when you scratch it anywhere, it hurts everywhere." There can, therefore, be no air pollution control program in a vacuum. Air conservationists must be prepared to co ordinate their policies with other programs and to ultimately see that air conservation is one part of a larger whole of related policies of environmental control. Here again, economics can be useful in balancing out a total program and fitting air conservation into proportion.

A policy that will help most of the people will undoubtedly hurt some, and many or most policy proposals founder on the rock of distributing benefits and costs. Thus, when it is proposed that air pollution in New York be alleviated by moving power plants to West Virginia, it is protested by saying that the 100 mountaineers who will be affected in the new location will suffer as much as 1 million New Yorkers in the old, and that therefore the move should not be made.

The economist stresses that the joint benefits should be maximized, and that the losers should then be compensated from the gains of the winners. This may be done, and, indeed, it is constantly being done, by adjusting tax assessments on property, purchase of easements, condemnation, and so forth. The economist must further stress, however, that our redistributive mechanisms are entirely inadequate, so that maximization of joint net benefits from public action is almost always blocked far below 100 percent of maximum by distributive problems.

We lack, first of all, a sense of community or polity over areas large enough to handle most air conservation problems. Second, we lack any consensus as to what comprises the proper *status quo ante delicte* from which departures should be compensable. There is a pervading uneasiness about accepting the present distribution of property as a base, the historical origins of which might better not be examined. But there has also been an unwillingness to meet this question head on, so that the discipline offered by economics does not give us adequate counsel on the subject. There is, however, a general feeling that property has always been received, held, and bought subject to taxation and the jeopardy of increased taxation, so that the tax mechanism is a fitting one for redistributing the gains and losses from public actions.

Air may be regarded as a common domain to be managed under public tenure, as the Bureau of Land Management administers many western grazing lands. Invasions of the domain by polluters may then be regarded as trespassing, and taxes on polluters and other controls can be justified as constraints on trespass and/or rentals or royalties for use of public resources. The beneficiaries of pollution control—the owners of lands protected from pollution— might also be expected to pay higher taxes for the maintenance of their access to the unpolluted air domain, just as they pay for flood control or police protection.

Some might think that air conservation should be supplied without cost to the beneficiaries, since pure air is a "natural" condition. However, the ownership of superior natural resources is itself a special privilege, subject to taxation; and maintaining pure air for some imposes sacrifices on others who must use the waste-disposal capacity of air. Unless we draw an invidious line between two groups or two needs for using the air, it would seem both equitable and economical to weigh them in the same balance. We object to the presumptuousness of the polluter who acts as though he could appropriate all the air to his own use. But it is just as presumptuous for nonpolluters to extend their domain over the common air in the opposite way by prohibiting almost all pollution without balancing their gains against the costs to others.

This is less true as there is less chance of escaping from pollution. However, when it is much easier for the victims of pollution to escape by moving to another area than it is for polluters to remove or abate the offense, as might often be the case, then a reasonable philosophy should leave room for the former solution. The Bureau of Air Management would allow more or less pollution, depending on the relative values involved, always pursuing the basic goal of maximizing the joint benefits. Taxation could then be used to compensate the losers from the gains of the winners.

Taxation as a Method of Restraint

The polluter may bear the costs of control in at least three different ways: (i) He may discontinue the operation altogether; (ii) he may modify it to reduce noxious emissions; or (iii) he may pay the public a royalty for invading the air resource. In the third alternative, the polluter compensates the damaged parties by lightening their tax load.

The tax method of constraint and redistribution has several advantages, not the least of which is that taxation is incremental and permits very fine gradations. Taxation can also be automatic in the sense that it operates to fine some activities and reward others without specific court or police action. For example, a tax on diesel oil acts to discourage its use in any quantity, including those uses that are too small to reach the threshold of police action or lawsuit.

Another advantage of the tax approach is that air management is not a net drain on the treasury, but a source of revenue, and that by the simple recognition of the unexceptionable facts that air is a valuable resource and is a common domain.

The economist resists any concept of a "minimum tolerable standard" of air quality to be maintained for all persons at all times and places. As in other traits, individuals differ in their sensitivity to air pollutants, probably along a normal frequency distribution curve. We are fortunate to have the most sensitive 1 percent in the population since their function is similar to that of canaries in a mine; they warn the rest of us. It would be prohibitive, however, to keep all air at all times at the high standard of purity required by this 1 percent of the population. There is a trade-off between preventive measures, and one reasonable preventive would be that hypersensitive people avoid certain areas and occupations.

However, it is not only a matter of sensitivity but also one of personal preference. Many people prefer to accept the risk, or even certainty, of shorter life in return for higher income, or a warmer climate, or urban diversions, and so forth. Many people see life as so hazardous in any event that the additional risk from air pollution is negligible. Those who do not agree have no license to impose their preferences on all.

There is also a question of relative income. Air quality, beyond some standard, must take second place to food, clothing, and shelter. People who are barely able to afford these basic necessities will not be very squeamish about air quality.

Air pollution follows the usual economic law of variable proportion, or increasing and diminishing returns. In this case, the "returns" are negative, but the law refers to the effect of varying proportions, whether the effects are good or bad.

Following the law, the incremental or marginal effects of the first doses of pollution are small and dissipated. There follows a stage in which marginal effects rise rapidly, with the average effect lagging behind. The marginal effect reaches a maximum and then tapers off, with the average effect still catching up. The average effect reaches a maximum when it equals the marginal effect; then they both decline, in what is known as stage II, or the stage of diminishing average returns. Finally, marginal effects become zero and we enter stage III, that of diminishing absolute or total returns.

The damage that is caused by emissions at any specific time and place depends entirely on the stage of pollution that has already been reached by the ambient air. In the early part of stage I, and again during stage III, there is little purpose in controlling air pollution since the incremental damage is small. It is during the later part of stage I, when incremental damage is very high, that control has the greatest benefit.

In the usual textbook analysis of the law of variable proportion, the variable input—for example, fertilizer on land—has positive effects, and the object is to use it most economically. Under that assumption, the conclusion is quickly reached that stages I and III are to be avoided, and all economic combinations of fertilizer and land should be carried out during stage II.

In relation to air conservation, the variable input is air pollutants, and the effects are negative. Our goal is not to maximize the effects

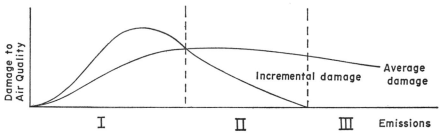

Fig. 1. Principle of diminishing returns.

but to minimize them, or to use the "input" as ineffectively as possible. The conclusion is therefore exactly the reverse of the textbook case: avoid stage II, and keep all combinations in stages I and III. In stage I, emissions would be diluted below a level of great concern. In stage III they would have saturated the air so fully that no further damage was possible, as in an air refuse zone. Figure 1 illustrates the principle of diminishing returns.

The difficulty with stage III is that any area of extreme air pollution, an air refuse zone, is bound to be surrounded by a circle of less dcnse pollution, as in stage II, since pollution density does not usually change abruptly from very high to very low. The air refuse zone would be feasible, therefore, only if it could be segregated from inhabited areas so that the stage II penumbra wasted itself on lands of little value, or else was kept low by natural barriers, winds, topography, and so forth.

Therefore, measures for controlling sources or standards that are unrelated to the condition of the ambient air would be viewed by economists with some skepticism. Ideally, control measures would seek to determine the incremental social cost of air pollution, and impose exactly those costs on the polluter, no more and no less. Naturally, great departures from the ideal must be accepted, but those who insist that ambient air standards be considered would have the weight of economic analysis on their side.

It should be noted, however, that the incremental cost of air pollution does not by any means increase linearly with concentration. On the contrary, it rises rapidly to a maximum during stage I, while the air is still relatively clean, and then falls, even before concentration has surpassed stage I and moved into stage II, the stage of diminishing average returns.

The implication is that if controls are worth imposing at all they are worth tightening quite stringently. That is contrary to the spirit of some conclusions promoted by the "ambient air school." It might also be implied that low population density should be encouraged, but, in the overall balance, this has aggravated more than it has ameliorated pollution.

Economic Motivation

Control technology has provided a considerable range of option in reducing emissions. Most of these techniques may be described in general economic terms as entailing the substitution of capital for demands on nature, with nature being represented by sources of fossil fuel and the air. Some examples of how economic policies might work toward the goal of substituting capital equipment for demands on nature follow.

1) *Exemption of control equipment from local property taxes.* Local property taxes vary widely among jurisdictions, but we may take 2½ percent of equalized market or true value as a roughly representative figure for cities in the United States in 1964. If we apply that 2½ percent to equipment with a 40-year life, it would come to 100 percent of initial cost during that period. This overstates the burden, of course, because payments stretched over 40 years are not as burdensome as a lump sum payable immediately, but when we account for that factor by discounting the future payments by 5 percent per year we still arrive at a lump-sum equivalent of about 43 percent. That is, a 2½-percent yearly property tax on control equipment is the equivalent of a 43-percent immediate lump-sum tax. Thus,

$$0.025 \times \frac{1 - 1.05^{-40}}{0.05} = 0.025 \times 17.2 = 0.43$$

It would serve air conservation, therefore, to exempt equipment for pollution control from property taxes.

This might seem like a subsidy to be borne by other taxpayers, but actually it is not. By exempting the new equipment from taxation, the rest of the property becomes more valuable. That is, the benefit of tax exemption is "capitalized" into the value of the site. Therefore, the tax levy might be as high as before. The difference lies in the fact that it is no longer contingent on installing control equipment. The polluter pays more taxes whether he installs the equipment or not because his land now has a higher assessed valuation.

The policy would be more effective if it were carried further, to exempt not only control equipment but also combustion equipment. This would encourage a generally higher standard in combustion equipment and more rapid replacement. There would then be a tendency for control equipment to be roughly commensurate in quality with basic combustion equipment.

2) *Fast write-off of control equipment.* This proposal is simply a subsidy for control equipment, imposing additional burdens on other taxpayers. As such, it is less attractive from the standpoint of distributive equity than the first proposal since it imposes the cost of pollution control on nonpolluters and nonbeneficiaries. Economists generally feel that, if subsidies are to be paid, they should be direct, explicit, and specific. Otherwise the initial purpose is often lost in the shuffle.

Fast write-off does have the advantage of being subject to federal control where interstate airsheds are involved. However, there is no way of adjusting it to the different needs of airsheds.

3) *Fuel taxation.* This is an indirect royalty on the invasion of the air resources. It would be most effective if higher taxes were imposed on cheaper fuels and sulfurous oils, while highly refined fuels were exempt. (Combining this principle with that of exempting control equipment, it would also be desirable to exempt refining equipment that is designed to increase the percentage of fuel burned.)

Like most indirect measures, fuel taxation does not exactly hit the bull's-eye. It discourages all use of fuel, regardless of time or location, and thus has some uneconomic side effects. No impetus is given to methods of control technology that operate on principles other than economy of fuel. It has no effect on air pollution from other sources, such as burning trash.

The great advantage of fuel taxation is relative ease of policing. Since most fuels come from a few basic sources—refineries or whole-salers—the cost of control at these points is so much less than it would be if emissions from every exhaust and vent were metered that fuel taxation might often be the backbone of an air pollution control program.

Fuel taxation as currently practiced does not consider questions of air pollution. Indeed, the least noxious fuels are the ones that are most highly taxed. Air conservation would prescribe a radical reversal of such practices, which reflect the elasticity of supply and demand rather than motivation for air conservation.

4) *Taxation of emissions, or air-depletion royalties.* Where phys-ically and institutionally feasible, the most perfect constraint on the invasion of the common air resource is to put a price on it. Such a price would constitute a royalty that is paid to the public for exploit-ing a limited natural resource. The royalty set should equal the incremental damage in time and place. It should be based on direct metering of emissions, adjusted for composition between noxious and inert gases.

Such a royalty might be compared to a tax on sewers, such as many municipalities impose. It is much like the effluent charges that are imposed in the Ruhr Valley and which have been proposed in several reports on water pollution abatement in the United States. It is closely analogous to the tax of $3 per acre-foot levied by Orange City, California, on invasion of the ground water resource.

The royalty approach has a number of advantages: (i) It gets directly to the point, constraining exactly what is intended to be constrained, with no side effects. (ii) It imposes costs on offenders, and lets them escape to the extent in which they ameliorate the offense. (iii) It is continuously in effect, independent of sporadic "crackdowns" and let-ups. (iv) It is graduated to the severity of the offense. (v) It permits pollution to continue to the extent that the cost of abatement would exceed the damage to air quality. (vi) It decides between necessary and unnecessary pollution. (vii) It continues to be effective even when polluters have met a minimum standard below which police regulations would not apply. (viii) It is noncatastrophic in application, allowing polluters to make their own best adjustment to the new constraint and in their own time.

By thus minimizing needless hardship it permits a more stringent basic standard to be set than with clumsier controls. (ix) It is based on performance rather than on any arbitrary technique or material. (x) It does not wait on "the gadget," but takes effect immediately, motivating polluters to minimize their damage with all the means and ingenuity at their command. (xi) It is adjustable for place and time of emission. (xii) Those who can dispose of wastes cheaply by other means will do so. Use of the air will be reserved for those who have the greatest need.

Air pollution royalties would not be a complete substitute for conventional regulation, even if full metering were feasible. Some pollutants are so dangerous that absolute prohibition under all circumstances is necessary. Some pollutants are released so rarely that metering would not begin to repay the cost of installation.

Another objection to this scheme is that it presupposes a system of prices and costs that are true indices to the alternatives. But this is not always true. For example, a taxpayer in the 90-percent bracket would deduct 90 percent of the royalty as a local tax, and feel only 10 percent of it as a constraint. Again, the damages inflicted on surplus farm commodities supported far above their true value would tend to be overstated.

It is still possible to use the price mechanism as a guide by taking such factors into account and modifying procedures accordingly. However, this will increase the possibility of error.

5) *Licensing of polluters.* A variation of the royalty system, where full metering is not feasible, is to sell licenses to polluters, the price being determined by the capacity of the licensed process and facility to pollute the air. The amount of capacity licensed should be limited to an amount considered optimal.

Of importance to the equity and efficiency of licensing is the fact that fees should be kept at high levels as determined by competitive bidding. A weakness of the scheme is the notorious propensity of licensing systems to degenerate into political footballs, with early licensees establishing squatters' rights that grow in value with time and give them a monopoly.

This weakness need not be fatal, however, if it is foreseen and guarded against from the start. The degeneration of licensing systems for liquor, import quotas, taxis, use of water, and tobacco allotments may be clearly traced to the beginnings of the schemes when no provisions were made for periodic reevaluation through competitive bidding. The founders of the schemes were perhaps innocent of economic principles, or were gulled by others who were not, into creating valuable privileges for them.

6) *Increasing the scale of combustion processes and equipment.* This topic will be treated more fully later. However, the measures just discussed would generally tend, *inter alia,* to increase the scale of smaller operations since this is one means of increasing combustion efficiency.

7) *Accelerating replacement of older equipment.* This topic will also be discussed later. The foregoing measures would generally tend to increase frequency of replacement by adding to the cost of keeping older equipment in operation.

The use of chimneys and high stacks to remove airborne wastes from inhabited areas is, of course, a basic control measure so ancient that it could be assumed that there is no room for further progress along these lines. Nonetheless, economic policy could enhance its effectiveness materially.

Stacks are capital, and all our analysis of tax treatment of capital used in the modification of processes applies equally to them. Some economists regard it as ill advised to tax any improvements, but the case is especially strong when the improvement serves primarily to please his neighbors and not to help the improver. Where the motive of self-interest is weak, tax policy needs to fortify it, not further weaken it.

With regard to air-depletion royalties, they should be graduated inversely with the height of stacks.

The effectiveness of high stacks is enhanced by a high population density. First, it requires high density to support combustion processes on a scale large enough to spread the cost of a big stack over a large output. Second, where the population sprawls out over a wide area, some of the advantage of elevation is lost through air turbulence before the pollutants are adequately dispersed or inactivated.

There is a time and place for everything. The time and place to pollute air is downwind. This may be achieved by varieties of zoning.

A very crude form of zoning would be to simply consign all "industry" to one preselected area. Progressively more sophisticated practices will select those activities that can bear the cost of abating pollution and let them locate more centrally.

By such zoning, a community buys cleaner air at the cost of increased transportation. Where that is cheaper than other methods, it seems a worthy addition to a panoply of controls. The optimal location for the zone is where the increase in transportation costs equals the decrease in pollution damage.

For the fullest realization of net benefits, zoning constraints should be couched in terms of emission royalties or license fees graduated by location rather than by black-and-white prohibitions here and permissions there.

The activities most likely to select a location in a "smoke zone" are the export industries, sometimes called "basic." Export industries generally have less need for a central location than local service industries and they will not pay a premium for central land. These industries also generally yield fiscal surpluses and are much in demand by communities. Zoning policy must, therefore, supply enough land for smoky industry to prevent the policy from breaking down under pressure for more space.

One means is to enlarge the smoke zone, but the larger the zone, the less land remains for others. In order to make zoning work, therefore, downwind land zoned for air pollution should be subject to a substantial annual tax. This would minimize underuse and speculation in industrial sites and let a small zone support a large industrial base. Similarly, land protected from pollution should be subject to an annual tax in order to guarantee that the sacrifices made to protect the land are not wasted.

As the wind rose becomes more symmetrical, with no location that is consistently downwind, locational segregation becomes a less advantageous policy. It finally amounts to the banishment of heavy pollution to outlying locations where their damage may be inflicted on cheap land and sparse populations. The zone might be entirely in one quarter, or it might be stretched into a belt completely surrounding the city. The reason for the second choice would be to keep the level of ambient air pollution down in stage I (see Fig. 1) where the incremental damage from pollution remains low. The choice between the two policies depends very much on particular conditions and is too complex to elaborate here.

Population Dispersal as a Solution

There has long been an instinctive assumption that air pollution was a congestion problem brought on by the excessive use of a small air mass and was to be alleviated by bringing more air into the system: that is, by dispersing the pollution over a wider area and diluting a given volume of pollutants with more air. The experience of Los Angeles, however, demands that the old saw that "dilution is the solution to pollution" be seriously questioned. Even though Los Angeles labors under unusual natural disadvantages, it is striking that the city with the lowest density of population should have the worst air pollution problem of any major American city. Moreover, there is no general evidence to correlate air pollution with high density. Why?

Many of the benefits expected from population dispersal proved illusory.

1) The contribution of urban open spaces to natural air recovery is negligible, roughly comparable to their contribution to the city water supply. Big cities must import both air and water, basically, from the wide open spaces. The oxygen output of vacant urban land is hardly enough to compensate for the output of allergenic substances.

2) Dilution is a good principle if the city is in stage I of increasing average return to pollutants (see Fig. 1). In stage I, reduced intensity serves to reduce the average effectiveness per dose of pollution, which is good. However, in some cities, reduced intensity has increased the average effectiveness of pollutants to deteriorate air by giving them more air per measure of pollutant. This would occur when the nature and intensity of pollutants had put them in stage II, diminishing average returns. In that stage, increased intensity would reduce the average effectiveness, so reduced intensity increases it.

3) Economists distinguish between variable proportion and variable scale. When we add air to a city by dispersing the population we are changing both, and the scale factor works against air con-

servation because now more air must be moved to change the city's supply, and that takes more time. Pollution damage is a function of exposure time as well as of intensity.

4) Available dump sites for disposal of trash by sanitary landfill recede so far into the back country that the removal of such wastes by truck becomes an increasingly costly alternative to incineration. Milwaukee, for example, is on the verge of a major shift to greater incineration, forced by a shortage of dump sites within 30 miles.

Thus, if wind velocity is 5 miles per hour, an upwind emission needs 4 hours to traverse a 20-mile belt of urban sprawl, as opposed to 2 hours at twice the population density and a 10-mile belt. In addition, in the wider belt there is a higher probability of irregular wind direction to slow the exhaust of pollutants. There is also higher probability of photochemical reaction among pollutants from many independent sources.

Increasing the area of a city also adds to the transportation cost of segregating polluters, thus weakening that weapon against pollution. The distance from the center of the city to the air refuse zones becomes greater, and *a fortiori* farther from the opposite extremity of the city. After some point, that forces a new air refuse zone to be created.

If we regard the city as a "target" that emissions should miss, the larger city is more difficult to avoid. Emissions dispersing inside a given angle will cover a much larger arc in 20 miles than in 10—the area polluted increases with the square of the distance from the source. In addition, air turbulence increases the angle of dispersion as pollutants travel greater distances. Thus, air refuse areas must be located farther from a larger city than from a smaller one in order to achieve the same degree of segregation.

The same factor decreases the effectiveness of vertical segregation in a larger city. More smoke reaches inhabited areas as the distance between the stack and the open country increases.

In addition to the fact that diluting the air does not produce the expected benefits, new problems are created by urban sprawl: (i) There is an increased number of jurisdictions whose policies must be coordinated. (ii) Physical separation increases the per capita number and reduces the scale of combustion facilities. Central heating, for example, gives way to smaller furnaces. Larger facilities can afford better proportioning of inputs, professional operations, taller stacks, and better controls. It is also easier for them to monitor and police. (iii) Dispersal of settlement means an increase in transportation, and part of the social cost of this increase is its contribution to air pollution. In some cities motor vehicles have become the primary source of emissions, either directly or from the oil refineries for which they create the market and need.

Dispersal increases the distances that must be traveled. It reduces walking and the use of public transportation, thus raising emissions per mile traveled. By reducing scale of engines used for motive power it reduces overall combustion efficiency in transportation. It has thrown electric power almost completely out of transit facilities.

In general, then, the policy of diluting air pollution through urban sprawl must be judged a failure—some would say a catastrophe at least in the extremes to which it has gone. Air conservation is better served by the containment of urban sprawl. The various policies to that end are too complex to discuss here, except to note that our various recommendations are all made with that as a correlative objective.

The condition of the ambient air determines, as we have seen, how tight a constraint on air pollution is most economical to impose, especially since the pollutant content changes with time. Nature renews and exchanges air continually, but not steadily. It might be said to afford us some short-run "storage capacity" for absorbing pollutants. This capacity has seduced us into thinking that we could continue to cram pollutants into the air indefinitely. Even though its potential usefulness has been badly abused, we should not be blinded to the possibility of using the air intelligently.

A sophisticated control program will, and many already do, tighten controls when the ambient air condition moves toward the top of stage I, and will relax them when the air reservoir is emptied. The "smog alerts" in Los Angeles are a crude example— crude because the control has only two positions, "on" and "off," with no gradations in between.

If measurement and monitoring were free or cheap, an elaborate system of full metering and flexible pricing would be desirable since it would be possible to constrain emissions optimally and achieve the maximum social benefits at a minimum cost. It is probably premature to elaborate any such scheme now, although it is a direction in which to point for future policy development. Metering is costly and crude, and we must try to do without it.

An alternative is to require licenses for polluting the air (see earlier discussion). Several classes of licenses might be issued. Class A licenses might allow pollutants to be released under all conditions below the "smog alert" level; class B licenses would become inoperative at a lower concentration of pollutants; class C at a still lower level; and so on through as many classes as could be administered or policed.

Alternatively, licenses might be graduated according to the number of hours per day they were effective, or particular times of day, or particular wind directions. Licenses could also be limited with regard to location.

The big drawback to using licenses as a control device is a quantitative one. Since emissions are not actually measured, the license must be based on some putative surrogate for actual emissions, such as emission capacity, type of operation, and so forth. If the license fee is high enough to be effective, it will be high enough to provoke evasive action by the licensee, and he will be motivated to use his licensed capacity more intensively than would otherwise be optimal. Short of actual metering, there seems little remedy for this.

Timing controls might be integrated with location controls, and policing might be eased by limiting class A licenses to certain areas, and so forth.

Since most combustion engines lose efficiency with age, it is important that public policy should supply the motivation to replace equipment in good time. It is especially important in connection with imposing new controls on pollution, because it will be difficult to withstand the inevitable pressure to exempt ancient and honorable polluters from the control process, under the prescriptive or grandfather clause principle, and the new controls will not become effective until the old and exempted equipment is replaced.

The importance of this factor may be grasped by considering the low replacement rate of the typical urban building. If the average life of a building is 100 years, which is not too far from the fact, we

replace only 1 percent each year. New furnaces may be installed
sooner, but there is no guarantee that grandfather clauses will not
be so written that they will expire only with the building.

For effective air pollution control, therefore, the inevitable pressures to recognize prescriptive rights to pollute air, based on historical priority, should be resisted as much as possible. If established firms and plants may pollute the air, while new ones may not,
the latter are burdened with a serious competitive disadvantage
commensurate with the cost of abating pollution. In this case, the
very existence of laws to control pollution acts perversely to discourage abatement because the cost differential will retard replacement. The prescriptive right to pollute the air becomes a valuable
private asset, to be nurtured and exploited as long as possible.

It is also worth noting that, by anticipating the fact that prescriptive rights will be recognized, a motive is created in advance of
control to establish and maintain a "history" of air pollution, since
history is the basis on which prescriptive rights are granted. That
has quite clearly been the effect of the prescriptive rights principle
applied to the use of water in 17 western states, for example.

Aside from resisting prescriptive rights, public policy can serve
air conservation by revising the present relationship between taxes
and the age of buildings and machines and equipment. Motor
vehicle taxes, for example, generally decline with the age of the
vehicle. They are, on the whole, too low to have much effect
either way, but to the extent that they do have an effect, they tend
to retard replacement. Yet it is clearly the old "oil burners," with
their plumes of blue smoke, that contribute more than their share
to air pollution. Motor vehicle taxes should at least remain fixed
with age, and preferably rise, thus forcing old cars off the roads
sooner. Although some old cars burn fuel more completely than
some new ones, we have ruled out the possibility of full metering
of exhausts and other emissions. Statistically, age is highly correlated with poor carburetion.

With respect to real estate, under present practice, assessments
are progressively lowered as buildings age and obsolesce and become
more offensive to their neighbors, and assessments are raised when
the nuisance is abated by demolition and renewal. Thus, the tax
on buildings serves to retard the replacement of aging buildings.
This also applies to all their component parts, including heating

plants; in this case, as we have seen, the tax rate is high enough to have a material impact.

In the case of buildings, it is not necessary to propose that assessments increase with age, since buildings, unlike vehicles, rest on sites to which the taxes may be shifted and which tend to rise in unit value with time. Without abandoning the *ad valorem* principle, it is possible to accelerate the replacement of buildings by exempting them from the real estate tax. The benefit of tax exemption is capitalized into the value of the site, so that the same tax levy can be collected from the average parcel as before. But the tax would not be lowered as buildings and heating plants deteriorate, nor would it rise when they are replaced. Thus, the tax system would accelerate replacement, or at least stop retarding it, and hasten the day when pollution abatement laws enacted today will actually go into effect.

Equally effective would be a reform of federal income tax practice, which presently operates against demolition and renewal. If the buyer of an old building spares it from the wrecker he may depreciate a large part of its value, even though many previous owners have already done the same thing. But if he clears the site, his entire purchase price is considered as payment for the land and is not depreciable. This fiscal bias against renewal may be remedied simply either (i) by disallowing multiple depreciation altogether or (ii) by requiring realistic allocation of most of the value of old buildings to the nondepreciable land element. Reform (ii) could be accomplished without new legislation by changing administrative definition and practice. However, this would require reeducation of the entire Internal Revenue Service, and a new law might be a simpler expedient.

Role of Electric Power

The transmission of electric power is of special importance to air conservation since it affords a sovereign means to segregate combustion from power delivery. Portland, Oregon, provided an excellent example of air pollution control when it substituted electric energy for local combustion. Even the scrap steel mills use electric power.

New developments in long-distance power transmission at 500,000 volts open important new possibilities for increased substitution of electric energy for local combustion. Plants at Johnstown, Pennsylvania, and Morgantown, West Virginia, can now serve the New York and Philadelphia markets.

Conceivably, all combustion might be centered in large, efficient thermoelectric plants, remote from population centers but close to coal fields, saving in coal transportation costs what is lost in electric "wheeling" costs. Costly urban distribution networks for gas, coal, and oil could be eliminated and their functions could be assumed by increasing the capacity of the electrical network. It is much cheaper in the long run to increase the capacity of one distribution network than to maintain one or more additional and separate ones.

One drawback to this solution is the fact that, in generating electricity, 100 percent of the fuel calories is not converted into electric power. However, the percentage of potential power output that is lost to nature is probably less than what is lost to the tax collector. Power meters are favored devices for collecting taxes. Because there are many substitutes for electric power, the demand is quite elastic, and, therefore, the taxes on its generation, distribution, and consumption serve to hold down consumption, keep unit costs of distribution high, and thereby doubly discourage the substitution of electric power for local combustion.

Another factor in establishing rates for electric power that interferes with optimal air conservation policy is the custom of charging uniform rates over wide areas, in spite of differential costs of service. Rates should be lowest in densely populated areas where distribution costs are lowest and near load centers, which should in turn be near centers of population. These areas are also the ones where it is most important that electricity be substituted for combustion. Present policy bleeds the centers to subsidize the outlying regions, thus promoting electric consumption in areas where it is less important to promote it. Furthermore, such a policy tends to encourage urban sprawl, and this, in turn, inflates distribution costs and makes electric power more expensive for everyone.

In the interests of air conservation, it would be helpful not to tax the generation, transmission, and distribution of electrical energy, and not to tax home and industrial apparatus for reconverting it to heat and work. Increased consumption would cause the rates to be lowered and the resulting decline in unit costs would permit still further reductions in rates. Universal availability of abundant and cheap electrical energy would make it feasible to outlaw the burning of fossil fuels in areas where it is necessary and sharply curtail it elsewhere.

The question immediately arises of how the lost revenue will be recouped? The answer is not as difficult as it first appears. The availability of cheap energy makes land more valuable in the area served, and the revenue lost from electric taxes may be recouped from land taxes with no additional burden on the landowner, who, after all, is the one who had been paying the electric taxes. He simply pays in a different way, and in return he has cleaner air and cheaper electricity, which is a fair exchange.

Many economists go further, and hold that distributive networks not only should not be taxed but should also be subsidized so they can charge very low rates equal to their marginal costs, which are below average. They have tended to apply this reasoning to all distributive networks, but considerations of air conservation would clearly make it most relevant to electrical networks. Gas distribution is economically analogous in most respects, but differs in that gas combustion contributes, although less than other fuels, to air pollution. When that social cost is added to the conventional monetary one, the full social marginal cost of gas delivery and combustion, where the ambient air is congested with pollutants, may be higher than the average unit cost.

This does not rule out gas in all cases. Where the choice is between gas and soft coal, the arguments made here for electricity would apply to gas, the less polluting fuel. However, there are few areas where electric power is not a feasible alternative.

Any such proposal would, of course, be resisted by many people, especially those who see their interests threatened: oil and gas owners, coal-carrying railways, and fuel distributors. Since it would also appeal to the self-interest of other groups, their interest, coupled with that of the public, might be effective politically.

A more difficult problem is that posed by the small size of the taxing jurisdictions. If a power-consuming city reduced or eliminated taxes on thermoelectric facilities, there would be little change in power rates if the facilities were largely located in other jurisdictions. Indeed, one community's sacrifice of tax revenue simply adds feathers to the goose for others to pluck. This problem is not insoluble, however, if the electric system is in one state. State assessment of rails and utilities and state equalization are established methods of restraining localities from competitive overtaxation of these networks. It is also within the power of each sovereign state to classify property as the legislature sees fit and to tax some classes more lightly than others, or not at all, or in different ways.

With interstate systems the problem is more difficult. What would prevent, let us say, West Virginia from capturing the benefits of New York's reduction of taxes on electric power if it were generated in West Virginia? One possibility would be strict interpretation of the commerce clause, with the Federal Power Commission in effect acting as a national board of equalization to prevent West Virginia jurisdictions from taxing power exported to New York. In view of the lenient attitude often displayed by the Supreme Court toward *de facto* taxation of interstate commerce, wrapped only in specious subterfuges, this approach may not be very promising. Another approach is through expansion, or threatened expansion, of federal power generation and distribution at very low rates. To meet the competition, states would have to cut taxes on private power plants.

None of this will be easy, but the potential gains warrant the consideration of drastic measures. Unless we can break through the tangle of interests vested in current tax practices, we can realize only a fraction of the latent contribution of Edison's inventions to human welfare in general and to air conservation in particular.

In summary, we have tried to show that economic analysis, in conjunction with other disciplines, may be of service in combating air pollution. The policies discussed are not represented as the right ones for every time and place, nor as a complete list and optimal balance of all feasible policies. Instead, we have tried to furnish a number of examples of the usefulness of economic analysis to air conservation, in the hope that this may be the beginning of more concentrated interdisciplinary research into the subject, and a bridge for the early movement of research findings into public policy.

References

1. Carr, L. J., *Situational Analysis* (Harpers, New York, 1948).
2. Gillitte, J. M., and J. M. Reinhardt, *Current Social Problems* (American Book, New York, 1933), p. 4.
3. Bossard, J. H. S., "Comment" on "The natural history of a social problem," *Am. Sociological Rev.*, **6**, No. 3, p. 329 (June 1941).
4. Fuller, R. C., and R. R. Myers, "The natural history of a social problem," *ibid.*, pp. 320–329.
5. Arndt, G. W., "Community response reactions to a horrifying event," *Bull. Menninger Clin.*, pp. 106–111 (May 23, 1959).
6. Festinger, L., *A Theory of Cognitive Dissonance* (Stanford Univ. Press, Stanford, Calif., 1957).
7. Parson, T., and N. J. Smelzer, *Economy and Society* (Free Press, Glencoe, Ill., 1956).
8. Long, N. E., "The corporation and the community," *Ann. Am. Acad. Political Social Sci.*, pp. 118–127 (Sept. 1962).
9. von Bertalanffy, L., *Problems of Life: An Evaluation of Modern Biological and Scientific Thought* (Torch, New York, 1960).
10. Alinsky, S. D., *Reveille for Radicals* (Univ. of Chicago Press, Chicago, 1945).
11. Riesman, D., "Private people and public policy," *Bull. Atomic Scientists*, p. 207 (Mar. 1959).
12. Lasswell, H. D., "The structure and function of communication in society," in *The Communication of Ideas*, L. Bryson, Ed. (Harper, New York, 1948), p. 37.
13. Lazarsfeld, P. F., B. Berelson, and H. Gaudet, *The People's Choice* (Columbia Univ. Press, New York, 1948).
14. Katz, E., "The two-step flow of communication: An up-to-date report on an hypothesis," *Public Opinion Quarterly*, **21**, 61 (spring 1957).
15. A Guide to Questionnaire Survey Design is presented by E. Katz and P. F. Lazarsfeld in *Personal Influence* (Free Press, Glencoe, Ill., 1955), pp. 335–380. See also L. C. Freeman *et al.*, "Locating leaders in local communities: A comparison of some alternative approaches," *Am. Sociological Rev.*, **28**, No. 5, pp. 791–798 (Oct. 1963).
16. Katz, E., and P. F. Lazarsfeld, *Personal Influence* (Free Press, Glencoe, Ill., 1955).
17. Merton, R. K., "Patterns of influence," in *Social Theory and Social Structure* (Free Press, Glencoe, Ill., 1957), pp. 387–420.
18. Larsen, O., "The social effects of mass communication as a research problem," *Sociologiske Meddeleser*, **5**, No. 1, pp. 23–42 (1960).
19. Hunter, F., *Community Power Structure* (Univ. of North Carolina Press, Chapel Hill, 1953). Hunter's study pioneered the study of power structures and utilized reputational techniques to establish leadership patterns. His findings showed that in a southern city there were groups of influentials with close intercommunications.
20. Miller, D. C., "Decision making cliques in community power structure: A comparative study of an American and an English city," *Am. J. Sociology*, **64**, 299–310 (Nov. 1958).

21. Hanson, R. C., "Predicting a community decision: A test of the Miller-form theory," *Am. Sociological Rev.,* **24**, 662–663 (Oct. 1959).

22. Sanders, I. T., "Public health in the community," in H. E. Freeman *et al.,* Eds., *Handbook of Medical Sociology* (Prentice-Hall, Englewood Cliffs, N.J., 1963).

23. Englebert, E. A., Ed., *The Nature and Control of Urban Dispersal* (Univ. of California Press, Berkeley, 1960); Studenski, P., "Metropolitan areas, 1960: Voluntary cooperation is not sufficient, areawide government is needed for selected functions," *National Civic Review,* **49**, No. 10, pp. 537–532 (1960); and Milner, J. B., "Town and regional planning in transition, *Can. Public Administration,* **3**, No. 1, pp. 59–75 (Mar. 1960). These articles show a consensus among planners that the traditional municipality is no longer considered adequate in size for effective planning. There is need for larger agencies with clear powers.

CHAPTER 7

Air Pollution and Urban Development

Air pollution, other than that from nuclear explosions, is primarily a big city problem. Or more accurately, it is a metropolitan or regional problem, since small communities in the same region will be affected if they are downwind of the industries, power plants, automotive exhaust, and other pollutants of large cities. Air pollution is created and experienced principally in the large metropolitan region, and all forecasts indicate that the overwhelming proportion of the nation's population will be living in metropolitan areas in the future (see Chapter 3). Thus, the changes that are taking place in metropolitan areas must be understood in shaping air pollution strategies.

Unfortunately, these changes are not easily understood. One could reasonably assume that an area that doubles its population within a certain period—say 25 years—will have increased air pollution. But will double the population mean double the air pollution? Or will it mean more than double, because the additional population will permit a certain critical mass of purchasing power or interest groups to support new activities that were not previously possible? Thus, will doubling the population create three times the air pollution that previously existed? Or, might the reverse situation occur? For example, the additional population might be able to support industries and commercial establishments in such a fashion that formerly marginal operations would be able to adopt new methods of processing, using fuel or other technological changes that reduce air pollution.

What is the effect of greater and greater extensions of the urbanized area, with greater decentralization of residences, places of em-

307

ployment, shopping areas, and recreation? One could reasonably assume that this physical swelling of the metropolitan area would increase air pollution because of the inevitable increase in motor vehicle miles. After all, mass transportation is uneconomic where distances are great and the population density is low. However, is air pollution that is spread thinly throughout a large area dispersed effectively under typical weather conditions?

What about the politics of air pollution control programs? Since local officials might believe, whether rightly or wrongly, that they will lose industrial development to nearby, rival communities if they impose strict controls and their neighbors do not, would local areas find state-wide rather than local standards more palatable in the long run? Would politicians dare to tax the use of automobiles so severely that this form of transportation would be drastically curtailed? (The automobile is completely woven into our fabric of jobs, living patterns, and consumer preferences.) Would the control of air pollution be more readily accepted by the public because of losses to amenity rather than because of threats to health? Cigarette smoking seems to be a pleasure that most people do not want to relinquish, even after evidence of a threat to health; are people today more likely to respond to an appeal to their pleasure than to their health?

What kinds of land development patterns seem best for air pollution control? What community resources would be needed? If the metropolitan area were to be planned for optimal development, taking into consideration many different goals, of which air conservation would be only one (some others being efficient transportation, full employment opportunities, varied educational, cultural, and recreational facilities, and attractive housing for all groups), how much would have to be sacrificed in order to attain this goal? Would the air environment be more subject to improvement because it was part of a package of community betterment, or would it be less so because of the necessity to allocate resources among many goals?

What are the consequences of remedial suggestions for conserving the air? For example, if, as some have suggested, power plants and industries that emitted pollutants were required to locate downwind from the community, would there be any assurances that the emissions would not pollute a neighboring community now or in the future? What would be the costs to industry to locate there, in terms of land and access to markets and employees? (Would land price rise because of a monopoly situation?) What would be the cost to the community in terms of new transportation, utilities, and other facilities? Does the community have enough suitable land downwind to accommodate the amount of industry it anticipates? Would increased motor vehicle traffic for goods and employees cause more air pollution than was reduced by the new location? How would existing industries be forced or induced to move?

A Multiple-Focus Approach

These are the kinds of questions that should be raised in strategy planning for urban air conservation. If a single-minded approach is used to solve the air pollution problems, with no consideration being given to the changes that are taking place in the community as well as to other community concerns, it is probably doomed to failure. However, a single-focus strategy offers the most logical solution to air pollution. For example, it might recommend closing down all industries that emitted more than a certain amount of pollutants and forbidding the establishment of new industries that were not free of pollution. It could recommend an extensive mass transportation system and the banning of private automobiles. It could require coal-burning power plants to locate at the pit. It could forbid all home fireplaces and incinerators. These are logical solutions, and if they were adopted, air pollution would certainly decrease markedly. But the recommendations, although logical, would simply not be acceptable. Nor would modified versions be any more acceptable, unless the proposals were so modified that they would, in effect, do very little to curb air pollution.

On the other hand, if air pollution control were put into a multiple-focus context, there is no assurance that a better air environment would be obtained. If it were placed in such a context, the people of the community, acting through their elected officials, might decide that they preferred not to pay the costs of securing a better air environment. That is, having had the alternatives clarified for them, they might still prefer to continue the development patterns that had been shown to create air pollution. (This possibility assumes that air pollution is not at a level that would seriously endanger human life.) However, if a major threat to life were shown to exist, then the seekers of improved air environment could concentrate on technological and managerial solutions, such as perfecting the fuel cell for automobiles (eliminating its own air pollution defects, for example), improving the heating of homes and rubbish disposal, revamping industrial processes, or substituting new products.

The citizens of metropolitan areas are neither aware of the threats of increased air pollution nor of the relationship of air pollution to development patterns. With the exception of such cities as Los Angeles and Pittsburgh, where there has been heightened public awareness of air pollution through adverse experience, those who are responsible for urban development—the industrialists, the sub-dividers, the businessmen, the mayors, the local legislators—are only vaguely concerned about air pollution. None of them wish to contribute to air pollution by their own actions or those of others; they either are unaware of the implications of their actions (or lack of them), or they see no compelling reason to alter them. Even the city planner, who is a municipal official professionally committed to improving the future environment, has typically ignored air pollution problems.

The city planner operates in a middle ground between the research scientist and the public. He should be an ally of the specialist in air pollution control; he is already sympathetic toward public action for amenity as well as health purposes, although in most communities he has not been involved in programs for controlling air pollution. The city planner rarely has an ideological hesitancy in dealing with problems that transcend municipal boundaries. He knows about the nature of the community, its physical, economic and social character, and the way in which it is changing. When staff resources permit, the city planner is in a good position to help prepare a multiple-focus strategy for community improvement, including improvement of the air environment, assuming jurisdictional difficulties on the size of the area are worked out.

A Case Example: The San Francisco Bay Area

It would be highly desirable to select a metropolitan area for intensive analysis and the preparation of a multiple-focus strategy for environmental improvement, including the improvement of the atmospheric environment. It is not possible to do so here. The following data on the San Francisco Bay Area illustrate the extent of the changes under way in the metropolitan areas of the nation and the tension between what might be desirable from the viewpoint of air pollution control and what is likely to happen if present trends continue.

The estimates that follow should not be assumed to be correct; they are a convenience to give some concreteness to problems that must be dealt with at specific places at specific times. Two myths of the social sciences are that estimates of the future can be based on holding constant other factors than the ones being examined and on the continuation of present trends. But other factors are not constant. And present trends do not continue unchanged. Unforeseen occurences are likely to intervene: an economic inflation, new technological developments, or changes in governmental policy. The ghosts of extrapolation, once vivid and now moribund and mocked, haunt forecasters. What, for example, happened to the "gloomy" demographic forecasts of the 1930's?

Nevertheless, the extension of present trends has virtue—it is an approach that at least helps to clarify one alternative future direction, and it helps to change the situation if the prospect is sufficiently displeasing to enough people.

*   *   *   *   *   *

The San Francisco Bay Region is part of an airshed that resembles a lopsided H, the western leg of which is greatly foreshortened in comparison with the eastern leg, which extends north above Sacramento and south below Bakersfield. The western leg extends south and east of Santa Cruz (1).

Winds flow both eastward from the San Francisco Bay Region into the valley and from the valley north and west to the bay. This means that the air pollution of Sacramento, Stockton, Fresno, Bakersfield, Oakland, and San Francisco could all contribute to the pollution of intervening areas (and to one another, if the air is not self-cleansed between urban centers). Full analysis of the air pollution situation in the San Francisco Bay Area, therefore, should include urbanization, industrialization, and use of motor vehicles in all the communities in the airshed. In this brief analysis, the San

Francisco Bay Region is limited to the nine counties that border San Francisco Bay. The San Francisco–Oakland Metropolitan Area covers only six of these counties: San Francisco, San Mateo, Santa Clara, Alameda, Marin, and Contra Costa. The Bay Area Air Pollution Control District covers these same counties. However, the established control district, which is bold in its administrative responsibility in comparison with prevailing practice, is not bold enough to deal with the geographic extent of pollution in the Bay Region.

Man influences the quality of air in other ways than by the pollutants he introduces. One of the factors, for example, that should be considered in analyzing airshed microclimatological data is whether temperatures are rising as a result of increased urbanization, and if so, where, how much, and with what effect. The loss of heat from buildings, reflection, steam, smoke, and vehicles may add a few degrees to the local temperature. In turn, this rise may affect moisture retention or moisture precipitation. Extensive planting or removal of trees may affect the moisture content or cleansing power of the air.

In the Bay Region, the gradual filling of the bay for building purposes may markedly alter the cooling and warming effects of a large body of water on the air and the surrounding land. It has been estimated that, if all the shallows less than 18 feet deep were filled in, the bay would then be reduced to about 25 percent of its present size. Such a drastic shrinkage would affect the climate and the character of the air environment.

Changes in the Bay Region

The nine counties of the San Francisco Bay Region had 3,639,000 people in 1960. In it there are more than 80 cities, the principal ones being San Francisco, Oakland, Berkeley, and San Jose. San Jose has had the most recent rapid growth, increasing in population by 121 percent between 1950 and 1960. The rest of the Bay Region increased in population by about one-fourth during the same period, roughly the rate of increase for the 212 metropolitan areas designated by the U.S. Census. Most of the increase in the Bay Region is accounted for by migration from other parts of the country.

Just as the population in this and other metropolitan areas of the nation has increased, so has the geographic extent of the metropolitan area. The U.S. Census has periodically revised the definition of a metropolitan area. The territorial expansion of the San Francisco Bay Region, as Davis and Langlois point out (2), increased by about eight times during the period 1910–1960—from 452 square miles to 3314—while population increased by only about five times. (The nine-county area covers 6990 square miles.) Thus, the average density of population has been decreasing rapidly since 1930. Today, people may feel more crowded than those who lived at higher densities at an earlier period because present-day residents are farther from the open countryside. There are also peak travel periods, such as during the daily journey to and from work, or when Candlestick Ball Park is emptied on a Sunday afternoon, or during Christmas shopping, or during the return to the Bay Region on a holiday weekend. People thus feel more crowded because more of them are trying to travel on the highways than ever before. In the metropolitan area, however, Davis and Langlois point out that "the 1960 density was down to approximately what it had been about 95 years ago."

Most forecasts suggest an increased use of land, a decreasing density of population, and a further decentralization of economic activities. The U.S. Department of Commerce report, "Future Development of the San Francisco Bay Area: 1960–2020," is one of the more conservative estimates. It classifies 52 percent of the Bay Region's land resources as suitable for urban purposes and predicts that developed urban land will increase by 1980 from 15 percent of the total to almost 25 percent of the total. Other estimates point to the possibility that 75 percent of the land resources of the Bay Region will be used for urban purposes by 1980, compared with 12 percent in 1962. This would mean multiplying land utilization by six times and halving the number of people living in each square mile.

The discrepancy in these forecasts is not important in itself. Obviously there would be very different implications for both community services and air pollution if 75 percent of the vacant land were in use by 1980 or if it were less than 25 percent. However, in either case the cost of providing municipal services would go up because of the increased dispersal of the population. The amount of

open space in the first forecast becomes minuscule when compared to
the present country-like landscape of much of the Bay Region. (Of
course, those who enjoy vacant land as an amenity today do not pay
for it; they benefit from the willingness of property owners to defer
development until property values rise.)

From the point of view of air pollution, an extended, dispersed
but urbanized, low-density type of development will rely heavily
on automobile transportation since it is uneconomic to serve
such areas by mass transportation. Whether the air pollution from
automotive exhaust will disperse into rather thinly settled, but
stretched-out development (the first forecast), or whether it will be
emitted into the more built-up but still low-density development
(the second forecast) is open to question. In either case, there will
be a greatly increased use of automobiles. Since developers and in-
vestors favor single-family, low-density housing, by 1980 development may stretch well into the Napa Valley, to Livermore, and to
Santa Cruz. Some new garden apartments, of higher density than
single-family homes, will undoubtedly also be built in outlying
areas.

The new dwellings will not all be for sale. For the first time
since the great depression, the proportion of rented housing has
been rising. At first glance, rented housing seems to indicate a
tendency toward centralization and higher densities; this is not the
case. Although new high-rise luxury apartments are being built in
San Francisco, most of the new rented units are in the newer
suburban areas and are low-density developments. Even renewal
projects in central San Francisco do not have the net effect of holding or attracting back to the city people who have left. The projects
typically lower the densities of residential neighborhoods rather than
raise them.

Much of the suburban growth is the result of migration to the
region, but some of it is due to the influx of people who formerly
lived in San Francisco, Oakland, or Berkeley. The percentage of
the population who live in the heart of the city has gone down,
both relatively and, in some cases, absolutely. The population of
both San Francisco and Oakland declined between 1950 and 1960.
This does not necessarily mean that the residential density in the
center of the city decreased. Per acre residential crowding may in-

deed have gone up, to the extent that nonresidential properties displaced residential. And, of course, daytime densities are much greater than population figures reveal. It has been estimated that one-quarter of San Francisco's work force commutes into the area each day (and that this amount will rise to one-third by 1975). Daily commutation is a base figure; to this is added the people who do not live in San Francisco but who go there for recreation and shopping, and also for the city's cultural, health, and professional facilities.

Three widely used estimates for the total population of the Bay Region by 1980 vary from an increase of 57 percent over the 1960 figure of 3,640,000 to an increase of 80 percent. (The actual increase in population between 1940 and 1960 was 110 percent and during the 10-year period between 1950 to 1960 it was 36 percent.) This discrepancy is great enough to mean that more specialized projections of population groupings, for example, the aged, are even more tentative. Traditionally, the old—the age group particularly sensitive to air pollution—have lived in the central part of the city rather than in the suburbs. People 65 years and older make up 12.5 percent of San Francisco's population, 8.9 percent of the San Francisco–Oakland metropolitan area, and only 6.9 percent of the more decentralized, more recently developed, San Jose metropolitan area. Also, 2½ times as many dependent aged live in San Francisco County as in Marin or San Mateo. However, if retirement communities for the aged become popular—that is, the suburban residential developments that can save on community facilities since no schools are needed (residence may be restricted to those who are 50 and over)—there may then be some change in the settlement patterns of the most readily detected victims of air pollution.

Employment

Many areas in California depend upon defense contracts for employment. Los Angeles County, for example, is first in the nation in the dollar amount of defense contracts, and other areas in California also rank high. The very rapid growth of population in San Jose and its vicinity is due to its development of defense industries. In contrast, San Francisco County (the same area as the city of San

Francisco) does not depend on this source of employment, being only 50th in the country in defense contracts. Much of the population growth in the San Francisco Bay Region is supported by a more stable employment base than that prompted by the Cold War.

Manufacturing accounts for more than 20 percent of the non-agricultural employment in the Bay Region as compared with about 30 percent nationally. Trade and government each make up another one-fifth; in the case of trade, the Bay Region's proportion is the same as that of the nation, and in the case of government, it is somewhat more than the national proportion. Services, which make up 15 percent of the Bay Region's employment, also exceed the national percentage as does employment in transport, finance, and construction.

This diversity of employment would suggest that in the San Francisco Bay Region air pollution from industry would be less than in other areas. Such an assumption is unwarranted because the amount of pollution is linked to processes, fuel and raw materials, firing practices, and not to the number of workers. Also, in many respects, the metropolitan areas of the United States are becoming more like one another. Thus, differences in income during the last few decades have diminished, although they have not disappeared. Similarly, the kinds of employment in metropolitan areas are becoming more similar. While manufacturing has been diminishing in importance in manufacturing centers, it has been growing more important in the Bay Region.

The Department of Commerce estimated that three out of five jobs in the Bay Region serve the local market. As the population of California increases, the market within the state may become so large that many activities that were formerly considered uneconomic will become feasible. California already has a population as large as Belgium and Holland combined; by 1980 it may equal that of Spain. After a certain critical mass of population is reached, it may be strategic from the standpoint of production or distribution —or even politics—to fabricate many of the items that are now merely assembled or distributed. The new integrated Bethlehem Steel plant is an example of a processing industry that is now deemed feasible. Its construction in the Bay Region will probably spark metal-working industries. Other industries in which growth is probable, according to Poland (3), in addition to electronics and space industries, are "refineries, petrochemical and other chemical industries, computer production, food product industries, the packaging and container industry, aluminum fabrication, printing and publishing, furniture, and industrial service and supply."

As the United States becomes increasingly dependent on the importation of ores, fuels, food stuffs, and other bulky raw materials, there will be a greater concentration of heavy processing industries on the coasts and, because of the St. Lawrence Seaway, on the shores of the Great Lakes. Ships could carry the raw materials to their destinations without transshipment.

Increased dependence on imports and exports would suggest more intensive development of water and adjacent sites in the Bay Region, almost without regard for the proportion of new development attracted to southern California. Communities in the Bay Region are already vying with one another for industrial and commercial development and find that the shores of the bay—and filled-in land—are attractive from the standpoint of supplying additional industrial sites and additional tax money.

From the point of view of heavy industry, location on or near the bay has tremendous advantages, among them propinquity to port facilities and water transportation, flat topography, water for cooling purposes, access to labor supply, and linkage with a freeway system. From the point of view of air pollution, heavy industrial or power plant development on the bay shores is unfortunate. Prevailing winds carry pollutants to the residential areas on the eastern shores and then, if they are strong, into the valley beyond. (If they are weak, and there are inversions, the emissions can be trapped in the Bay Region.) Moreover, the presence of industry on the bay shores would generate a great deal of movement of goods and passengers; the air pollution from trucks, commuter automobiles, ships, airplanes, and railroads may be more difficult to cope with than the pollution from the industries themselves.

Urban Transportation

The San Francisco Bay Region is the only major urban complex in the country that is constructing a rapid transit system to meet some of its transportation needs. Three counties, San Francisco, Alameda, and Contra Costa, have joined together to build the 75-mile network, costing $925 million. The system will link downtown San Francisco, Oakland, and Berkeley, and will extend to Richmond, Fremont, and Concord. The system will be electronically controlled and high speed, with trains running at 70 miles per hour, with 90-second headways at peak hours; it is designed so that it can be extended to complete the ring around the bay (running to San Jose) and eastward to Livermore should this extension be desired. There will be no parking in connection with downtown stations but it will be provided at outlying stations, with capacities for off-street parking that range from 400 to 2000 cars, and with a total capacity of 29,000. The system is predicated on feeder bus service as well as outlying parking. The system is based on fares that will be no more than the out-of-pocket automobile expense to destinations; the chief appeal of the system, which hopes to divert automobile drivers, particularly during peak journey-to-and-from-work hours, is that of time saved.

What will be accomplished by the rapid transit scheme, either in its modest three-county network or in its extended, proposed form? From the viewpoint of air conservation, the rapid transit system should result in an urban transportation system with no more (or not much more) motor vehicle traffic than exists at present. Desirably, motor traffic should be reduced to allow for additional industrial pollution. It is impossible to predict how people will respond to a high-speed transit facility before it has been built, but it seems extremely unlikely that a situation favorable for air conservation will be achieved. With the increased decentralization of industrial, commercial, retail, cultural, professional, and other services and residences, many work trips, as well as nonwork trips, will not be conveniently served by the rapid transit system. Where there is more than one rider per car, the rapid transit fare will exceed out-of-pocket automobile expenses and the tendency will be to use the automobile. Many people will find it inconvenient to get to the rapid transit by another form of transportation, to transfer to rapid transit, and then to transfer again to another form of transportation in order to get to their final destination. They will prefer the one-mode transportation (automobile) even if this means enduring the irritations of congested traffic and even if the total time is somewhat greater than it would be by the rapid transit system.

Also, no matter how successful the rapid transit system, it will not handle goods, which will continue to be carried mostly by truck.

A more important consideration, however, is that rapid transit is not the only new form of transportation being built in the Bay Region. By the middle of 1962, one-half of the 650 miles of California's District IV approved new freeways and expressways were constructed. (District IV includes Santa Cruz County and excludes Solano County, but is otherwise identical to the nine-county Bay Region). Although a comprehensive transportation plan (for all forms of transportation) for the entire region has not been prepared, it seems unlikely that there will be no new highway projects in the Bay Region in the near future. Various levels of government have additional bridge crossings and highways to serve these crossings under consideration; it can be assumed that there will be strong political pressure from the automobile-loving consumer and from other interests for these additional facilities. Indeed, the Transit District assumed that by 1975, 32 freeway lanes would be built in the six-county area in addition to the 48 now in use.

Rapid transit should be expected to do more than absorb the present regional bus traffic. In 1962 there were less than 10 million passenger trips made by transbay coach, less than one-half of the trips that were made in 1950 when the crossing was by rail, the tracks of which have since been removed. The total of interurban transit trips were more than cut in half between 1945 and 1960, from 67 million to 30 million.

By 1975 the Rapid Transit District hopes to carry 55 percent of all peak-hour, peak-direction passenger trips across the Bay Bridge, compared to the 40 percent that were carried by buses in 1959. It also expects to carry about 35 percent of peak-hour, peak-direction traffic through the Berkeley Hills and less than 25 percent at two other gateways in the three-county region. Roughly 100,000 automobile trips per day are to be diverted to rapid transit. From the viewpoint of coping with traffic and congestion at the hours of most intensive demand, rapid transportation could make an important contribution. From the viewpoint of air pollution control, however, the transit solution, even if it meets the expectations of the Transit District, is only a minor portion of the whole. There are now about 4 million daily trips in the three-county area, 7 million in the entire Bay Region. These figures presumably will rise to 5.2 million and to 11 million, respectively, by 1975. The Transit District estimate that it would carry 258,600 trips per day means that it would absorb only about 5 percent of the passenger travel (in trips, not miles) in the three-county area, and 2.5 percent of the trips in the entire Bay Region.

Whatever the success or lack of success in diverting the regular automobile commuter to the transit system, rapid transit will undoubtedly perform a standby service to the automobile commuter. When cars are being repaired, when the weather is poor, when another member of a one-car family uses the car, the automobile commuter may turn to rapid transit.

Rapid transit may possibly be sufficiently attractive and convenient and appropriately enough located to discourage one-car families from becoming two-or-more-car families. At present, two out of every five families with incomes of $10,000 or more have at least two cars. In 1959, 24.3 percent of the families in the San Francisco–Oakland Metropolitan Area had incomes of $10,000 and more, as did 26.1 percent in the San Jose metropolitan area. In Palo Alto, the average per capita household income in 1962 was estimated to be more than $10,000 and that in San Mateo was $9217. According to Resources for the Future, the gross national product will double by 1980. There is no reason to believe that the number of families in the Bay Region will not share in the increased income.

Interestingly enough, the nine-county Bay Region has a lower ratio of passenger cars to population (1 to every 2.38 persons) than the state of California (1 to every 2.28 persons). This is due to the lower car ownership ratio in the city of San Francisco (1 to every 2.66 persons). While estimates for the nation expect consumers to have 100 million cars by 1975, or one car for every 2.35 persons (approximately the present Bay Region ratio), the ratio of the Bay Region is expected to go to one automobile for every two persons by 1980. Whether or not the number of automobiles will double between 1960 (1.5 million) and 1980 (3 million) as has been estimated, the likelihood is that the number of motor miles traveled will increase faster than the rate of automobile registration. The California Department of Public Works estimated in 1958 that the miles traveled in the state would triple by 1980; although a prediction was not made specifically for the Bay Region, all evidence seems to point to a larger and larger urbanized area and to a greater number of destinations to which motorists will be attracted.

Though rapid transit gives no promise of absorbing a large portion of the daily passenger trips in the Bay Region, and thus reducing the air pollution caused by motor vehicles, then Zettel points to an asset of the system usually overlooked, that is "its large reserve capacity, and consequent ability to meet the potential demands of the long-range future" (4). Presumably, if the population grows beyond what is expected in 1975, or economic conditions worsen and people cannot afford cars, or air pollution gets out of hand, or highways and parking lots are saturated with cars, then the reserve capacity could be utilized.

Household Operations

Heating residential properties is less of a problem in the Bay Region than in many parts of the nation since temperatures are mild and the coldest season (rarely below freezing) is of short duration. Most of the heat is supplied by natural gas, with electricity being used in some of the more expensive units; coal and oil are rarely used.

However, burning rubbish at home is encouraged because of the lack of municipal responsibility for collecting refuse. In San Francisco, Oakland, and San Jose, private haulers remove garbage and trash on a fee basis; in Berkeley the home owner may contract with either the city or a private company for service on a fee basis. Permits are issued by the fire department for burning leaves and other debris, and the home owner is under considerable cost incentive to burn paper and other flammable rubbish in home fireplaces or incinerators.

If the communities in the Bay Region wish to curb the burning of rubbish at home, they will have to assume the costs of either policing burning regulations or collecting trash. If trash is collected, then the problem of disposing of solid wastes must be solved and how air pollution will be affected by the operation of trucks must be considered.

Impact on Air Pollution

The U.S. Public Health Service has intensively measured tiny solids suspended in the air and solid organic matter that is soluble in benzene. The average for 189 cities in the United States for at least 20 readings per year from 1957 to 1961 is 104 micrograms per cubic meter for pendent solids and 7.6 for organic matter (5). San Francisco is below these averages (66 and 6.6 micrograms per cubic meter) and so are Berkeley (79 and 6.1) and Richmond (63 and 4.3). Oakland is below in pendent solids (87) and above in organic matter (10.0), while San Jose is above in pendent solids (106) and below in organic matter (7.3). In terms of these figures, the Bay Region fares much better than most other large communities in the nation: for example, Los Angeles (169 and 19.2), Birmingham (126 and 9.7), Phoenix (207 and 13.9), Denver (110 and 10.3), Wilmington (175 and 11.9), Atlanta (99 and 9.5), Chicago (187 and 14.2), Louisville (132 and 9.1), and Boston (131 and 11.2). Comparative measurements for gases are not yet available.

According to the Bay Area Pollution Control District report, "Air Pollution in the Bay Area" (1958), Oakland had 69 low-ventilation days—weather conditions equivalent to the "smogwarning" type of Los Angeles—during the 2-year period of July 1956 to July 1958, while Los Angeles experienced 164 such days. Thus, although the incidence of inversions coupled with weak winds was less than half that of Los Angeles, still almost 1 day in 10 posed an air pollution threat. The weather conditions did not occur randomly but peaked at certain times of the year; for example, half the days in November 1956 were low-ventilation days.

The Bay Area has recognized the seriousness of its air pollution problem to the extent of establishing a control district. The nonspecialist is probably very little aware of present levels of air pollution, its costs, or its potential threats to health, discomfort, amenity or property. At least this is probably true most of the time. The air may seem a little hazier; it is no longer possible to see San Francisco from the hills in Napa; sometimes heavy smog makes driving dangerous; some industries may be readily identified as visible polluters. But the buildings are clean, eyes and noses are rarely irritated, and the loss of view is often attributed to topography, climate, and meteorology rather than to these factors plus air pollution.

Yet this very sketchy suggestion of growth trends in the Bay Region points to the likelihood of markedly increased emissions. The prospects are for an increased population with higher incomes settling in low-density residential developments; a smaller center of the city in relation to the surrounding growth; a swallowing up of the countryside; greater and greater extensions of the metropolitan area, with more scattering of commercial, shopping, recreation, professional, and even cultural facilities; more ownership and use of cars; and more industrial development, with heavy industry particularly favoring a location along the bay. All this suggests that the San Francisco Bay Area could rival Los Angeles in air pollution.

If these trends were to be made clear to the residents and the decision-makers in the Bay Region, it is possible that strong remedial actions would be adopted to preserve the quality of the air environment. The San Francisco area is one place in the nation that is not only endowed with beautiful vistas, but is also self-consciously proud of its urban amenities. Properties with a view have a value of thousands of dollars more than equivalent properties without a view. Taxpayers are willing to consider removing an elevated highway structure that strikes them as ugly. They have supported a costlier renewal project than other proposed solutions because the one selected was more beautiful. They are willing to spend millions of dollars of city money (plus state and voluntary contributions) to save a unique but crumbling architectural structure (the Palace of Fine Arts by Bernard Maybeck). With beauty a political issue—there are save-the-bay, save-the-redwoods and other active conservationist groups—the air environment might well become an important cause to many for aesthetic reasons as well as for reasons of health.

Implications for Public Policy

This sketchy discussion of the possible growth in the Bay Area Region is intended only to give some insights into the discrepancy between what is likely to happen in American urban communities if public policy does not intervene, and what should happen for air conservation purposes. The case example was not meant to be a condensed version of all the elements that should be considered in a strategy for environmental improvement.

It is the thesis of this chapter, and indeed of this report, that a thorough study of the physical, economic, and social community and alternative future development patterns is as important for air conservation programs as the scientific analysis of the causes, character, and effects of air pollution. Only as the behavior of the people of the region is analyzed can judgments be made on which commitments can be altered.

It is also the contention of this chapter that those people—consumers, taxpayers, government officials, entrepreneurs—who are not fully informed on air pollution matters are also uninformed on other implications of community changes. Air conservation must be placed within the context of a multiple-focus strategy for community improvement, if decision-makers are to be able to make meaningful decisions for the future well-being of the entire region.

References

1. See map in "The control of air pollution" by A. J. Haagen–Smit in *Scientific American,* **210**, No. 1, p. 27 (Jan. 1964).
2. Davis, K., and E. Langlois, *Future Demographic Growth of the San Francisco Bay Area* (Institute of Governmental Studies, Univ. of California Press, Berkeley, 1963), p. 3.
3. Poland, O. F., *Economic Trends in the San Francisco Bay Area* (Institute of Governmental Studies, Univ. of California Press, Berkeley, 1963), p. 25.
4. Zettel, R. M., *Urban Transportation in the San Francisco Bay Area* (Institute of Governmental Studies, Univ. of California Press, Berkeley, 1963), p. 45.
5. *New Medical Materia,* pp. 20–21 (Feb. 1963).

Index

Acrolein, 30, 97
Additives, to gasoline, 111, 125, 130, 248
Adiabatic lapse rate, 34, 51–52
Aerosols, 62, 63, 97, 112, 114, 159, 254
Afterburners, 76, 98, 103, 131, 238, 243, 245
Agriculture
field wastes, 244, 246
use of economic poisons in, 149–152
Air
analyses of, for fallout, 179, 182
as a natural resource, 4, 5, 12, 195, 281, 286, 297, 298
Air conservation
cost of, 41, 216–223
economic analysis of, 281–304
factors to consider, 309–310
programs, 195, 216–232
public policy for, 3–19
social analysis of, 273–281
Air Conservation Commission, recommendations of, 6–8, 17–19
Air pollution, 26–32
control of, 36–39
cycle of, 50–51
development of, 23–25, 273–275
disasters, 5, 61, 63, 251
dispersal of, 51–54
economic motivation to control, 290–296
federal grants to control, 209
metropolitan problem, 307–310
stages of, 288–290
transport of, 32–34
Air Pollution Control Association, 258
Air Pollution Medical Studies Unit (California), 255
Air Quality Section, Division of Air Pollution, U.S. Public Health Service, 154
Air quality standards, 7–8, 101, 129, 225, 249–260
Air sampler, 154

Aitken, John, 89
Alamo, Nevada, 187
Albany, New York, 184
Aldehydes, 89, 91
Alfalfa, 64
Alkalies, 68
Altonah, Utah, 187, 188
Aluminum, 65
Aluminum industry, 134, 135, 140
American Conference of Governmental Hygienists, 85, 129
Ammonia, 68
Ammonium sulfate, 66
Annexation, of a suburban area, 205
Apricot, 135
Argon-41, 159
Aromatics, 89
Arsenic, 129, 145
Asbestos, 145
Asparagus, 246
Atlanta, Georgia, 322
Atmosphere
mathematical model of, 54–55
removal of pollutants from, 45, 119–121
to dispose of wastes, 36, 57, 238
Atomic Energy Commission, 163, 164, 165, 169, 177
Atomic energy installations, 160, 161
Automobiles. *See* Motor vehicles

Bacteria, 109
Baghouses, 67, 265–267
Baiting, 150
Bakersfield, California, 311
Baltimore, Maryland, 95, 138
Barium-140, 159, 179, 180
Beans, 95
Beets, table, 116
Belgium, 316
Beltsville, Maryland, 102
Benefit-cost analysis, 282–283
Benzo [a] pyrene, 118, 141, 144

325

M/